NEW HANDBOOK OF THE HEAVENS

was written and revised on the basis of the authors' experience in presenting astronomy to the Junior Astronomy Club of the American Museum of Natural History and at the Hayden Planetarium in New York. Other prominent scientists and writers have applauded the results:

"The authors are to be congratulated upon an excellent, dependable, and most useful book..." Dr. Clyde Fisher, Hayden Planetarium, New York.

"The beginner star-gazer, young or old, is offered one of the best introductions to the study of the sky available today." Arthur Draper, Director, Buhl Planetarium, Pittsburgh.

"The sort of book the layman enjoys because it gives him everything he needs to get started..." Harry Hansen, New York World-Telegram.

"Good introduction to astronomy for those who do not wish outright textbooks." Scientific American.

D1263194

McGRAW-HILL PAPERBACKS
IN SCIENCE, MATHEMATICS AND ENGINEERING

New Handbook of the Heavens
Herbert J. Bernhard
Dorothy A. Bennett, A.B.
Hugh S. Rice, A.M., Ph.D.,
Research Associate, Hayden Planetarium

Revised Edition

McGraw-Hill Book Company, Inc.
New York   Toronto   London

NEW HANDBOOK OF THE HEAVENS

Copyright, 1941, 1948, *by the* McGraw Hill Book Company, Inc.

REVISED EDITION

VIII

Preface

WE HAVE enjoyed knowing the stars. We are among
the thousands who have found them old friends,
to which we can turn time after time for refreshing thoughts
and relief from the worries and troubles of every-day life.

We have written this book so that others might share
this companionship with us. It has been prepared as simply as possible, and it tells of things that anyone can
see and understand for himself merely by looking up at
the heavens.

But we have found that a great many people, having once
looked up, want to lend wings to their explorations by using
field-glasses or telescopes. To most such "home astronomers" their instruments have a limited use, and so we
have included a few telescope suggestions that may be of
help to our readers as they grow more ambitious, and to
advanced students as well. We have also included carefully
prepared lists of the finest celestial objects available for
observation.

We wish to express our appreciation and thanks to James
B. Rothschild for his examination of the text and his
valuable criticisms; to Leon Campbell, secretary of the
A.A.V.S.O., for reading the chapter on Variable Stars; and
to Dr. Charles P. Olivier, director of the Flower Observatory, for his assistance with the meteor-shower tables.
Miss Levett Bradley is responsible for the execution of a
number of the more detailed diagrams.

We hope that our efforts, meant both to be read at leisure and to aid actual observations in the field, may reveal to you not merely a new world—but an unsuspected universe!

THE AUTHORS

Contents

[vii]

* CONTENTS *

Illustrations

[ix]

[x]

New Handbook of the Heavens

1

Introduction to the Heavens

IT IS fun to know the stars. When night gathers overhead thousands of them appear. There are bright stars and faint ones, near suns and far. Some seem scattered at random over the sky while others seem mingled in patterns.

And there are exciting events that are always occurring among them. Once in a while a new star appears, and if you know the old ones you can always pick the new one out. There are the changing phases of the moon and the moon's shifting place along the zodiac. Then there is the possibility that one of those wandering objects, the comets, may appear. If you know the stars, you can easily pick out the visitors from space. And one night, as you are watching the sky, brilliant shooting stars will flash through the heavens. You can add a really important bit of information to astronomy if you know how to watch them and keep records of them.

With even a box camera you can make a permanent record of some celestial events. The rotating earth will shift your camera beneath the stars, and across the photographic plate those distant suns will trail bright arcs. The moon as it drops behind the trees will leave a gradually dimming trail as its light passes through more and more atmosphere and is therefore absorbed.

When you have made your first step into observing the sky you can always go farther. Build a telescope and you can explore the depths of the universe. Double stars and clusters, variable stars and nebulae—all lie within your reach.

Most intriguing of all is the fact that the sky is so full of fascinating things that there is more than a lifetime's entertainment there. In one night one can find many of the star groups, perhaps observe several of the planets, identify dozens of features or more on the moon, and with the telescope spot numerous double stars, clusters, and nebulae. The next night the same sky will hang overhead but there are thousands of double stars, hundreds of variable stars, innumerable markings on the moon, and a limitless wealth of still undiscovered wonders within reach of the telescope. The next season a whole new realm of the heavens will be there to explore.

There is a real satisfaction in knowing which stars to expect in summer, what different stars will decorate winter skies, which planets shine in the morning sky, what others remain in the west after the setting of the sun.

Long ago people traced pictures among the stars. They carved these heavenly figures on stones in Babylonia, drew them on papyrus in Egypt, fixed them on marble in Greece, and painted them on buffalo skins in the American west. These ancient constellation figures can still be recognized, for the stars seem to stay the same in relation to their neighbors for a lifetime and even a thousand years. Really, they are all drifting in space, but they are so far away that their motion cannot be noticed in a lifetime. To the unaided eye they seem fixed and permanent in position.

Even though they do seem fixed in relation to one another, all the stars appear to move together around the earth. Long ago people thought they actually did circle the earth once each 24 hours the way the sun seems to do. But then it was discovered that the earth itself was turning on its axis and that the apparent motions of the sun and stars were the result of this movement of the earth.

There is one star, though, that does not seem to change

much. It is the brightest in the Little Dipper. Its proper
name is Alpha (α), its family name, Ursa Minor; hence the
star is called Alpha Ursae Minoris and is nicknamed pole
star. Hanging over the north pole of the earth, over one end
of the axis on which the earth turns, it is the brightest star
close to the north celestial pole. All the stars seem to rotate
around the north star, which itself makes a small circle
around the celestial pole every 24 hours because it is really
$1\frac{1}{4}°$ away from the true pole. To the casual observer
it appears to be quite motionless and always to occupy
the same place for any one latitude in the northern
hemisphere (where *pole star* means the *north star*).

However, Polaris, the north star, has a different position
for every latitude within that hemisphere. In the New
England states it is about half-way up the northern sky;
whereas at the north pole it is overhead. At the equator,
however, the pole star is just at the horizon. So if you
travel to the north, the pole star climbs higher the farther
you go. When you sail south, the star drops lower and
disappears if you cross the equator into the southern
hemisphere. There the south polar region of the sky comes
into view, and in the same fashion these stars climb higher
above the southern horizon as one travels from the equator
toward the south pole.

Just as there is a pole of the sky over the earth's pole, so
there is a celestial equator that hangs over the terrestrial
one. It is, of course, everywhere 90° from both poles just as
it is on earth. The earth and sky can be considered two great
globes, one within the other. It is 360° around any circle
such as the earth's equator, for instance. The half-circle
from the north pole to the south pole is 180° and the quar-
ter-circle from the equator to the pole is 90°. If the pole
star is half-way up the sky in the north, then the equator is
about half-way up in the south. Of course, to most people
this doesn't make any difference, but to sailors and surveyors it is important. They use such marks of reference

in the heavens as a means of establishing points of reference on the earth.

So excellent an index of one's latitude is the altitude of the pole star that it has guided sailors since earliest time. Even today this and other stars are used by modern aviators in crossing the trackless ocean.

No one has ever walked around the earth with a measuring tape, yet we know that it is about 25,000 miles in circumference. This is possible to compute approximately when you know the distance between two points on the earth on the same meridian of longitude and then can measure the height of the pole star in each place. Thousands of years ago Eratosthenes in Egypt first determined the size of the earth by a similar method. He believed the world to be round and knew consequently that its circumference measured 360°, as does any circle. Hearing from a traveler that the sun appeared at a different height when viewed at the same time from two different cities, he measured the difference in height in degrees. Having this figure, and comparing it with 360°, he knew what part of the earth's total circumference was represented by the distance between the two cities. When he measured that distance he was able, by simple multiplication, to estimate correctly that the earth is about 25,000 miles around.

In the same way, no one has ever walked through the earth from pole to pole, yet we know that it is about 7900 miles in diameter. It is possible to figure this out again because we know the earth is round like a baseball. We can measure a baseball and then discover how much farther it is around it than through it. If it is 3 inches in diameter it will be roughly 9.4 inches around. There is a definite mathematical relationship between circumference and diameter in any circle, and we can apply the same rule to the earth.

By other mathematical means, it is possible to measure the 93,000,000 miles distance of the earth from the sun. Our world is one of nine planets that move around the sun. The

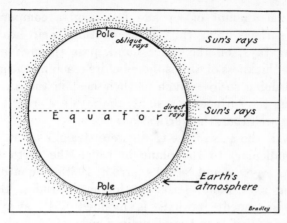

INSOLATION

Insolation depends upon the inclination of the sun's rays, and also the absorption of the atmosphere when we consider equal areas, a constant output of solar energy, and equal distances from the sun. Our diagram shows these two effects, closely connected with the change of seasons. In high latitudes, a bundle of solar rays is spread over a larger area and thus is less concentrated than a similar bundle of rays in lower latitudes. Similarly, it is evident that oblique rays pass through a greater thickness of atmosphere, consequently losing much of their lighting and heating power.

sun is always shining, so one side of each planet is always light. And as the planet rotates upon its axis, an observer on that turning globe sees the sun apparently rise and set.

In considering the motions of the earth, it is convenient to assume that the sun's position is a constant one. Since the earth does not move in a perfect circle around the sun, it is sometimes nearer and sometimes farther from it. In January we are about 3,000,000 miles closer to the sun than in July. The varying distance does not make winter and summer, however. The actual shift of the season comes from quite different causes. The earth is round, wrapped about with a blanket of air, and tipped upon its axis. Sunlight must penetrate the air before it can warm the earth beneath. Vertical rays of sunlight which strike directly down upon the planet are the most effective, as the accompanying diagram shows, because they pass through a

[7]

minimum amount of air and fall upon a comparatively small surface area, thus concentrating their heat. The slanting rays, on the other hand, pass through a much greater thickness of atmosphere before reaching the ground, and in doing so lose much of their heat in the air. Then, reaching the surface on a slant, the rays are spread over a greater area than the vertical ones.

Now if the axis of the earth were straight up and down (perpendicular) to the plane in which the earth moves, vertical rays would always strike at the equator, and slanting rays would strike at higher latitudes. But the earth is tipped; its axis is inclined $23\frac{1}{2}°$ away from the perpendicular to the plane in which it moves about the sun. As the world moves round the sun with its axis always tipped at the same angle and pointing in the same direction, first one pole and then the other is nearest the sun. The direct rays shift from $23\frac{1}{2}°$ north of the equator to the same distance south of that imaginary line. The sun shines alternately $23\frac{1}{2}°$ beyond the north and then beyond the south pole. The days grow long in the northern hemisphere and then become short. These are the underlying causes for the change of the seasons.

As the seasons come and go, one can see the changes in the sun's position that bring the seasons about. During some months, the sun is higher in the heavens at noon than during others. And, too, it seems to shift its place constantly against the background of stars as the earth moves around it. The sun's light is so scattered through the air that the sky is too bright for us to see the stars, but they are always there. On rare occasions a solar eclipse makes it dark enough in the daytime for us to see them. We discover that the stars close to the sun in summer are the very ones that we see in the night skies of winter. Of course, if the eclipse occurs in winter, we see stars near the sun that we saw on the nights of summer.

There is a particular section of the sky that the sun and

planets always occupy. The ancients recognized it and divided it into constellations, all but one of which represented some animal. It was called the zodiac, or band of animals, and along this path the sun seems to move.

As the earth revolves around the sun it makes the sun assume an apparent motion among the stars—really a "reflection" of the earth's true movement. Although we cannot observe it quite as easily as the daily rising and setting of the sun, we can detect it as the ancients did. They noticed that each evening after the sun went down certain stars of the zodiac could be recognized above the sunset point. As the nights passed, the same stars set earlier and seemed to go to meet the sun. The stars that were above the western horizon at sunset at the beginning of the month would set with the sun at the end of the month. Thus the sun seemed to progress from west to east along the center of the zodiac.

Pursuing its monthly path around the earth, the moon moves regularly among these same stars, as do the planets at various intervals. The moon's path, always close to the sun's, crosses it in two places. Where the orbits cross, eclipses occasionally occur. Either the moon comes between us and the sun and hides the latter, or the moon enters the earth's shadow and is darkened. Because of the eclipses that occur here the sun's path was named the ecliptic.

But the earth is tipped upon its axis, and as a result of this the celestial equator is inclined to the ecliptic and crosses it. Where equator and ecliptic cross are the equinoxes—points along the sun's apparent path reached near March 21 and September 23 each year. From these points in the apparent path, the sun's rays strike the equator directly, and all over the earth there is equal day and night.

After the equinox times, the situation changes. Climbing north of the equator after March 21, the sun's vertical rays reach latitudes north of the equator. On June 21 or 22, the sun is at its most northern point. Then it takes the northern

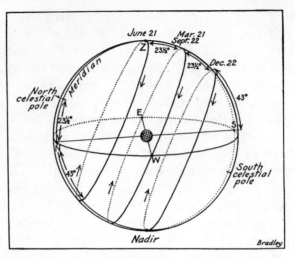

THE SEASONS

At different seasons of the year, the noon sun appears at different altitudes to an observer at any one station. Our diagram is drawn for any locality in latitude 23½°N. Most important cause of the change of seasons, as illustrated in this diagram, is the difference in length of day and night at different times of the year, for the length of the sun's path above the horizon indicates the daylight hours.

half of the earth longer to turn through sunlight than through the night. The northern nights are short; days are long. This is the time of the solstice—summer for the north but winter for the south. Each day after late June the sun goes south. It reaches the equator September 23. Fall begins, and day and night are equal again as the sun's most direct rays fall at the equator. After this the sun continues to go farther south and by December 21 or 22 it has dropped to the Tropic of Capricorn. The warm rays and the long days have gone south with the sun. The short and cold days of winter are in the northern hemisphere and the sun is very low in the northern sky.

As the sun changes its noon-time or meridian position, it also changes its place of rising and setting. At equinox time the sun rises exactly east and sets exactly west. On those days the sun is on the celestial equator. As the earth rotates on its axis, the sun rises in the east and seems to move across the sky on the equator, setting in the west. As the sun climbs north of the celestial equator it rises to the north of the east point, and sets to the north of the west point, reaching its farthest position in each case about June 21. Then as it begins to move back to the equator it again rises due east in September; but by December, when it is far south of the celestial equator, it rises to the south of the east point and similarly sets to the south of west.

Long ago the ancient peoples learned to tell the exact time of the seasons by watching the shift of the sun's place of rising and setting. Early monuments in China, Japan, Central America, and the American southwest were oriented to make observations of these changes possible. Even the Stonehenge of England was used for this purpose.

And of course as the earth turns on its axis each day the sun rises at different times for different longitudes. This makes a change in time that was not even thought of in the olden days before people could keep track of what was happening on the other side of the world. But now that radio connects the whole of our planet instantaneously, it is possible to be quite sure exactly what time it is in China as well as in New York. In fact it is possible actually to tell your longitude from the time—because the two are closely related. When the sun rises in London it is still dark in New York; on the other hand, it is already afternoon in Shanghai. People on the east coast of the United States must wait 5 hours for the sun to appear above their eastern horizon after it has come up in England. And in the same fashion, people in San Francisco must wait 3 hours to see the sun after it has come up in New York. Once this was merely interesting, but now it is used to help locate the positions of ships at sea and the big clipper airplanes that fly the ocean.

All that is necessary to determine difference in longitude is to know the time of any two places on the earth and from

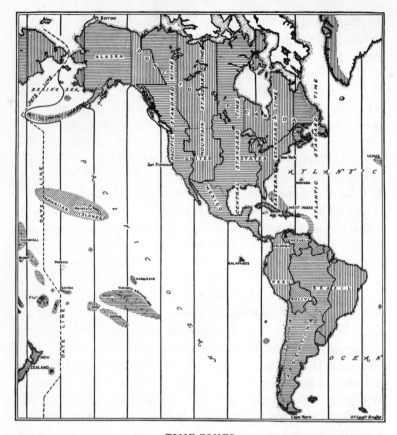

TIME-ZONES

The earth is divided into 24 standard-time zones, each 15° wide in longitude. This section of a U. S. Coast and Geodetic Survey diagram shows only the western hemisphere. The time in all stations of any one zone normally differs by a full hour from that in adjoining zones, and zones vary in outline according to the convenience of localities within. Diagonally shaded regions indicate the few areas where standard time does *not* differ by one whole hour from adjoining zones.

this you can tell the east-west distance between them. The usual method is to use Greenwich time as a standard from which to measure, and then figure local time from the altitude of the sun or other astronomical data and the tables in an ephemeris or nautical almanac. The time difference is directly convertible into longitude distance between the observer and the Greenwich meridian. You can use stars instead of the sun, and they are really preferable. So modern ships and airplanes all carry a clock that shows Greenwich civil time, and radios with which to check the clocks. This is now called by astronomers Universal time, because it is used the world over for the establishment of longitude and for many other scientific purposes. Stations located 15° of longitude to the west of the Greenwich meridian have local time reading one hour earlier than Greenwich time; stations 75° to the west, or in the Eastern Standard time-zone, have their local clocks 5 hours earlier than Greenwich time. So it is around the world. One can tell his time by the sun wherever he is on the earth. Comparing that with the Universal time he can establish his position east and west of the prime meridian. One of the most important things that time does then is to help fix positions on the earth; and so it is possible to tell latitude from the pole star or the sun, and longitude from the sun or the stars.

Star-gazing is like a magic carpet that can carry you away millions of miles from home and remove you far from the affairs of every day. You need only to put your head out the window to start upon this trip of exploration into the outermost reaches of space, where one can sense the immenseness of the universe and the remarkable law and order that prevail there.

2

Stars around the Poles

WHEREVER one lives upon the earth, there are certain stars that he can see night after night. At the north pole of the earth, for instance, one always sees the same stars—they never set and are visible at all hours every night. As the earth turns on its axis each 24 hours the whole sky seems to circle, with every star at a definite and constant height above the horizon. Those near the horizon seem to move parallel to it, and those overhead circle in a direction opposite to the hands of a clock. Every star seen from the pole is circumpolar, but these are in only half the sky; the other half never rises at the north pole and is forever invisible from that point.

Suppose, though, that you were to leave the north pole and go as far south as Minneapolis. This city, and all others in the same latitude, are exactly half-way between the equator and the poles. The pole star, therefore, hangs half-way down the sky instead of at the zenith where it was seen from the north geographical pole. In Minneapolis all the stars in view on any night still seem to move around the pole star, but some of them, rising out of the east and climbing above the southern horizon, will sink from view in the west and be out of sight for some time during the night. Above the northern horizon there are certain stars that continually swing around the north celestial pole and never disappear. Since they are in view for every hour of every night they are among the easiest to find and identify.

MIDNIGHT SUNS

In this photograph, the sun's motion is like that of a circumpolar star. The camera, located in northern Alaska, was opened at 12-minute intervals as the sun dipped down toward the horizon in a shallow arc, then gradually rose again. The sun at the exact moment of local midnight is almost hidden behind a mountain peak of the Endicott Range. (*Photograph by Stephen Rychlew.*)

They are the keystones of constellation study—the circumpolar stars. They form an easy guide to other near-by groups.

If our journey be extended and we continue to the equator we find the pole star at the horizon and no stars circumpolar, for all of them both rise and set. Our pole star, Polaris, lies at the northern horizon, and off at the southern horizon the south celestial pole is located. Continuing our journey to the south, we would find the south polar region rising higher. When we reached Tasmania the south celestial pole would be nearly half-way up the sky. Again a group of stars would circle the pole, remaining in view through the whole of the night. But at this pole they move in the opposite direction, clockwise. After reaching the south pole we would find that every star south of the celestial equator had become circumpolar. For each latitude there is a different group of circumpolar stars.

You can easily discover what stars are circumpolar for your locality by measuring the altitude of the pole star or looking up your latitude in the atlas. Any star that is no farther from the pole star than the pole star is from the horizon will be circumpolar. Like this circumpolar area which is always visible, there is from the same latitude an equal section in the other hemisphere always invisible.

[15]

As you go from equator to pole the circumpolar area increases. As you go from pole to equator it decreases.

Since the greater part of the population of the United States and of many parts of Europe lies in the middle latitudes, most people are familiar with the stars that are circumpolar for the middle latitudes of the northern hemisphere.* Among these the Big Dipper (or Great Bear), the Little Dipper, Cassiopeia, Perseus, and others are well known.

The Big Dipper, properly known as Ursa Major, is composed of seven bright stars. Four stars form the bowl, three the handle of the Dipper. The same three stars that we see as the handle were employed by the Greeks and Romans to make the tail of the Great Bear. The four we use to make the bowl they used in picturing the bear's hind quarters. Despite the different pictures that have been made with these seven stars, their arrangement has always been much the same. The Egyptians described them as a hippopotamus; yet they saw the same arrangement that we find today.

Five of the Dipper's stars seem to be of the same brightness, and two are fainter. All the stars that we can see with the eyes alone have been classified according to their brightness and placed in six arbitrary groups. The 20 at the top of the list are $2\frac{1}{2}$ times brighter than the greater number of stars in the second-magnitude group. The next type, the third-magnitude stars, are $2\frac{1}{2}$ times less bright than those of the second-magnitude group. This proportion is used throughout the scale.

Some 9000 stars can be seen with the unaided eye all over the earth throughout the year, but only some 2500 to 3000 at any one time in any one place. They range from the sixth

* Stars visible in mid-northern latitudes are shown as they appear at any hour of any night, on a rotating planisphere, the *Star Explorer*. Planet positions are also given. This star-and-planet chart may be obtained for 50 cents from Star Explorer, c/o Dr. H. S. Rice, Hayden Planetarium, New York 24, N. Y.

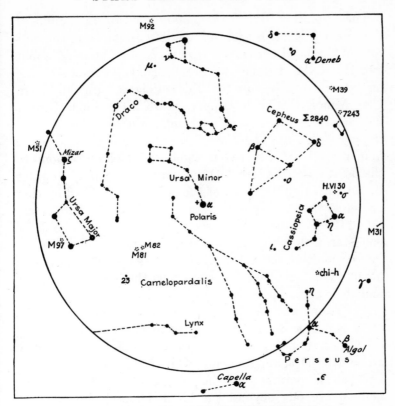

NORTH CIRCUMPOLAR CONSTELLATIONS

magnitude to the first, and the first-magnitude stars are 100 times as bright as the faintest stars that we can see.

There are a few stars brighter than first magnitude. These are reckoned on the same scale. Stars $2\frac{1}{2}$ times as bright as first magnitude are designated as zero magnitude. Stars brighter than that are labeled *minus*. Thus Sirius, our brightest star, is magnitude −1.58. The lowest value represents the greatest brilliance. So Polaris is among the second-magnitude group and five of the seven stars in the Great Bear are of this same brilliance. It is no wonder, then, that the Big Dipper is easy to find at a glance and Polaris easy to locate when one follows the pointers of the Dipper.

The "pointers" are the two stars opposite the handle of the Great Dipper. By following a line drawn from the bottom of the bowl through the pointers and extended about five times the distance between them, one comes to the pole star. To make sure that this is Polaris one should learn Ursa Minor, the Little Dipper, as well. The Little Dipper has Polaris in the end of its handle, the brightest star in the constellation. There are three stars in the handle and four in the bowl. The two in the bowl which correspond to the pointers of the Great Dipper are considerably brighter than their neighbors. Just as the pointers are called by that name, so the corresponding stars in the Little Dipper are called the Guardians. They seem always to swing about the pole star. Columbus mentioned these stars in the log of his famous journey across the ocean and many other navigators have found them useful in measuring the hour of the night and their place upon the sea.

The Dippers are so arranged that when one is upright the other is upside down, and their handles extend in opposite directions. Winding in between the two Dippers is part of Draco, the Dragon. The end of his tail lies almost directly between the pointers and the pole, and the coils of his long body curve out beyond the Little Dipper's bowl, swing back toward Polaris again, and finally turn toward the constellation of Hercules in a reverse "s".

After you have recognized the Great Dipper, traced the pointers to the pole star, and found the Little Dipper hanging from Polaris—you might trace a line from the pointers to the pole and extend it an equal distance, on the other side. There it will lead you close to a w-shaped group, Cassiopeia. Across the pole from Ursa Major and equally distant from Polaris lies this group that represents, some say, a big chair upon which the ancient queen of Ethiopia is seated.

In the course of a night Ursa Major and Cassiopeia circle the heavens like the opposite sides of a wheel. At 9 p.m.

May 1, the Great Dipper hangs upside down, Cassiopeia resembles a "w" right side up on the opposite side of the pole. As the earth turns, Cassiopeia climbs the northeastern sky while the Great Dipper drops down to the northwestern horizon. At sunrise in middle latitudes, their positions are reversed by a quarter turn. At 9 a.m. they have exactly changed places. But the next evening the Great Dipper is again high overhead, and Cassiopeia hangs just above the horizon.

Cassiopeia is a typical constellation. It is a group of stars that to us looks always the same. In fact, it appeared the same more than a thousand years ago when it first received the name and even longer ago than that when people first observed it. Yet some of the stars in this constellation are nearer to us than others, and all of them are separated from one another by millions of miles. From some other corner of the universe these same stars would not form the same picture. In this same corner of the universe at some other time their arrangement will be different. For all the stars are really drifting through space. The speeds and directions of hundreds are known. They are so distant from the earth that it takes several thousands of years for any change in their arrangement to be noticeable to the naked eye. Nevertheless in modern instruments their motion can be detected over a period of years, and we know that a time will come thousands of years in the future when many of the familiar star figures will be hard to recognize.

Some of the star groups are truly related. Five of the bright stars in the Big Dipper, for example, belong to the same family. The "open cluster" of its members moves as a group through space, all the stars sharing a common speed and direction of motion.

For a lifetime of a man upon the earth, through the passage of many generations, during the years of a millennium, the sky will look much the same. So the 89 constellations into which the sky has been divided today will be there

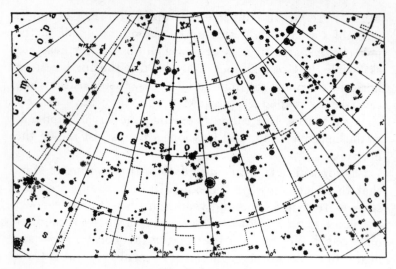

CASSIOPEIA, A CONSTELLATION

The star group as it appears in Schurig's *Himmels-Atlas*, showing the extent of
the constellation boundaries, methods of indicating the more important stars,
clusters, etc., and difference in magnitudes.

tomorrow and will serve as points of reference for men a
thousand years from now. Cassiopeia is just one of these
89, yet it is typical of the rest. Its borders include not just
the w-shaped figure that is so easy to see with the eye, but
many faint stars near-by that one must look closely to
find. Then, too, there are the double stars that lie within
this constellation area, which are only revealed as double in
the telescope. Here too are clusters of stars and hazy patches
of light that are called the nebulae. Stars that vary in their
light can be found in this area also. In one night one can
learn to find the "w" and to recognize Cassiopeia seated
upon her throne. Many nights must pass, though, before
one can easily pick out the boundaries of this "star state"
and find with his unaided eye all the stars that belong within
it. Many more nights may be spent in discovering those
hidden objects that lie within the reach of the telescope.

Near Cassiopeia is the section of the sky which the Greeks

named after Cassiopeia's son-in-law, Perseus. A straggling stream of stars that runs from Cassiopeia to the little group of the Pleiades depicts Perseus. He still holds in his hand the head of the Medusa, relic of his heroic adventure with the Gorgons. One of the wicked eyes of the snaky-haired monster still shines but seems to close now and then. For in Perseus is a "blinking star" that changes its light from day to day. Algol it is called, named by the Arabs the Demon Star. Another variable star in Perseus is Rho (ρ).

Algol is a common name, and Rho a scientific name. Not all stars have common names—only the brighter and more spectacular as a rule were named individually, but the astronomers must be able to identify any star in a constellation. The common practice of using Greek letters to designate different stars in the constellation has been followed for several centuries. Thus Algol is also Beta (β) Persei. Usually the brightest star of a group is called Alpha, the next Beta, and so on down the line. Of course, there are many stars within the boundaries of one constellation. When the astronomers ran out of Greek letters they used numbers, Arabic letters, and a system of codes that related the star to its place in various catalogs.

In Perseus there is another object that bears a Greek name too. A twin cluster of stars visible to the unaided eye as two hazy patches, Chi-h Persei. Similar objects to these, other double stars, and other variable stars lie within Cepheus, Camelopardalis, Lacerta, and Lynx—all constellations circumpolar for the middle northern latitudes. Most important of these is Cepheus, the husband of Cassiopeia and the King of Ethiopia. He lies almost in line with the Great Bear but on the other side of the pole star, in the Milky Way.

So many constellations are figures in Greek mythology that familiarity with the stories adds to one's pleasure in astronomy. You remember how Cassiopeia, Queen of Ethiopia, was so beautiful and vain. She aroused the jeal-

INHABITANTS OF THE HEAVENS

Among the stars, ancient peoples traced many figures with the aid of lively imaginations. This plate, showing the north circumpolar regions, pictures the inhabitants of one section of the sky—the Dragon; the Great Bear; the Giraffe; the Seated Lady; and others. (*From Burritt's Geography of the Heavens.*)

ousy of the Sea Nymphs and aggravated them into action. They went to Neptune demanding her punishment. Neptune ordered Cassiopeia to take her daughter Andromeda to the seashore and chain her to a rock. Then a huge sea monster would have devoured her, but Perseus happened along on his way from slaying the grisly Gorgons. He glided

[22]

down on his winged horse, Pegasus, took the Medusa's head out of his pouch, turned the sea monster to stone, and rescued the lovely lady. Then he restored her to her chastened mother, Cassiopeia, and her grateful father, Cepheus. All these are in the same part of the sky. Cassiopeia, Cepheus, and Perseus are circumpolar in mid-latitudes. Andromeda, Pegasus, and the sea monster are very near at hand.

Some persons do not care for mythology; they are more interested in the rich historical and geographic heritage of the stars. They recount the adventures of South Sea Islands sailors who follow the stars for thousands of miles over the trackless ocean. Or they point out that the Crow, Corvus, is known as Corbeau in French, Corvo in Italian, Rabe in German. The Hebrews called it Noah's Raven flying over the deluge. To the Arabs it was the Raven's Beak and to the Chinese a Redbird. So the stories of the stars take one over the world and back through time.

In Cepheus is one of the most famous of variable stars, Delta (δ) Cephei. By the way, when you use the Greek letter for the star, it is customary to use the genitive case of the Latin name of the constellation following. Thus it is Beta Persei instead of Perseus; Delta Cephei and Alpha Ursae Minoris. It is simple after you have once discovered what the system is. It is really a kind of universal language that people interested in the stars all over the world can use and understand, an astronomical Esperanto if you will, a kind of sign language that all nations can understand.

Of course people who live south of the equator will not choose the Big Dipper as their guide to the night sky— but rather the Southern Cross. Wherever you live there are familiar stars that remain in view night after night. These are the ones on which to begin. Then, as the seasons roll on, your explorations can branch out to include the new visitors of spring and summer and the changing stars of autumn and winter.

3

Autumn and Winter Stars

As DAYS begin to grow short and leaves fall from the trees, the nights of autumn grow longer and winter arrives. Then the greatest number of bright stars appears and the best of the meteor showers visit the earth. A knowledge of the constellations is a great help in reporting these shooting stars.

On September evenings a brilliant triangle composed of three of the 20 brightest stars in the heavens passes overhead. Vega, the blue-white sun in Lyra, the Harp, is one of these and is the fourth brightest star in the whole of the sky. Known as Alpha in the constellation of Lyra, it has as its neighbors four tiny brilliant jewels set in a parallelogram. One of its neighbors, Epsilon (ϵ), is a double star when examined closely. Between Beta and Gamma lies the magnificent Ring Nebula, within reach of a small telescope.

The second of the three stars in the big triangle is Deneb, the brightest star in the Northern Cross. Although the Cross is easy to recognize, the ancients visualized the same stars as picturing a Swan, and the proper name of this sky area is really Cygnus. The stellar area enclosed within the boundaries of Cygnus houses many interesting objects. There are 61 Cygni, the first star to have its distance measured; Beta Cygni, Albireo, one of the most beautiful of the double stars within reach of a small telescope; and the Coalsack that looks like a great cavernous hole in the sky.

The last corner of the triangle is marked by Altair,

principal star of Aquila, the Eagle. Altair shines in the Eagle's head and Deneb shines in the tail of the Swan. Thus the Swan flies in one direction down the Milky Way while the Eagle wings his flight in the opposite direction. Easiest thing to do on these nights of fall is to pick out the three bright stars and from them the star pictures of which they are a part.

After that, there are many other near-by constellations that are easy to identify. There's the tiny group of Delphinus, the Dolphin, below one arm of the Cross and over the head of the Eagle. Only five stars can be seen readily in this little group which some people call Job's Coffin. Even so, one can find here several interesting objects with the telescope. Gamma is a double star in the Dolphin's head, and behind his tail is a hazy patch which in the telescope is a cluster of countless stars.

Between Delphinus and Albireo at the head of Cygnus lies the image of an arrow. The constellation, made of five faint stars, is labeled Sagitta. Between Sagitta and Cygnus lies an even more inconspicuous figure, Vulpecula, the Little Fox from Aesop's fables. Prize object in this area is the Dumbbell Nebula—an oddly shaped telescopic patch of misty light.

Sagitta and Vulpecula require real searching. So save them for the time when you are looking for new fields to conquer and feel an irresistible urge to find something that your fellow star-gazers have not yet discovered. Actually, of course, Cygnus and Aquila, Delphinus and Lyra are remnants of the nights of summer. They are crossing the south in the early evening in early autumn. As the hours pass they will sink to the west and disappear before the dawn. Driven before them will go the stars that hung in the west in the early evening. There are Boötes, off the curve of the Dipper's handle, and Corona, Hercules, Ophiuchus, and Sagittarius.

When trying to describe the location of one constellation

in relation to another, we must have some method that will always work. At first it might seem as though the easiest thing would be to say to your fellow astronomer, "When you find Orion, Sirius will be just below and to the left". This might apply when Orion is on the meridian and your friend in the northern hemisphere. However, it would be incorrect 3 hours earlier or 3 hours later on the same evening in the same locality, and it would be just the opposite in the southern hemisphere. In the long run, it is not wise to use the terms *above* or *below*, *right* or *left*, *up* or *down*, when giving directions in the sky.

It is far better to start out correctly. Imagine the sky a huge sphere overlaced with circles like a spherical bird-cage. All the *hour-circles* pass through the poles, but other circles at right angles to these are parallel with the equator and are called *parallels of declination*. There is one hour-circle that is very easy to visualize—the *meridian*. When you face due south you can imagine it running from the horizon through the *zenith* or overhead point, on to the north celestial pole, and down to the horizon. (Out of sight it continues on through the south celestial pole as the *anti-meridian*.) Suppose, then, that Orion seemed to be just over the south point on the meridian. To describe Auriga properly you would say that it was *north* of Orion. It is between the head of Orion and the north celestial pole. However, Lepus is *south* of Orion, because the great circle that started at the north pole and passed through Auriga strikes Lepus beyond Orion on its way toward the south celestial pole.

Through the belt of Orion runs the celestial equator. Every star between the equator and the north celestial pole is said to have a declination north. Objects between the equator and the other pole are said to have a declination south. Just as the whole sky is overlain with lines through the poles similar to the meridian, one for any star anywhere, so at right angles to the hour-circles may be imagined other

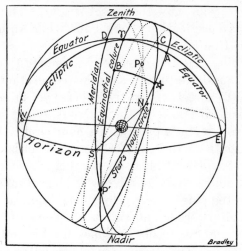

THIS MAY BE DIFFICULT

But it's worth studying! The diagram representing the celestial sphere, with the earth at the center, shows the coördinates of the equator system, and of the ecliptic system. We have chosen an object (★) which has the following coördinates as measured along the lines of the diagram:

ϒ—Vernal equinox
B★—Right ascension
A★—Declination
ϒ C—Celestial longitude
C★—Celestial latitude
CϒA—Obliquity of ecliptic
DWE around the circle to A—Hour-angle
P,P'—Celestial poles
N,E,S,W—North, east, south, west—cardinal points
Arc from D on equator westward around the circle to ϒ—Sidereal time

lines parallel to the equator—parallels of declination. Every star everywhere has such a parallel of declination.

All the stars that we can see have long since been carefully plotted on the framework of hour-circles and parallels of declination. This framework can be used by an observer any place on earth and any time of day or night.

The declination of an object is measured in degrees north or south from the celestial equator. If the figure has a plus sign before it, you know the object is north; if it has a minus sign before it, you know the object is south. Thus Capella in Auriga has a declination about $+46°$, while Alpha Leporis has a declination about $-17°$.

In describing celestial directions it is safest to use the terms north and south only, in this connection, (always in reference to directions on the sphere, *not* in connection with the cardinal points of the compass as applied to the horizon). From a star's place on its hour-circle its distance north and south of the equator can be described. To tell its place east and west along its parallel of declination we must have a similar point of reference. The vernal equinox is that point—the place where ecliptic and equator cross and which the sun passes about March 21. The east-west position is called right ascension and measured from the vernal equinox in hours. The distance is measured *eastward* from this equinox to the point where the hour-circle that goes through a star crosses the equator. Obviously the right ascension of a star, which is given in hours, is similar to geographic longitude, while the declination of a star is similar to geographic latitude and is given in degrees.

Each star has a permanent place on the celestial sphere, where it can always be found. For instance, Betelgeuse (Alpha in Orion) is located near right ascension 6^h, declination $+7°$. However, this is more than you need to describe how to find Sirius in relation to Betelgeuse. First find the two stars, connect them with an imaginary line, and note the line's direction *with respect to the hour-circles and parallels of declination*. It will be seen that Sirius lies south of Betelgeuse and to the east, on the celestial sphere, while Aldebaran lies to the north and west in the direction of the setting sun. The relationship between these stars will every time and everywhere appear the same and can always safely and accurately be described in this manner.

There is another system for describing the stars' positions—altitude and azimuth. Since this system depends upon the observer, it is variable with time and place. The

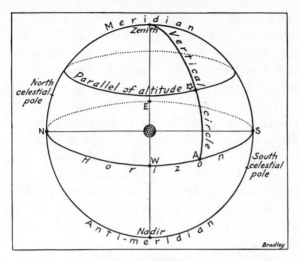

ONE METHOD

of locating objects on the celestial sphere is that employing altitude and azimuth —the coördinates of the horizon system. Altitude is the height of the object above the horizon as measured along the vertical circle, *A* to ★, where ★ represents object. Azimuth is the distance of the object, measured either along the horizon or "parallel of altitude" from the meridian to the object's vertical circle. In astronomy, it is measured from south point westward (*S* to *A*), but in navigation it is measured from north point eastward (*N* through *E* and *S* to *A*).

altitude, of course, is the star's height above the horizon in degrees; the azimuth is the distance in degrees measured westward from the south point of the horizon around the circle to the point where the star's altitude circle meets the horizon. In navigation, however, the zero point of azimuth is at the north point of the horizon. It is well to know these coördinates—especially for navigation—but for most astronomical purposes the right ascension-declination system is more in use.

Off in the east of the sky early on the nights of autumn are Pegasus, Andromeda, Triangulum, Aries, Pisces, and Aquarius—properly the stars of fall. Most characteristic of all these groups is the great square of Pegasus. To the ancients he represented the white winged horse that inspired the poets of old and carried Perseus through the sky after he had slain the Medusa. To a modern boy, however, this section of the sky looks like a baseball diamond. There are the home plate, first, second, and third base, even the right- and left-field foul-lines, and the catcher.

In the old story, Perseus was riding upon Pegasus when he looked down upon the shores of Ethiopia and there saw Andromeda chained to the rock. Appropriately then, the constellation of Andromeda lies very near to Pegasus. In fact, they share one star in common, Alpheratz, frequently mentioned by Anne Morrow Lindbergh in *Listen, the Wind*. Andromeda was the daughter of Cassiopeia and Cepheus and finally the wife of Perseus. Since they are all close together in the heavens, it is easy to find them and to remember them.

The corner stars in the square of Pegasus are so bright that the area inside the square looks quite like empty sky. On a clear night, though, a person with good eyesight can count well over half a hundred stars inside the square. With the telescope he can see many more. Some of these are double, and some are grouped in clusters.

When you are searching the square of Pegasus for the stars that you can recognize, look along Andromeda for a hazy patch often called Messier 31. When you have finally located this misty patch, just barely visible to the eye, it is hard to believe that it is actually made of 100,000,-000,000 suns like the one that we see each day. It's so distant that only the telescope and camera combined can show its true nature. They reveal it to be a whole universe of stars like the Milky Way galaxy of which we are part. While you have your telescope there, be sure to turn it toward Gamma Andromedae, for this star is a beautiful double that can be easily separated with a small telescope.

Once familiar with Pegasus and the long line of Androm-eda, you will have no difficulty in recognizing the v-shaped group of Pisces to the south, as well as the two smaller constellations, Triangulum and Aries, in this same region.

The Triangle lies just south of Gamma Andromedae, and
Aries hangs an equal distance south of Triangulum. The
star Gamma in Aries is also a double easy to resolve. Much
more important, however, is the fact that long ago, when
the zodiac was first recognized, the sun's place was in Aries
on the first day of spring. Since then, Aries has been called
the first sign of the zodiac, even though the motion of
the earth's axis has slowly caused a shift in the place of the
sun at the time when spring begins.

In modern times, the sun is seen against the background
of Pisces, the Fishes, when it crosses the equator about
March 21. Here, therefore, is the vernal equinox, a reference
point from which the positions of all celestial objects are
reckoned.

Along the zodiac beyond Aries and Pisces lies Aquarius,
the Water Carrier, and past him toward the west, Capricornus, the Goat. Capricornus follows after Sagittarius, the
Archer, and it disappears beneath the western horizon on
autumn evenings.

South of the zodiac is Cetus, the Whale. In this constellation area a variable star shines, named by Hevelius, Mira,
the Wonderful. A strange "blinking" star, Mira takes
about 3 months to change from second magnitude to sixth
and finally vanishes from naked-eye sight, reaching tenth
magnitude in nearly a year. Its variation changes it from a
star as bright as Polaris to one invisible to the unaided eye.

As Cetus comes out of the southeast early on autumn
evenings, Taurus, the Bull, rises in the east and follows
after its zodiacal neighbor Aries. Taurus has many claims
to fame. In the time of the Egyptians it was the most
important of the 12 groups along the path of the sun, for
the vernal equinox was located there at the time. The
Bull's eye, Aldebaran, is one of the 20 brightest stars. In
the Bull's face is a little cluster of brilliant stars, the
Hyades. On the Bull's shoulder is the famous group of
the Pleiades, often called the Seven Sisters, sometimes the

Stars of the Autumn and Winter Skies

The map above shows positions and accepted geometric patterns for all the constellations visible at 9 p.m., November 6 in latitude 40°N. Identification of the star groups may be made by comparison with the chart on the opposite page.

In use, this map should be held overhead and oriented according to the compass points indicated. It will then show the stars as they appear in the sky. The stars visible here at 9 p.m., November 6 will also be visible at 7 p.m. December 6 and at 11 p.m. October 6.

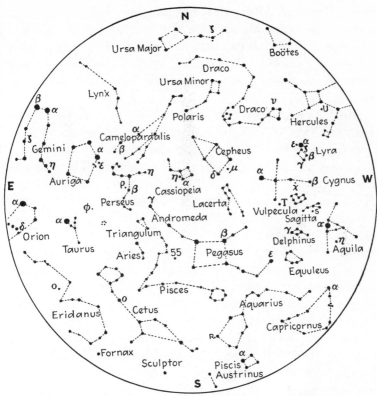

Chart of Autumn and Winter Skies

The map above shows the accepted geometrical patterns of all the constellations visible at 9 p.m., November 6 in latitude 40°N. Chief stars listed for study in the chapters on "Double and Multiple Stars" and "Variable Stars" are indicated, as are the first-magnitude stars, which are the following:

α Geminorum—Castor	α Tauri—Aldebaran	α Aquilae—Altair
β Geminorum—Pollux	α Lyrae—Vega	α Piscis Austrini—Fomalhaut
α Orionis—Betelgeuse	α Cygni—Deneb	α Aurigae—Capella

Seven Brothers. Although it has long been called the Seven Sisters, there are only six stars that can be seen at a glance, whereas at least 250 can be recognized in the cluster with a telescope. Sometimes November is called the Pleiad month because this group is so prominent in the eastern sky in the early evening.

Most spectacular group of the winter season is Orion, the Hunter. Two first-magnitude stars, Betelgeuse and Rigel, decorate this constellation area and several of the second brightest are included within its boundaries. Three bright stars equally spaced in a straight row form the belt of the Hunter, three more represent the sword, and five are prominent in the figure of the man. Betelgeuse in the right shoulder, Bellatrix in the left, Rigel in the left foot and Saiph in the right are easy to recognize. Two of the stars of the belt are fine doubles, one in the sword is in a magnificent nebula, the star in the right shoulder is one of the largest known, and Rigel has about the greatest intrinsic brightness of any star.

Since the belt of Orion shows the location of the celestial equator, Orion's head and shoulders belong to the northern hemisphere, and his legs and feet lie south of the celestial equator. Since all diurnal motion of the sky through the hours of the night takes place parallel to the celestial equator, it is well to know the location of Orion's belt. It can also guide you to the eye of the Bull and the nose of the Big Dog. Trace along the belt toward the northwest of Orion and you come to Aldebaran in Taurus. Trace along the belt toward the southeast of the Hunter and you encounter the brightest star in all the sky, Sirius, the Dog Star. Although the Greeks and the Romans identified this brightest star with the Dog, the Egyptians interpreted it as the beak of a bird. Watching for the time when Sirius rose just before the sun, the Egyptians measured the length of the year and devised a fairly successful calendar.

Sirius is one of the nearer stars. Although some 50 trillion miles separate it from the earth, it is very near compared with other stars. That helps to explain its brightness (its magnitude is −1.58), and also makes clear why the Dog Star is one of a number of suns that seem to have shifted in relation to their neighbor stars since people first made record of the sky. Hipparchus discovered that in his time Sirius and Vega both seemed to appear in slightly different relation to their neighbors than they did to the Egyptians. Prompted by this discovery he made careful study and finally noticed the shift of that reference point, the vernal equinox, too. He decided that the place of the sun on the first day of spring was creeping slowly westward along the zodiac with the centuries. Thus he is credited with the discovery of the precession of the equinoxes. Now we know that, as 26,000 years pass, the earth wobbles once upon its axis like a dying top. This motion makes the position of the celestial pole and consequently that of the equator shift continuously against the background of stars. As a result, different stars become pole stars; and the position occupied by the sun on March 21, as it crosses the equator at the vernal equinox, slowly shifts along the ecliptic with the centuries.

Although precession makes the stars' places appear to change in relation to points of reference in the sky, it does not affect their relationship to one another. However, the actual motions of the stars themselves will change the stars' places in the course of time. Many thousands of years are required before most of the stars change noticeably their apparent places, but for Sirius the change is more easily observable because it is so near.

Companion to the Big Dog, Canis Major, with its brilliant first-magnitude Sirius, is the Little Dog, Canis Minor, with its bright star Procyon. Between the two Dogs a group of faint stars represents Monoceros, the Unicorn. Monoceros, however, is like Vulpecula, Lacerta, and Sagitta —a real test of the star-gazer's seeing ability.

Just as there are two Dogs so are there twin boys, Castor

and Pollux. The Twins belong in the zodiacal constellation Gemini, one of the 12 star groups along the ecliptic. Castor and Pollux are much closer together than Sirius and Procyon, since about 4° separate the first pair but four times that distance separates the latter.

Of course, this is just the way they appear on the celestial sphere when seen from the earth. From some other place, their arrangement would seem different. Actually millions upon millions of miles lie between the Twins, and one is nearly twice as far from us as the other. Describing their relation to each other in degrees is just like drawing their places on a map. One point upon the map may represent a mountain 18,000 feet high, while another point upon that flat paper may represent an ocean depth many miles below sea level. So a map of the sky represents the stars as we see them and gives no indication of the fact that some may lie 10,000 times as far away as others.

Gemini could be called the "Times Square" of the sky, for like the cross-roads of the world it entertains all kinds of visitors. On its way around the zodiac, each month, the moon passes through its boundaries. Once each year at the summer solstice the sun passes near Eta Geminorum, and summer begins in the northern hemisphere. Shooting stars each year in December seem to radiate from Gemini. Close beside Eta, in 1781, Sir William Herschel discovered a new world, the planet Uranus. Beside Delta Geminorum, in 1930, Clyde Tombaugh finally identified a tiny speck upon the photographic plate as the ninth planet in the sun's family—Pluto. Double stars, variable stars, clusters, nebulae can all be located within the boundaries of this constellation area.

No wonder, then, that the nights of winter in the northern hemisphere offer great reward to the star-gazer. The brightest stars, the most spectacular constellations, the longest nights—all these serve to make the cold season ideal for observation of the stars.

4

Spring and Summer Skies

LEO, the Lion, is one of the 12 zodiacal constellations and among the most ancient of star groups. Its sickle-shaped head and triangular tail are easy to identify as it crosses high over the southern horizon early in the evenings of April and May. One easy way to locate it is to find the Great Dipper in the north and follow the pointer stars in the opposite direction from the pole star. Down through the bottom of the Dipper bowl, an imaginary line will lead right to the head of the Lion and on to the brilliant star Regulus in his heart.

It is said that this group received its name because the sun's station was here when the early Egyptians watched for the inundations of the Nile. At this season the lions came down to drink, so a likeness of a lion was pictured in the stars. The brightest star in the group, Regulus, is one of the nearer neighbors of the sun, and it is over 140 times as luminous intrinsically as the sun. It is the faintest of the first-magnitude stars. Because it is one of the 20 brightest stars, is prominent in the zodiac, and is especially close to the ecliptic, it has been carefully plotted and constantly watched for centuries.

Hipparchus, in comparing the skies of his day with charts made hundreds of years before his time, discovered that Regulus and certain other stars appeared to have changed their positions. Not the stars, but the framework of reference imposed upon them, had shifted. This westward precession has now carried the autumnal equinox along the ecliptic to a point in western Virgo just south of the Lion's tail. Leo possesses a blue second-magnitude star, Denebola, or Beta Leonis, in the tail, and one of the sky's finest doubles, Gamma, in the sickle. The yellow-and-green stars of which it is composed can be seen with a 3-inch telescope. A larger glass than this is necessary to give proper separation to the triple components of Alpha, for, although Regulus itself is first magnitude, its companions are eighth and thirteenth magnitude.

Gamma in Virgo is also a double with an eighth-magnitude companion—one easily visible in a 3-inch glass. The same telescope will find a rich field of clusters and nebulae between Leo and Virgo. Herschel was so impressed with the multitude of the telescopic objects there that he called the region the "realm of the nebulae".

The only first-magnitude star in Virgo is Spica. A blue-white sun of great brilliance, Spica is so far away that its light requires 192 years to travel across the space that separates it from the earth. Since light travels 186,000 miles a second, 6 trillion miles a year, it is obvious that Spica must be brighter than the sun but unbelievably farther away. It has a tiny invisible companion which was discovered while analyzing its light with a spectroscope.

Cancer, the Crab, is the next zodiacal group west of Leo. During the month in which the sun appears to pass through this section of the zodiacal band, the Crab is, of course, invisible. It is inconspicuous most of the rest of the year, as well, for only faint stars compose the figure. A misty patch in the center of the constellation is called Praesepe. It is really a cluster of thousands of suns so distant that only on a clear night can they be seen with the naked eye; only with a fair telescope can they be separated, even at the edge of the group.

Between Cancer and the horizon can be found a little pentagon of stars that picture the head of Hydra, the Sea-serpent. The most extensive constellation of the whole sky, Hydra winds beneath Cancer, Leo, Virgo, and Libra. A full 120°, one-third the way around the heavens, the spangled serpent stretches. Yet over its whole length it has but one bright star, a second-magnitude one in its heart. Cor Hydrae, the Heart of Hydra, is properly called Alpha Hydrae, and another name is Alphard.

Several small constellations are arranged along the back of the serpent. Close to Alphard, in fact lying directly between Alphard and Regulus, rests Sextans. A little farther to the east Crater, the Cup, balances on the serpent's back south of Denebola in the Lion's tail. Still farther toward the tail, close to Virgo, perches Corvus, the Crow. Corvus, by the way, is a convenient little group to know. If you ever want to locate the Southern Cross, just find Corvus, and Crux is directly south of it. One can always find Corvus by starting with the Great Dipper, following the curve of the Dipper's handle south to the bright star Arcturus, continuing on about the same distance to sparkling Spica, and then south again an equal distance to Corvus.

Next group along the zodiac east of Virgo is Libra, the Scales, once represented as a balance of justice. The constellation is almost a square, or diamond, between Scorpius and Virgo. Alpha in Libra is a double star separable with field-glasses, while Beta is the only bright green star in the heavens.

Far more spectacular than either of its neighbors, Scorpius is the best known zodiacal group of the summer months. With its brilliant red star, Antares, and its long curving tail, the Scorpion is easy to recognize. Antares is a giant sun 400 times the diameter of our own and tremendously distant from us. It was well known to the ancients, and modern astronomers have found that it has a tiny green companion. Antares is occasionally hidden by the moon and, when such an occultation occurs, is a startling sight to observe with the telescope.

Stars of the Spring Skies

The map above shows positions and accepted geometric patterns for all the constellations visible at 9 p.m. March 6 in latitude 40°N. Identification of the star groups may be made by comparison with the chart on the opposite page.

In use, this map should be held overhead and oriented according to the compass points indicated. It will then show the stars as they appear in the sky. The stars visible here at 9 p.m. March 6 will also be visible at 7 p.m. April 6 and at 11 p.m. February 6.

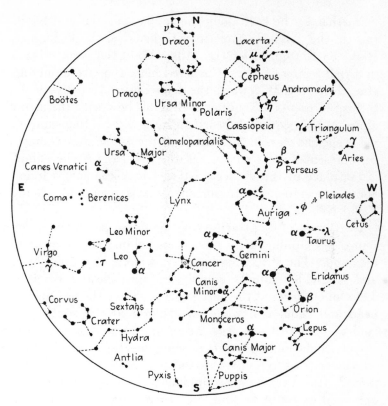

Chart of the Spring Skies

The map above shows the accepted geometrical patterns of all the constellations visible at 9 p.m. March 6 in latitude 40°N. Chief stars listed for study in the chapters on "Double and Multiple Stars" and "Variable Stars" are indicated, as are the first-magnitude stars, which are the following:

α Aurigae—Capella	α Geminorum—Castor	β Orionis—Rigel
α Leonis—Regulus	β Geminorum—Pollux	α Canis Majoris—Sirius
α Tauri—Aldebaran	α Orionis—Betelgeuse	α Canis Minoris—Procyon

Farther to the east along the zodiac, one can find Sagittarius, the Archer, sometimes called the Milk Dipper. Right on the border of the Milky Way, the Archer is set in a rich region of stars. Gathered here, too, are numerous star clusters that reward the telescopist. Actually Sagittarius represents a Centaur holding his bow with the arrow aimed at the Scorpion's heart. In India several thousands of years ago the stars in this section of the zodiac were thought to represent a horse's head. Off the tip of the Archer's bow is the place of the winter solstice, where the sun is found about December 21. Important in this region too is the Trifid Nebula.

Northwest of Sagittarius is an immense pentagon which represents Ophiuchus, a physician, holding the Serpent in his hands. The straggling figure runs along the Milky Way and is divided almost equally by the celestial equator. Thus an observer at the north pole could see the physician's head and shoulders, while an explorer at the south pole could see his feet and legs. According to an ancient story, this constellation represents Aesculapius, the first physician, who attempted to revive Orion after the Scorpion had killed him. In the vast area of Ophiuchus a new star suddenly appeared in 123 A.D. and five others have appeared since then. Despite the fact that Ophiuchus is not considered one of the 12 zodiacal constellations, the sun spends $18\frac{1}{2}$ days within its boundaries while passing from Scorpius to Sagittarius.

Next group to cross the meridian after Sagittarius is Capricornus, the Sea Goat. Composed of relatively faint stars, the figure is fairly easy to recognize in a dark sky because of its symmetrical shape. Really it looks more like a butterfly than like a goat. Represented as a goat by the Babylonians, it was imagined to be an antelope by the Hindus, a narwhal by the Aztecs, an ox by the Chinese. As long ago as the year 2449 B.C. the Chinese observed and recorded a gathering here of all five planets visible to the unaided eye. The careful observer may find a star of sapphire-blue less than 1° north of the star 15 Sagittae.

Through this group passed the sun long ago when it reached its greatest declination south. Therefore, the place where the sun was seen overhead at that time was called the Tropic of Capricorn. Because of the precession of the equinoxes and the westward motion of the points of reference in the sky, the sun is no longer in this constellation when it is overhead at latitude $23\frac{1}{2}°$ south (on the Tropic of Capricorn). The term is still used, however, just as we still use the Tropic of Cancer, although the sun similarly no longer appears in the constellation of Cancer when overhead at latitude $23\frac{1}{2}°$ north.

Following the Goat across the meridian, Aquarius, the Water Carrier, is the next group along the zodiac. On the stones of the Babylonians it was represented as a man with a water jar, although the Arabs imagined it a mule carrying water barrels. There are no bright stars in the whole area and the group is not easy to identify. The easiest way to locate it is to find Fomalhaut, a first-magnitude star just south of it, and the corner of Pegasus just north of it. Then with considerable imagination you can trace out the water jar, the holder of the jar, and a stream of water pouring into the mouth of the Southern Fish, Piscis Austrinus.

Most prominent of all the spring groups, Leo can be seen in the early evening from March to June. Succeeding it Boötes dominates the early evenings of July and August with the crown in Hercules close by. Directly south of Corona, Scorpius is the outstanding zodiacal group for the summer season. The appearance of Capricornus above the southern horizon signifies late night hours of summer or the evening hours of the coming fall, to observers in the northern hemisphere. When Fomalhaut crosses the south in the early evening, summer is over; and high above, the great Square of Pegasus warns us of the presence of autumn and the approach of winter. When once more the winter

Stars of the Summer Skies

The map above shows positions and accepted geometric patterns for all the constellations visible at 9 p.m. July 1 in latitude 40°N. Identification of the star groups may be made by comparison with the chart on the opposite page.

In use, this map should be held overhead and oriented according to the compass points indicated. It will then show the stars as they appear in the sky. The stars visible here at 9 p.m. July 1 will also be visible at 7 p.m. August 1 and at 11 p.m. June 1.

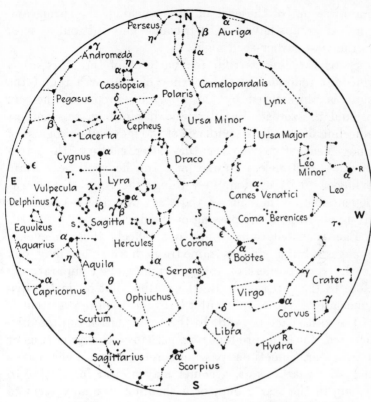

Chart of the Summer Skies

The map above shows the accepted geometrical patterns of all the constellations visible at 9 p.m. July 1 in latitude 40°N. Chief stars listed for study in the chapters on "Double and Multiple Stars" and "Variable Stars" are indicated, as are the first-magnitude stars, which are the following:

α Aurigae—Capella	α Aquilae—Altair	α Boötis—Arcturus
α Cygni—Deneb	α Leonis—Regulus	α Virginis—Spica
α Lyrae—Vega		α Scorpii—Antares

stars rise out of the east in early evening, the spring and summer groups have run their course and drift out of sight in the west earlier each night.

So as the seasons roll, the patterns of the stars are a constant reminder of the journey of the earth round the sun, as represented by the apparent circuit of the sun around the zodiac. Familiar and fascinating, this endless wheeling of the sky is evidence of the inevitable progress of time. Year after year, century after century, the earth pursues its timeless course, and the heavens bear mute evidence to its motion. Few things there are that are as dependable as the shift of the stars with the seasons, the rising of the sun, the passing of the days.

Each constellation group that reflects these heavenly changes is but a window-frame through which one may look to the very borders of space. Bright stars comparatively close to the earth compose the outline, but off in the distance are others even brighter but faint to our eyes because of the vast space beyond. In the constellation outline may be a red star or a rare blue one, perhaps a cluster of suns or a twin star. Sometimes passing close at hand, much nearer than the nearest star, a comet may appear for a time to belong in the star group, or a shooting star may seem to fall from that familiar section. They are but passing visitors, framed for the moment on that section of the sky. A planet, too, may swing this way, and for a time seem one with the other members of the constellation, but as it moves on in the confines of its orbit, another constellation will soon offer it a background. Transient minor planets are occasional visitors within the constellation outline—but near and fast-moving, they too soon journey on to some other region. A framework, the constellation gives a view into the distant depths of space beyond the very limits of our own galaxy, and off to the neighborhood of other island universes.

Constant for the period of a human life and the entire

span of a nation's history, the constellations are almost imperceptibly affected by time. Each of its members a sun moving through space, perhaps alone, perhaps in company with other members of the family—that sun in time will leave some of its neighbors far behind. The familiar figures, slowly shifting through the centuries, will one time dissolve their present outlines as their members become absorbed into new patterns.

But through all the memory of one man the constellations are more constant than the rock of Gibraltar. They offer a guide-post to time, direction, season. They present a pass-port to distant and mysterious regions of space.

5

Stars of the Southern Sky

MOST of the ancient observers of the sky lived in the northern hemisphere, so south of the equator the heavens seem reversed. The constellation of Orion depicts a man standing on his head, the familiar Scorpion waves his tail in the air, and even the Big Dog balances on his nose. Of course, the inversion of the constellations does not occur all at once, for they shift slowly overhead as one travels on the surface of the earth.

Suppose a traveler leaves New York City for the south. As he journeys toward Florida, the stars in the south rise higher, those in the north drop closer to that horizon. If it were an evening in May, he would have his first glimpse of the Southern Cross off the tip of Florida. By the time he reached Havana he would find it well in view. If he should go to the equator he would see the cross one-third of the way up the sky; and at Lake Titicaca, Peru, half-way from horizon to zenith. His journey on through the southern hemisphere would carry it higher and higher.

This same Southern Cross is a guide to the south celestial pole. Like the Great Bear in the north, it indicates the location of the pole and therefore is often employed by navigators seeking to establish their place upon the earth. In May and June it can be found early in the evening above the southern horizon, clearly outlined by four stars of almost equal brilliance. Alpha is at the foot of the figure, nearest the south pole. Gamma is at the top, Beta and

CRUX

A magnificent close-up of Crux, the Southern Cross, showing the famous "Coalsack" dark nebula to the lower left. It lies in a rich region of the Milky Way. When transiting the meridian, the two stars forming the top and foot of the cross are nearly perpendicular to the horizon, and the group becomes a stellar timepiece. (*Union Observatory, Johannesburg, South Africa.*)

Delta in the arms. Gamma is a reddish star, bright to the eye but faint on the blue-sensitive photographic plate. Kappa is also a reddish star and one that appears fainter on the photographic plate than in the sky. Surrounding Kappa, though, are over 100 stars in a cluster.

From top to bottom this Southern Cross, Crux, measures 6°—no taller than the distance between the pointers of the Dipper. It covers, in fact, an area about one-half that of the bowl of the Dipper—about $\frac{1}{2900}$ of the sky. But, while within the Dipper's bowl only nine stars are visible, there are within the boundaries of the small constellation Crux 32 stars within reach of the naked eye.

Southeast of Alpha Crucis is the well-known Coal-sack nebula which looks like a great black hole in the sky. When William Herschel saw the first of these objects on his survey of the northern skies he was much impressed, and it is said that he called his sister to the telescope to see the "hole"— a window into outer space. It was to be expected that his son John, exploring the southern skies, would label any similar dark lanes by the same name. But modern astronomers disagree with the Herschels and no longer regard these dark areas that are scattered so generously in the Milky Way as holes. Probably they are great dark clouds of dust and gas that absorb the light of stars that must lie beyond them. Sometimes the "dark nebula" beneath the arm of the Cross is known as the Black Magellanic Cloud.

Two other features of the southern skies bear Magellan's name; they are two hazy patches like detached portions of the Milky Way. There is nothing like them in the northern heavens, and Magellan's expedition reported them to northern peoples among the curiosities seen in the other half of the world. Since then they have always been called the Greater and the Lesser Magellanic Clouds. Also known as Nubecula Major and Nubecula Minor, they are among the first sights for which one searches the southern skies.

[50]

The Greater Cloud is about 7° in diameter, nearly 14 times the full moon; the Lesser, not even 4° in diameter, covers an area not as large as Crux. A full moon occasionally brightens the sky so that it is a little difficult to locate the smaller cloud, but even then the large one can be found with ease.

Examination of these two clouds has shown that they are made of all types of celestial objects that exist in our Milky Way. There are bright stars and faint ones, red stars and blue ones, large suns and small ones, variable stars, star clusters, gaseous nebulae, dark nebulae—a complete array. The Clouds of Magellan are island universes and close neighbors of the Milky Way galaxy which is our home. The small cloud is about 84,000 light-years distant, the large one about 75,000 light-years. When one recalls that light travels 186,000 miles a second and traverses 6 trillion miles in a year, then these floating families of stars seem far away. Photography brings out a haze of stars around them, and their distance apart is about 30,000 light-years.

The Magellanic Clouds are irregular in shape and present a straggling appearance that contrasts sharply with the great spiral in Andromeda and other island universes. Some 3000 variable stars have been recognized in the clouds, among them some which enable astronomers to measure their distance. The Large Cloud is rich in super-giant stars, and 30 globular clusters have been recognized there. In the Greater Cloud is S Doradus, a super-giant variable, 500,000 times as bright as the sun. Some 180,000,000 miles in diameter, it is, except for some super-novae, intrinsically the brightest object known. There too, surrounding 30 Doradus, is the Great Looped Nebula, the largest known gaseous nebula in the universe.

After you have found the Southern Cross and picked out the Clouds of Magellan, the next objects to attract attention are Alpha and Beta Centauri. First and second brightest stars in Centaurus, they are often called Guardians of the

SMALLER MAGELLANIC CLOUD

A companion of the Milky Way Galaxy in its endless trip through space, the Lesser Magellanic Cloud is visible to the unaided eye in Tucana. It has the same types of stars and nebulae as our system. (*Harvard College Observatory.*)

Cross. If you draw an imaginary line through Delta and Beta Crucis (along the cross-bar of Crux), it guides you to these bright stars in Centaurus. The constellation, which represents a figure half-man and half-horse, is one of the largest in the southern sky. It is nearly 45° in length, almost half the distance from the horizon to the zenith.

A particularly interesting and magnificent star is Alpha Centauri. Not only is Alpha Centauri the third brightest star in the heavens, but it is our nearest binary system. The components of Alpha (A and B) occupy 80 years for a revolution around each other. More than this, Alpha happens to be a multiple star, composed of the binary and a third, faint companion (C). The latter, Proxima Centauri, is visible in the telescope—with magnitude about 10.5— and is the nearest neighbor to the sun, being about $4\frac{1}{3}$

light-years away. Although Proxima is over 2° away from Alpha and its companion B, yet it is connected gravitationally with the latter system and is moving through space nearly parallel to it, actually in an enormous curve around Alpha with a period probably over 300,000 years.

Another object in Centaurus for which the amateur astronomer always looks is Omega (ω) Centauri, a hazy patch of light that is the brightest of the globular clusters. This cluster, 18° northwest of Alpha Centauri, is a fine sight with field-glasses and even more beautiful with the telescope. It is composed of some 50,000 stars, more than 100 of which are variable. Brightest and nearest of the 100 or so globular clusters known, this one is some 20,000 light-years distant from the earth.

After a casual glance at the constellations in the south, one is struck with a difference in the constellation figures and names. Although there are some old-fashioned subjects like Ara, the Altar; Columba, the Dove; Musca, the Fly; Pavo, the Peacock; Volans, the Flying Fish; and Corona Australis, the Southern Crown—there are many more modern figures. One finds a Clock, or Horologium; a Compass, Circinus; a Furnace, Fornax; an Easel, Pictor; a Telescope, Telescopium; and even an Air-pump, Antlia. Most of the southern constellation names that we use are of recent origin, for they were not known to the ancients, and all have been described since the time of Magellan.

There are some 27 constellations within 40° of the south pole; whereas in the north only 15 are represented. There are five first-magnitude stars circumpolar for Sydney, Australia, but none in the circumpolar regions for New York. In all the southern sky there are 10 first-magnitude stars, while 13 are visible north of the celestial equator. The section of the heavens circumpolar for 40° south is one richer in constellations and bright stars than an equal area in the northern heavens. In all, the 89 constellations for the whole heavens are about equally divided between the hemispheres and some 6000 stars easily visible to the naked eye are shared almost equally by both hemispheres.

There is no south pole star similar to Polaris in the north. Though no bright star hangs just over the pole, Sigma Octantis, a $5\frac{1}{2}$-magnitude star in Octans, the Octant, is the nearest naked-eye star to the pole. It is not exactly at the pole but about 1° away and so makes a small diurnal circle as the earth spins. Aviators and navigators of the southern hemisphere named the region around Sigma Octantis the south polar pit, because of its lack of bright stars. Of course it is important to know the location of the pole in estimating your latitude in the southern hemisphere. One way to locate it roughly is to draw an imaginary line from Gamma at the top of the Cross through Alpha at the foot and prolong it five times that distance. Another way is to draw an imaginary line from the Large Cloud of Magellan to the smaller one and "turn the corner" an equal distance toward the Cross.

Canopus, or Alpha Carinae, is the brightest star in Carina, the keel and hull of the old ship Argo, which lies near the Small Cloud of Magellan. With magnitude −0.9, Canopus is a super-giant star 40 times as bright as the sun and over 650 light-years away. Well known to the ancients, it was a favorite of the Egyptians and the Babylonians. Another interesting star in this region is Eta Carinae, one of the most remarkable of variables. On a map of 1677 it was ranked with the fourth-magnitude stars. In 1837, however, it was brighter than Canopus, in fact as bright as Sirius. Then it began to fade, had disappeared to the naked eye by 1868, and now can be found only with a telescope as a faint eighth-magnitude sun.

Another part of the ship is Vela, the Sails, northwest of Crux. With Kappa and Delta in Vela, and Epsilon and Iota in Carina, one can make a cross which is almost the exact replica of Crux, although slightly larger. Since this figure is often confused with the real Cross, it is frequently called the False Cross. A line from the top of this figure to the bottom and prolonged five times that distance does not lead to the south celestial pole but off toward the Great Cloud of Magellan. A navigator would find himself far from his destination if he should steer by the wrong cross.

Northwest of Crux lies Vela, but east of Crux beyond Centaurus is Circinus, the Compass. Alpha Circini is the joint of the Compass, while Beta and Gamma are the two points. Not far away one can recognize Triangulum Australe, the Southern Triangle. This is a counterpart to Triangulum in the northern hemisphere, just as Corona Australis is a southern duplicate of the Northern Crown. The Southern Crown lies near the tail of the Scorpion and not far from Ara, the Altar, and Norma, the Level. All these small constellations are composed of second- and third-magnitude stars.

There is one extremely long constellation in the southern hemisphere, Eridanus, the River. It begins near Rigel in Orion, very close to the celestial equator, traces its winding course from Orion to Cetus, past Fornax to Phoenix, and on to Hydrus. The first-magnitude star Achernar, at the southern end of the River, lies about 15° from the Small Magellanic Cloud, and the northern end of this "Mississippi of the Sky" is near the great nebula in Orion. Omicron Eridani is a beautiful triple star well worth examining with a telescope. In this same constellation is located an extraordinary planetary nebula, a great globe of dust and gas surrounding an eleventh-magnitude star. If one traces the course of Eridanus he finds nine constellations along its boundaries: Hydrus to the south, Orion, Lepus, Caelum, and Horologium to the east, Taurus to the north, and Cetus, Fornax, and Phoenix on the west.

The Toucan houses the Lesser Magellanic Cloud and the globular cluster 47 Tucanae. Some 20,000 stars in the cluster blend together to appear as a single star of fourth magnitude. Hydrus encircles the other border of the Lesser Cloud

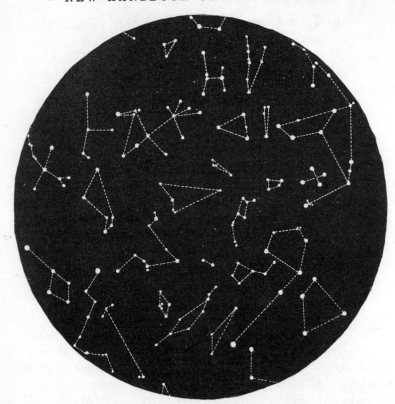

Stars of the Southern Skies

The map above shows the positions and accepted patterns for the constellations within 50° of the south celestial pole. Identification of the star groups may be made by comparison with the chart on the opposite page.

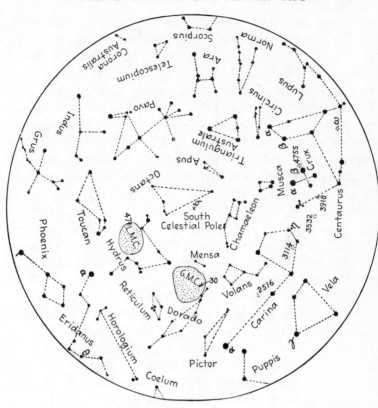

Chart of the Southern Skies

The map above shows the accepted geometrical patterns for the constellations within 50° of the south celestial pole. All the stars listed for study in this chapter are indicated, as well as the first-magnitude stars, which are:

α Carinae—Canopus	β Centauri
α Eridani—Achernar	α Crucis
α Centauri	β Crucis

Constellation names are the official ones in Latin, except Tucana, named in English on the chart.

[57]

of Magellan. Between Hydrus and Dorado, the Swordfish, are the Greater Magellanic Cloud and the tiny constellation Reticulum. Between Dorado and Carina can be found Pictor and Volans. Mensa, the Table Mountain, and Chamaeleon lie nearer to the south celestial pole than Dorado or Carina. Musca, the Fly, lies between the south celestial pole and Crux, while Apus is south of Triangulum.

East of the Scorpion's tail, Corona Australis, Telescopium, Ara, and Pavo, the Peacock, are not far from the south celestial pole. South of Capricornus, the Goat, and Aquarius, the Water Carrier, lie Piscis Austrinus, Indus, and Grus, while nearer to the south pole than Cetus can be found Phoenix and the Toucan and Sculptor. Near the Hydra's head lie Puppis and Pyxis, part of the old ship Argo. The rest of the ship, Vela, and Carina are still closer to the south celestial pole.

For the star-gazer who spends much of his time in the north, it is interesting to know the relation of southern constellations to groups familiar in the north. For instance, on the same hour-circle to the south of Aries lie Fornax, Eridanus, Horologium, and Hydrus. In order, too, from Taurus to the south celestial pole, are Caelum, Dorado, and part of Mensa. South of Gemini, bordering right ascension $6^h 40^m$, lie Puppis, Canopus in Carina, sections of Pictor, Volans, and Mensa. South of Cancer can be discovered Pyxis, Vela, Volans, Chamaeleon, while along the same hour-circle with Leo are Antlia, Vela, Carina, and Chamaeleon.

Beyond Virgo toward the south pole we encounter Centaurus, Crux, Musca, and more of Chamaeleon. The hour-circle of $15^h 20^m$ through Libra also cuts Lupus, parts of Norma, Circinus, Triangulum Australe, and Apus. On the hour-circle through Scorpius can also be traced Ara, a bit of the Southern Triangle, and Apus, while near-by another cuts Sagittarius, then goes south through Corona Australis, Telescopium, and Pavo. South of Capricornus on

20^h40^m are Microscopium, Indus, and a bit of Pavo while 2 hours away, south of Aquarius, are Piscis Austrinus, Grus, Tucana, and some of Indus. A line through Pisces goes south to Sculptor, Phoenix, and Tucana.

In general these meridians have been selected as nearly central as possible on the zodiacal groups and on the average are 2 hours apart.

When one discovers that Crux lies south of Virgo, the Greater Magellanic Cloud is in the same hour-circle with Taurus, and the Lesser Cloud in the same right ascension with Pisces, it is easy to find the other neighboring groups.

Familiar and friendly to the people of the south, Crux, Alpha and Beta Centauri, the Magellanic Clouds, and the rich star fields of the Milky Way are foreign and fascinating to the traveler from the north.

6

The Planets

THERE were five of them, and they moved about among the "fixed" stars. Men who looked heavenward were quick to call them the planets, which meant that they were wanderers.

They were different from the stars in more ways than one. Not only did they wander, always staying within the constellations that lie along the ecliptic, but they shone with a steady light that was somehow different from the twinkling of the stars. Early astronomers knew very little about them, and it was not until Galileo turned his telescope on the skies that they began to learn. After that, but very slowly (at the rate of approximately one every 100 years), astronomers began adding to the number of the planets so that we now know eight in addition to the earth.

They are the sun's children, brothers and sisters of the earth, and all neighbors in the solar system. But they are not very close neighbors as judged by earthly standards. If, in constructing a diagram on the ground, we assume the sun to be stationary, and make a mark a little less than 5 inches away from it, that mark might represent the position of Mercury, the nearest planet to the sun.

At $8\frac{1}{2}$ inches we would make another mark, for Venus; and at 1 foot we could indicate the distance of our own earth. Mars would be $1\frac{1}{2}$ feet from the sun; and then, between 2 and 4 feet, we would make a series of marks to represent the asteroids—the minor planets which are

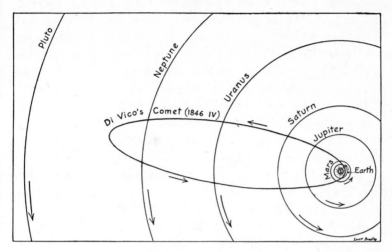

THE SOLAR SYSTEM

A plan view of orbits of the solar system. Drawn to scale, with one comet, Di Vico's, included, the diagram gives an accurate impression of the relative distances between the planetary orbits.

discussed elsewhere. We should have to pace off a bit more than 5 feet from the sun, though, to get to Jupiter's position; and $9\frac{1}{2}$ feet for Saturn; and then walk out 19 feet from the sun for the position of Uranus.

Still on the same scale, Neptune would be a full 30 feet from the sun and the newly discovered Pluto would be 40 feet. The earth, remember, was only 1 foot from the sun, and that foot represented an average distance of 93,003,000 miles—the astronomical unit.

As for size, the earth is large to us with its 7918-mile diameter. Yet Jupiter, the largest of the planets, is more than 10 times the diameter of the earth; and the entire planetary system of Mercury, Venus, Earth, Mars, Jupiter, Saturn, Uranus, Neptune, and Pluto would have to be multiplied six hundredfold to make a body as big as the sun.

And there we have, roughly, a picture of the planetary system as known today, although we have not included the zodiacal light, comets, meteors, and satellites. It is a picture drawn from the outside, of the planets as seen from a point over their orbits, and consequently a picture we can never see from the earth. For the observer here, with only his eyes to help him, there are five blazing points of light (and perhaps a sixth dim one, if he knows where to look for it).

One of these points of light is elusive. That is Mercury, which stays close to the sun like a child clinging to its mother's apron strings. Because you must look for it so soon after sunset, or before sunrise, there was a famous astronomer, Copernicus, who never saw the planet in all his life. There is also, however, the story of at least one amateur who has seen Mercury not once but 150 times.

It's all in knowing how. The planet is best seen as an "evening star" in the spring, and as a "morning star" in the fall. But there are *six* periods in every year when it is fairly well placed for observation, these periods occurring when the planet seems to us to be at its greatest distance east or west of the sun. These times are known, incidentally, as greatest eastern elongation (when the planet is an "evening star") and greatest western elongation (when it is a "morning star").

Obviously, since there are six periods, they are spaced approximately 2 months apart. During each of these periods, which last about 2 weeks, Mercury is visible in the morning or evening sky for only about 1 hour at a time.

When it can be seen, Mercury presents itself as a "star" of the first magnitude, varying in brilliance between Aldebaran and Sirius. Look sharply, and you will be able to detect its characteristic orange coloring; turn a 2- or 3-inch telescope on it and you will see that it undergoes phases similar to the moon's; they are explained in the diagram on page 65.

Under the best conditions details on the planet's surface are hazy and indistinct, but the famous Italian astronomer, Schiaparelli, was able to discover faint permanent markings, features which two equally famous American scientists

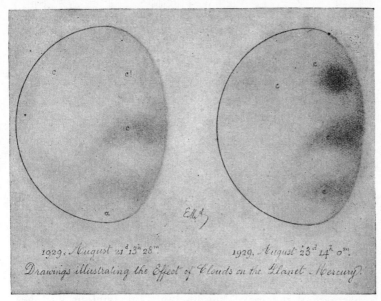

1929. August 21ᵈ 13ʰ 28ᵐ   1929, August 23ᵈ 14ʰ 0ᵐ

Drawings illustrating the Effect of Clouds on the Planet Mercury.

MERCURY

The smallest major planet known to man as seen by the Greek astronomer, E. M. Antoniadi, with Europe's greatest refracting telescope, the 32-inch instrument at Meudon. Existence of a slight atmosphere seems to be indicated by movable dust clouds which are different in the two figures.

corroborated. Edward Emerson Barnard described them as closely resembling the naked-eye markings on the moon, and Percival Lowell drew them as streaks.

Barnard's comment on a resemblance to the moon, by coincidence, points out the fact that tiny Mercury, with its diameter of 3000 miles, is not much bigger than the moon and is indeed smaller than two of the satellites of Jupiter. It is the baby of the planet family, if you except the thousands of asteroids.

And because it is so near the sun—only 36,000,000 miles away—Mercury at one point in its orbit receives 10 times as much heat and light per unit area as the earth. It keeps virtually the same face turned constantly toward the sun because its rotation period of 88 days is equal to its revolution period. On that eternally bright side of the planet lead would melt and run away in rivulets; and here too the sun never sets.

Over on the other side of the little sphere, however, it is cold enough to freeze not only water but some of the gases in the air, and here the sun never rises and the stars always shine. There is however, a fairly wide zone on Mercury, along the "dawn" and "twilight" lines, where the sun alternately rises and sets, because the planet's speed in its orbit varies while its rotation period remains constant. But even here the surface is unprotected by much of an atmosphere, and the constant change from hot to cold must result in a belt of great cracks and crevices between the side that is scorched by the sun and the side that is hidden in darkness. Mercury is an interesting but forbidding planet.

For the planet Venus, no exact rotation period, or day, has yet been satisfactorily determined, because of the impermanent nature of the markings on its cloud surfaces. Recent spectroscopic studies indicate a period of a few weeks. On Venus, however, the heat that pours down on the sunlit side is less intense because of two factors—its greater distance from the sun, and its atmosphere which, while it holds a great deal of warmth, distributes it evenly around the planet.

Venus and the earth might almost be called the twin sisters of the solar system. The orbit of Venus, which the planet travels in 225 days, is nearer to a perfect circle than that of any other planet, and that of the earth is not far behind in this respect. The two planets are approximately of the same size, Venus having a diameter of 7575 miles and the earth having one of 7918 miles, and they are closer together in space than any other major planets.

Nearness and heavy clouds around Venus account for the appearance of the planet in the sky. For Venus is not merely visible. With the exception of the sun and moon, she is the brightest object normally seen in the heavens and at

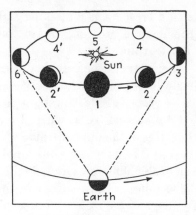

PLANETARY PHASES

Mercury and Venus, the two inferior planets, go through phases similar to those of the moon. Diagram shows:

1—Inferior conjunction
2 and 2'—Greatest brilliancy
3—Greatest western elongation (morning star)
4 and 4'—Gibbous phase
5—Superior conjunction
6—Greatest eastern elongation (evening star)

her best outshines Sirius, the brightest of the stars, by 13 times. Sometimes, when there is no moon to interfere, she is bright enough to cast a shadow.

And not only is she far more conspicuous than Mercury, she is also visible for greater intervals of time. Like the other planet, Venus is often out of sight on the other side of the sun, but these periods of invisibility are not nearly so frequent as those of Mercury. And, unlike the smaller planet, Venus can be seen for as much as 4 hours at a time, making her appearances in the same way as Mercury. She slides down the celestial vault, trailing the sun in the evening, and weeks later climbs into the sky before the sun in the early hours of morning.

In either case, turn a pair of binoculars on her. With a magnification of 10 diameters and upward you can see her going through phases like those of Mercury and the moon. And the thin crescent is a striking sight, a gleaming miniature of the moon's crescent phase, because at that time Venus is most brilliant.

Both of the inner planets, paradoxically enough, do this same thing and stand out most when only a small section of their illuminated surface is reflecting light to the earth. It's easily explained by noting that when they are in their "full" phase they are on the opposite side of the sun, which means, in the case of Mercury, an additional distance from the earth of over 72,000,000 miles and, in the case of Venus, one of 134,000,000 miles. (The figures are the diameters of their orbits, if you care to check.)

So they are brightest when near the earth. But not when they are at their very nearest, because then they are almost directly between the earth and the sun, and the dark sides of the planets are presented to us. The greatest brilliance comes at a certain critical angle between the greatest elongation east or west and the point directly between the earth and sun, when the nearness of the planet and the width of the crescent combine to the best advantage. The crescent Venus appears to us six times greater in diameter than the full Venus.

To return again to our field-glasses and telescopes, Venus in her crescent phase offers a yellowish-white surface to small instruments. If you turn a 6- or 12-inch telescope on the planet (and remember that thousands of amateur astronomers make such telescopes) you may be able to detect spots on the surface. It is a rare thing for such an instrument, but it can be done by patient and continued effort. These spots, by the way, are not on the surface of the planet proper, but on the upper levels of the cloud blanket that surrounds Venus. Barnard, with powerful observatory instruments, saw "large dusky spots" which he believed were not permanent.

The atmosphere of Venus remains an enigma to astronomers. It exists, but no one knows how deep it is because

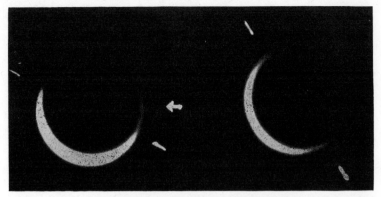

VENUS HAS A HEAVY ATMOSPHERE

And one proof of the fact is contained in this unusual photograph which shows
the reflected light of the sun appearing in the planet's atmosphere beyond the
horns of the crescent. (*Lowell Observatory.*)

of that same layer of clouds. When the planet goes through
one of its rare transits, and its disc is projected against the
sun, a light ring 25,000 feet deep is observed which is undoubtedly part of the atmosphere. Venus shows no positive
proof of oxygen or water vapor, although there is carbon
dioxid in the upper layers. Underneath there may be the
other necessary elements for life. Down on the surface, our
imagination may picture plant and perhaps animal life in
the midst of such a steaming swamp as characterized the
earth's early ages; we do not know. Absence of permanent
markings prevents our knowing Venus's rotation period.
Indications are that its day is a few earth-weeks long.

Mars is an excellent subject for small telescopes. It
presents its famous reddish color to the naked eye (a color
which persists on its surface when viewed with large instruments), and under a small telescope it offers opportunities
to observe details. Even so small an instrument as a 4- or
5-inch telescope will do, under the right "seeing" conditions.

Under a telescopic magnification of 200 to 350 diameters,
grayish or greenish markings stand out against the reddish
background. At less than 300 diameters the polar caps

appear, and so too does the dark wedge of Syrtis Major extending toward the north. Other dark areas can be picked up as well, and as telescopic power increases (try it sometime with a 6- to 12-inch reflector) the number of features visible increases.

There are several reasons why we know so much about Martian conditions and surface details. Mars has, of course, long been a subject of great popular interest, but many known facts would still be a mystery were it not for the amazing clarity of the planet's atmosphere. Slight clouds—whether of dust or some other composition—appear only infrequently, and the Martian air is so transparent as to permit excellent opportunities for study of surface detail.

Then, too, when the planet is in opposition—when the sun, earth, and Mars are in a straight line—it comes nearer, at 34,000,000 miles, than any other major planet except Venus. At times Mars may be observed going through a slight gibbous phase, although it never goes so far as to become a crescent, or even as to enter the "half-moon" phase.

Mars differs greatly from the earth in size, having a diameter of only 4216 miles. In almost every other point, however, she compares favorably and as a result has become the favorite home for life on one of the planets as conceived in the popular mind.

Nor does this suspicion of life on Mars necessarily remain outside the world of science, for many reputable astronomers—possibly a majority of them—believe that there is at least plant life on the planet. And the existence of vegetation presupposes conditions which might possibly support some kind of animal life.

The question of life on Mars probably got its start when the Italian astronomer Schiaparelli observed strange markings on the surface and termed them *canali*, which in his language meant channels. He was misinterpreted, though, and the lines became known as canals, a term which carried with it the implication of artificiality, of something which had been constructed by intelligent beings.

Percival Lowell observed these canals and expressed the open belief that they were constructed by an advanced race of beings who dug them to bring water down from the poles. But the character and extent of the canals is debatable, for to see them is a question of seeing detail at the extreme limit of visibility. Future telescopes may settle the questions about their nature for all time, although observers now report that they have seen sections near the canals turn blue-green in one season and dark brown in another.

Meanwhile, these are the known facts that figure in the arguments concerning life on Mars:

The atmosphere contains small amounts of oxygen and water vapor, which have been estimated quantitatively as $\frac{1}{1000}$ as much oxygen and 5 per cent as much water vapor as are found in the atmosphere of the earth. The equatorial temperature would probably support life as found on the earth, for it rises to 80°F. The axis of the planet is inclined to the ecliptic at substantially the same angle as that of the earth, which, combined with a similarity between the orbital motions and conditions of the two planets, would result in roughly approximate seasons. These seasons are twice as long, however, as those of the earth, because the year consists of 687 days—nearly twice that of the earth. The planet's day is nearly the same as the earth's, for it rotates on its axis in 24 hours 37 minutes.

The planet's polar caps vary in size with the seasons, too, a change which is synchronized with color changes in the region known as Syrtis Major, thought by some astronomers to be a vast area of vegetation. The composition of these polar caps may be either frozen carbon dioxid or frozen water. Because of color variations noted at the edge of the caps, many scientists are inclined to believe that when they melt they turn into a liquid and therefore are not carbon dioxid, which would instead immediately become gaseous.

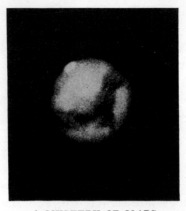

A MYSTERY OF MARS

Both the south polar cap and Syrtis Major, the dark, wedge-shaped area extending toward the north, which appear in this picture, seem to be related in some
manner. The polar cap shrinks and grows with the seasons, and as the polar cap
changes, color variations appear in Syrtis Major. The effect could occur if water
'rom a melting polar ice cap caused vegetation to flourish and grow, according
ᴐ certain authorities. (*Yerkes Observatory.*)

Mars is the first planet in the outward journey from the
sun (again, excluding the earth) which has any moons so
far as we know. There are two of them, tiny little satellites
which were discovered by Asaph Hall at the U. S. Naval
Observatory in 1877. They are too small to be picked up
with any but the largest telescopes, neither being more than
10 miles in diameter. But Phobos, the inner moon, runs
three laps around the planet each day, rising and setting
three times each 24 hours and rising, moreover, in the west
and setting in the east. When it passes the slower Deimos,
observers on Mars would see both of the satellites racing
each other across the sky, with respect to the stars beyond.

Mars, however, is not unique in its set of moons. Jupiter
carries with it a retinue of 12 satellites, four of which are
easily visible in small telescopes. To look at Jupiter and
its satellite system, we must let our gaze wander far beyond
the orbit of Mars and over the asteroid zone. The $4\frac{1}{2}$-feet
distance between the two in the diagram we planned at the

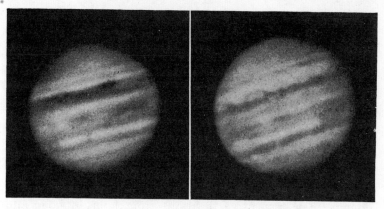

JUPITER

The surface of Jupiter, largest planet in the solar system, is belted by clouds which are characterized by intricate and ever-changing details. Actually, the atmosphere is composed of deadly gases at extremely low temperatures. (*Mt. Wilson Observatory.*)

beginning of the chapter was based on a scale in which each foot represented 93,000,000 miles. Jupiter, despite this greater distance, usually seems brighter than the red planet because it is so much bigger and because it reflects nearly three times as much as Mars does of the sunlight it receives.

Jupiter is the largest of the planets and curious astronomers have timed its speed of rotation upon its axis at 9 hours and 55 minutes. As a result of this speed, there is a huge bulge at the equator, so great that the diameter of the planet taken through the equator is 88,698 miles, or nearly 4000 miles more than from pole to pole.

A pair of binoculars or field-glasses shows a tiny disc—magnification of 18 times will do very well, but is even more than is needed. With a larger instrument, Jupiter resolves into a series of red, yellow, tan, and brown shadings, as well as a wealth of other telescopic detail.

Exceptionally good "seeing" is not necessary to get a clear view of Jupiter's surface markings, and frequently a slight haze or smokiness in the air will help to steady the image. The cloud belts, for which the planet is famous, will

appear in low-powered telescopes as parallel bands stretching across the disc. And another feature that the amateur
will—or may—be able to observe is the "Great Red Spot"
which was identified on drawings made of the surface in
1859 and has disappeared and reappeared during succeeding
years. A marking of perhaps similar nature, discovered early
in the twentieth century and known as the South Tropical
Disturbance, may also be observed.

But it is in its moons that Jupiter contains the greatest
telescopic treasure for the amateur. The four that are visible
run a merry race with each other around the planet and
change their respective positions from hour to hour and
night to night. They aren't hard to identify with an ephemeris, and they can be followed for hours as they speed in
front of Jupiter, throwing their shadows on the planet,
vanish behind its giant disc, or plunge suddenly into its
deep shadow. Binoculars will locate them, if outside the disc.

It is easier to watch one of the moons throw its shadow on
Jupiter than to watch the moon itself cross in front of the
planet. The satellites often become lost against the background when in transit and may drop out of sight—even
in large telescopes. The shadow, being a black dot, is fairly
easy to follow as it glides over the cloud surface of the planet
(and it may even change its shape at times because the
surface it passes over is uneven). The satellites in transit
require at least a 6-inch telescope, but the shadow thrown
on the planet is visible with a 4-inch instrument at
times.

Despite the fact that they seem to move haphazardly, appearing, perhaps, all on the same side of the planet one
night, then scattering around it the next, the four moons
of Jupiter present an orderly miniature of the solar system.
Now and then one of them may vanish; and very rarely all
four of them may be in front of or behind the planet. Yet
each has a definite period (which you may time for yourself
and then check with an ephemeris); each has a definite

RINGED PLANET

Saturn, ringed wonder of the solar system and second largest of the planets, together with Titan, one of its nine moons, just below the disc. Viewed with a telescope, the planet actually looks as beautiful as in any picture. (*Drawing by Antoniadi.*)

path; and every one of these four travels around the primary in the same direction.

Of the 12 Jovian moons the outermost three revolve in an opposite or retrograde direction, from east to west. This has given rise to discussion as to whether they might not be captured asteroids and therefore not originally members of Jupiter's system. The four easily visible in small telescopes are considerably larger and brighter than the others. It is worth mentioning that Ganymede and Callisto, of Jupiter's train, are bigger than the planet Mercury.

There is still another planet in the group that are classed as "naked-eye" objects, and although Jupiter may claim fame for its unrivaled system of moons, this other world—Saturn—has a set of rings that is unequaled in the entire universe. That is, our scientific caution prompts us to say, the rings are unequaled so far as we know.

In the eyepiece of a small telescope, they surprize observers with their beauty even though it be expected. Composed of millions of tiny moonlets, the rings appear as a thin, flat circlet poised some 7000 miles above the planet's equator. They are 41,500 miles wide from inner to outer edge, and by comparison with their width they are thinner than tissue paper—not more than 10 miles thick.

This microscopic thinness causes the rings to disappear when viewed edge-on. At such a time they are visible only in the most powerful instruments as a thin needle piercing the planet. At other times the rings may seem inclined upward or downward, for they are really inclined at an angle of 27° to the plane of the planet's orbit and lie in the plane of its equator. As Saturn moves around the sun we see them at varying angles—apparently from above, below, or edge-on, according to the planet's position with respect to the earth. They reflect so much light that when they present their broadest aspect to the earth, Saturn in the sky seems three times brighter than when the rings are edgewise. And when they are edgewise (which occurs every 15 years) they are invisible in small telescopes, nearly so for the very largest.

A medium-sized instrument shows the divisions of the rings clearly. The first one to resolve itself is the dark Cassini division, which divides the system in two and is not hard to detect with a small telescope. On the outer of the two rings thus formed, we may be able to pick up the faint, gray Encke division. And the word "may" is used advisedly, for the Encke strip is elusive and not always visible. On the inner ring there is a gradual shading off on the edge next the planet, a shading which melts into the misty gray border of the "crepe" ring. This foggy curtain on the inside of the ring system is comparatively transparent, and the shape of the planet can often be seen through it. The stars, too, because of the tenuous nature of the crepe ring, can be observed shining through it on occasions.

Saturn throws a shadow across its surrounding belt, a sharp black shape that outlines one rim of the planet; and the rings in turn throw a soft, neatly bordered band upon the planet. This latter shadow falls upon cloud surfaces similar to those of Jupiter, cloud surfaces that are belted just as those of the larger planet. But few details concerning them can be seen unless unusual observing circumstances prevail. Every so often a spot—probably related in nature to the Red Spot of Jupiter—appears, but none with the permanence of Jupiter's marking has yet been observed. The most recent one was a white spot which appeared in 1933.

Where Jupiter whirls upon its axis in a bit under 10 hours, Saturn requires 10 hours and 14 minutes. But Saturn, more oblate than Jupiter, has an equatorial bulge of 7900 miles. It is the second largest member of the sun's planetary family with an equatorial diameter of 75,100 miles.

In addition to her rings, Saturn has nine satellites; and as Jupiter has two larger than Mercury, so has Saturn one. Appropriately enough it is named Titan; it is nearly as large as the planet Mars. But most of Saturn's moons are unfortunately not easy to observe with small instruments, and lucky would be the observer who could pick up any other than Titan in a 3-inch glass. Were he equipped with a 4-inch telescope, however, he might be more fortunate. Taking extreme care to distinguish them from the stars, he should be able to identify Titan, Iapetus, Rhea, Tethys, and Dione (named in the order of observational possibility). Refer, of course, to the *American Ephemeris* for the numerous data necessary to identify them.

So far away from the sun is this planet and so slowly does she pace through the heavens that the earth, after completing a full revolution around the sun, has but to continue for 13 days before we can see Saturn in the same aspect (for example, opposition) as in the year before. If Saturn is far distant, consider the cases of Uranus, Neptune, and Pluto— the three planets discovered since invention of the telescope.

The first one was discovered by William Herschel in 1781,

more or less by accident. The astronomer was making a systematic survey of the stars when he noticed one that refused to remain in its place. That was the planet Uranus, which is about 31,000 miles in diameter and stays on an average of 1,783,000,000 miles away from the sun. It can be picked up as a naked-eye object by people gifted with good eyesight, and a forehand knowledge of where to look for it. At such a time it appears as a sixth-magnitude object.

A 9- to 12-inch telescope, magnifying from 400 to 500 diameters, is needed before Uranus shows any appreciable disc, and then it appears as a tiny green object with faint parallel bands. No permanent markings have been discovered on the surface, but characteristic cloud bands can always be observed with the largest instruments.

The planet has five satellites, all very faint and beyond the reach of any but the largest telescopes. And so amateurs, for the most part, must be content with locating the planet and mapping its path among the stars.

So, too, must we be with Neptune, though here the task of locating the object is more sport. The planet was discovered in 1846 by Adams and Leverrier, working independently on mathematical calculations; and its orbit is just about 1,000,000,000 miles farther out than Uranus. It can be seen with a 2-inch telescope and a magnifying power of 15 diameters; though its 30,000 miles of diameter does not become a disc until we use a telescope of 9 to 12 inches aperture.

At its brightest it is of the eighth magnitude, and the telescope shows a faint greenish color. Its two satellites are quite out of reach for amateurs, but Neptune offers one consolation to the telescopist—once located it can easily be followed for the rest of the season because it spends nearly 14 years in each section of the zodiac. And before you try to locate it you might try reading Appendix II, beginning on page 266, which describes the proper technique to use in hunting telescopic objects.

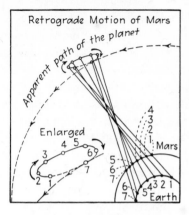

MARS IN RETROGRADE

When the planets are in position 1, Mars appears to be moving normally as seen from the earth. Gradually, however, the earth passes Mars and the red planet *seems* to move more slowly. As a result, in position 2, it apparently starts to move backward, assuming a retrograde motion. It continues until position 6, where the relative motions of the two planets having changed again, it once more assumes its normal forward motion.

If Neptune and Uranus have seemed far from the earth, then Pluto will make them seem near. For this little world, with ½ the earth's diameter, is now the outermost planet, as far as known. It takes 248 years for a single trip around the sun, and twice in each revolution, it crosses the orbit plane of Neptune.

Its orbit, most eccentric in the system, is farther from a circle than that of any of the other major planets. Pluto was discovered in 1930 as the result of years of search begun by Percival Lowell and finished by workers in the Flagstaff Observatory he had founded for planetary research. At that time it was in the constellation of Gemini, but it has since moved over into adjacent Cancer where it will be when you read this (unless you are a bit late), for it remains about 20 years within the borders of each star group. Needless to say, it is completely beyond the range of small telescopes and even taxes the power of a 15-inch refractor.

The giant planets (Jupiter, Saturn, Uranus, Neptune) are

similar to each other but differ widely from the earth, Venus, and Mars. Their atmospheres consist of great layers of the noxious gases, ammonia, and methane. Below this is an immense thickness of hydrogen, underneath which is a thick layer of miles of ice, and at the center the dense rocky core. The ammonia is in minute crystals and the methane gaseous. The cold is inconceivable; surface temperatures are about $-200°F$. on Jupiter to $-300°$ on Neptune. Conditions for any kind of life on these dark, cold, distant, and forbidding worlds would appear impossible.

There is a naked-eye observation which, if made accidentally and without beforehand knowledge of what is happening, is likely to send any amateur scurrying to the library for an explanation. It may be made for any one of the planets, including Mercury and Venus, which are visible when they present this phenomenon, and it consists quite simply of an apparent reversal of direction by the object under observation. Hence it is called retrograde motion.

A planet, Mars for instance, will be seen moving in its accustomed path west to east among the stars, then gradually slowing down, and finally moving east to west, nearly back in the direction from which it had been coming. After a short while, it will resume its old motion again. The explanation, which is clarified in the diagram on page 77, lies in the relative motions of the planet under observation and the earth. The earth has a greater orbital speed than the outer planets, and as it overtakes and passes one of them, that other planet seems at first to move more slowly, then actually to be moving backward. A similar effect results when passengers in one automobile pass another on the road going in the same direction. As the earth swings further along, in its orbit, the other planet seems to resume its former motion. In the sky, Mars and Jupiter apparently describe a retrograde "loop", while for Saturn, Uranus, Neptune, and Pluto, the loop is almost flat, and they seem to "backtrack" along their own paths.

7

The Moon

THE moon is one of the most fascinating of celestial
bodies and almost invariably the object oftenest
viewed by the telescope-user. On account of nearness and
size we see the moon with the naked eye and with small
optical power can observe a wealth of detail on the surface.
It can be observed scientifically with various types of telescopes and cameras, and it is often said we know the
topography of its surface better than we know some parts
of the earth.

The phases of the moon are so obvious a phenomenon
that they are noticed by anyone seeing the moon at any
time. The cause of phases is easy to understand. The moon
is a nearly spherical body and is half-lighted by the sun. As
it circles the earth, varying amounts of the lighted half face
the earth. Except at full-moon time, only a part of the
illuminated spheroid is visible to terrestrials—hence the
effect of phase.

At times of new moon, the moon is between us and the
sun, and at an eclipse of the sun, exactly so, with the moon's
disc silhouetted against the sun. At any other new moon
but that producing a solar eclipse, the moon passes by the
sun either north or south of the latter, and the sunlight falls
on the side of the moon away from the earth; hence the
object is invisible for this reason as well as being obscured
by the blinding glare of the sun. In a day or two after
new moon, we see a narrow crescent in the west after sunset,

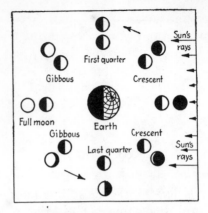

PHASES OF THE MOON

The earth's satellite is represented in the inner set of circles as it appears from
a point over the earth's north pole, while the outer set shows it as it appears at
different points in its orbit to an observer on the earth.

for the lunar globe is now *backlighted* by the sun, just as a
tennis ball held away from us and nearly in line with a
source of light is lighted up from behind and shows the same
crescent—but we know the rest of the ball is there, even if
not illuminated.

During the lunar month, the moon travels eastwardly
on the celestial sphere. Beginning with new moon, it takes
positions successively, more and more such that the directions of a line from the moon to the earth, and a line from
the moon to the sun assume a right angle. This is the first
quarter, one-fourth of the entire spheroid being visible (or
half of the disc); it is then in quadrature with the sun, or
90° away from it in longitude. Soon more than half of the
disc is seen—the "gibbous" phase—until finally at full
moon, all the half turned toward us is lighted up. Then
the longitude of the moon is 180° from the sun, putting the
moon directly on the opposite side of the earth from the
sun; this is also called *opposition*, at which time the moon
rises at sunset time. After full moon, the phases are repeated
in reverse order: the disc becomes gibbous, then at last-

quarter phase, and shortly before new moon a thin crescent can be seen over the eastern horizon before sunrise. The "age" of the moon is the time elapsed since the last new moon. The age of the full moon is about $14\frac{1}{2}$ days. "Crescent after new" is obviously to be found east of the sun, whether seen faintly in the daylight sky before sunset, or as a more brilliant object after sundown; whereas the "crescent before new" is found in the sky west of the sun, but in the eastern sky before sunrise.

The *terminator* is a word meaning the variable line between the illuminated portion at any moment, and the part in shadow. Inasmuch as the moon is a spheroid, the terminator is actually a complete circle around the moon, corresponding to the "circle of illumination" on the earth, but the part on the opposite side of the moon is always invisible to us. Generally speaking, if you were at the terminator any time between new and full moon, you would be having sunrise on the moon; similarly if you were on that section (which is seen from the earth) between full moon and new, you would be experiencing sunset.

The moon is of some real value to the people of this planet. Illuminating the landscape at night, for instance, it benefits us in all latitudes, the effect increasing as we go poleward. In very high latitudes the moon at certain times illuminates an otherwise dark sky during the "long polar night" when the sun does not rise at all for weeks. Again, the revolution of the moon gives us a basis for the measure of the month. Of greatest importance of any of the lunar effects are tides, and the moon is mostly responsible for these.

Tides are a phenomenon of regular rise and fall of the sea waters, commonly twice a day. While the earth rotates, the oceans pass underneath the moon whose gravitative attraction periodically raises the water level. Shipping would notice the effect at once if the moon were annihilated, for vessels would be unable to enter or leave many harbors, so that commercial and passenger trade would suffer untold losses.

Our moon lends itself particularly well to telescopic study, on account of its nearness to the earth and lack of atmosphere. Nothing on the moon prevents all the features of its surface from standing out clearly and being sharply defined in our telescopes and photographs. To be sure, we are unfortunate in always having but one face of our satellite open to observation yet that face presents a superb array of topographic features to delight the eye.

One who has not looked much at the moon with a telescope has no idea of the magnificent views to be encountered. Even an experienced observer of lunar landscapes repeatedly finds something new—that is, landscapes under new lights or conditions.

Aside from the purely astronomical sights, there are some phenomena, observable when the moon is near the horizon, that are caused by refraction effects of the earth's atmosphere and the origin of which has nothing to do with the moon. Under certain conditions, various refraction effects distort the moon's image into almost unbelievable shapes. The commonest effect is for the otherwise circular disc to become so flattened it is almost pumpkin-like. Nor does distortion stop here: occasionally the edges become serrated or saw-like; they even assume a step-like appearance, an effect almost indescribable. The bays or indentations "march" along the moon's disc moving perceptibly, even during brief observation, and often end with a part of the disc being separated entirely from the rest. Such effects are the result of varying density of a thick ocean of air on the earth's surface, with concomitant changes in refraction low over the horizon.

Any and all magnifications may be used on the moon. Even an opera glass will show the large gray plains, and a field-glass, some of the smaller features. But with high-power binoculars, magnifying 10 to 20 diameters, hundreds of objects can be identified, although they are still small. The smallest object that we have been able to distinguish with 18× binoculars is the mountain-ringed plain Lalande (15 miles in diameter), which means that hundreds of objects on the lunar surface are visible with low magnification.

But to do justice to our satellite, we should use a telescope. A 3- or 4-inch refractor opens up a vast field, while reflectors of 6 inches aperture and above will reveal marvelous details. Low powers are needed when we wish to include the entire disc for general examination. For more detailed work, put on higher magnification: 60 to 100 diameters are very satisfactory for examination of mountain ranges, chains of crater-like formations, and topographic details of intermediate size, while powers of 200 to 600 linear diameters are used for close-ups and details of the moon's smaller features, such as craters, peaks, and rills.

On the moon, all living organisms needing air for breathing would find it utterly impossible to exist for even a few minutes, unless they were equipped with special oxygen or air tanks. As far as we can detect, the moon's atmosphere is simply non-existent. We can prove by observation the absence of atmosphere. There is no ring of light visible around the moon at the time of a total eclipse of the sun. There are no clouds or areas of haziness visible. The satellite's limb stands out as clearly as the center of the disc, which would not be so if an atmosphere existed. Occultations of stars by the moon show an instantaneous disappearance or reappearance of the stellar image in a striking manner, which also could not be were an atmosphere to absorb the image gradually near the limb. On the moon, the sky would always be a night sky, except for the sun, with the stars—glowing steadily—visible right up to its edge. And one could see the larger asteroids, the great Milky Way, the mysterious zodiacal light, far more brightly than on earth, and even the prominences and corona of the sun. There would be no ocean of dust, haze, smoke, cloud, mist, and fog—no wind, no meteor, no aurora, no rainbow or halo, or any sound at all—and no twilight and dawn.

Resulting from the absence of air is another phenomenon —the enormous temperature range from about 215°F., where the sun is near the zenith, to about 240°F below zero during the lunar night. Likely there are no water bodies on the moon, as we cannot detect sunlight reflected on them. And there would be no wind or water erosion on the surface. Altogether an utterly desolate place, the moon shows no recognizable signs of habitation.

Galileo it was, who first observed the moon in 1610 with a telescope, and the satellite has held the attention of telescope-users ever since. Of the early moon students, Hevelius first published a chart of the whole surface. This chart was the best one for 100 years, and Hevelius was likely responsible for many of the names of the surface features. Riccioli published another map in 1651, replacing many of the earlier names with those of philosophers and scientists of the day. Over 200 of Riccioli's names for lunar formations are still used. Since his time, many others have been added.

The large surface objects of the moon are the gray plains, or *maria;* the lunar mountain ranges, peaks, ridges, hills; the mountain-walled plains or enclosures (such as Clavius), many of them effectually small plains; the mountain-ringed plains (like Copernicus); the crater-rings; craterlets and crater-pits; clefts, rills, valleys, and small features; and the bright rays.

The topographic feature largest on earth is the oceans, and the next largest the continents. On the moon the large gray areas known to the ancients as "seas" correspond perhaps to our oceans, or perhaps to the continents; it is difficult to make a good analogy. It is easy to tell why the ancients called them seas, for they *seem* to have been covered with water eons ago—or it may have been liquid lava (melted rock). Either the water or lava appears to

THE MOON—CLOSE UP!

Rugged mountains, stretches of barren plain, deep valleys, innumerable crater forms—all the rough-hewn features of the lunar surface are shown in this picture of the south polar region of the moon from Ptolemaeus to the pole. (*Mt. Wilson Observatory.*)

[85]

have overrun and melted and thus broken down many mountain ridges and left only remnants.

In the naming of the maria, the Latin designation of sea was used—*mare*—and the name for each denoted some idea fancied at the time. The original Latin names of the seas, bays, etc., are still professionally used in astronomy, even more than their English equivalents. Altogether there are about 30 of the gray areas. They include the following large maria:

Mare Crisium	Sea of Crises
Mare Foecunditatis	Sea of Fecundity
Mare Nectaris	Sea of Nectar
Mare Tranquillitatis	Sea of Tranquillity
Mare Serenitatis	Sea of Serenity
Mare Frigoris	Sea of Cold
Mare Imbrium	Sea of Showers
Mare Vaporum	Sea of Vapors
Mare Nubium	Sea of Clouds
Mare Humorum	Sea of Humors
Oceanus Procellarum	Ocean of Storms

Largest of the above is the Oceanus Procellarum, occupying the eastern regions of the moon. Besides these, there are other smaller maria, like Mare Smythii (Smyth's Sea), Lacus Mortis (the Lake of Death), and Lacus Somniorum (the Lake of Dreams).

The "seas" are quite dissimilar in appearance as to surface and extent. Small instruments indicate a level surface over most, but as the power is increased, more and more irregularities become apparent in the form of depressions, ridges, hollows, rills. The maria are darker than the rest of the moon; commonly the colors are different shades of gray, and in fact the naked-eye view of the "man in the moon" is formed by these darker areas appearing against the lighter surface.

Whether or not the maria were ever seas—now at least, they are and for millions of years have been what we call plains. Probably much of their surface is arid, desolate, and forbidding; surely it is subject to greater extremes of heat than we ever know on earth. On account of their indefinite outlines in places, it is difficult to estimate the proportion of the total lunar surface occupied, but the best opinion is that more than half the surface is covered by them.

Mare Imbrium, a great elliptical plain 750 miles long, is bounded on three sides by mountain ranges (the Carpathians, the lunar Apennines, the Alps), but the eastern side opens into the Oceanus Procellarum. Many other formations of great disparity of size are to be found in and around the region. Everywhere the surface exists at about the same level, although there are many low ridges in evidence, scattered over the surface. A particularly bright as well as rugged area is found just south of the mountain-walled plain Archimedes. In the middle of the Alps is a remarkable feature of unknown origin, the Alpine Valley. It is a unique thing, a narrow furrow about 5 miles wide and 75 miles long, with various details visible in a glass of good size. There is even a Mount Blanc near-by.

The Straight Range is interesting, a series of 12 or more peaks in one straight row about 45 miles long. This range can easily be seen in high-power binoculars, together with the Teneriffe Mountains, immediately west. Along the northeastern "shore" of Mare Imbrium is a beautifully curved "bay" known as the Sinus Iridum, which latter bay was probably once a *mare* all by itself.

On the north, the bay is bounded by peaks rising 15,000 feet or more above the interior, and containing several craterlets, and at the ends of this range are two promontories. Almost every conceivable lunar topographic feature can be found in Mare Imbrium, the crater formations existing in about all possible forms and sizes. Bright "rays" from Copernicus extend for miles over the plain.

The two hemispheres of the moon, northern and southern, are rather unlike (at least in the halves visible to us) as to mountainous characters: the southern parts (the *top* in lunar charts and photos) showing an array of hundreds of separate, circular crater formations, whereas the northern regions have several mountain ranges. The latter include the mountain chains surrounding Mare Imbrium, and the Haemus Mountains separating Mare Serenitatis from Mare Vaporum. Likewise, there are other ranges scattered over the moon, such as the Altai Mountains, the Riphaen Mountains, and some ranges at the moon's limb, like the Leibnitz Mountains. The limb mountains present an irregular rim to the moon, especially noticed during a total eclipse of the sun, and giving rise to the "Baily's beads".

Mountain ranges on the moon have many peaks with an average height of 5000 to 12,000 feet, and a few are considerably higher than that, as Mt. Huygens in the Apennines—18,000 feet. The range bordering Sinus Iridum is very steep and high, as can be detected in the telescope under the proper lighting. In the Leibnitz Mountains near the south pole, some of the peaks are said by the older selenographers to be much higher, attaining 26,000 to 33,000 feet, a figure which now appears to be definitely overestimated. Compare these elevations with Mt. Everest, the highest peak on earth (29,000 feet), remembering that the moon is only about $\frac{1}{4}$ the earth's diameter so that, comparatively, the mountains of the moon are considerably greater elevations.

The curved *mountain ridges* themselves are noticed in the regions of the maria, running miles in all directions, without any discernible system. They appear to have rounded tops, likely an example of erosion. Singularly enough, there are many unexplained mysteries about our satellite. What forces have been at work there to produce many of the features distinguished even in a field-glass, we do not know. The ridges are one of the examples of erosion; they seem to be worn down as compared to their original height and shape. The Riphaen Mountains are seemingly another example of erosion. There are also numerous iso-

CLAVIUS

A close-up view of the vast mountain-walled plain, Clavius, and surrounding region near the south pole of the moon. Many craterlets and other details are visible within the circular enclosure and on the ramparts. (*Yerkes Observatory.*)

lated mountains, as well as hills that are dome-shaped, and many of the latter have craters at their tops.

It has been the loose custom to call all the round crater-like objects simply *craters*. However, they consist of several types. The largest are the *mountain-walled plains*. The diameter is from about 60 to 140 miles. Only roughly circular or polygonal in shape, they are surrounded by mountain walls, which in some cases rise little above the level of the surrounding land. Yet they are impressive and conspicuous,

[89]

for the inside is depressed below the general level outside the ramparts or enclosing walls. Clavius is the largest of all—being 140 miles across—but seen in perspective, near the south pole of the moon, it may look smaller than Schickard and Grimaldi. Ptolemaeus, near the middle of the moon, is another of this class. Inside Clavius can be seen a group of smaller crater rings, each 5 to 30 miles in diameter, together with other craterlets and elevations.

In some cases, however, as Archimedes in Mare Imbrium, the interior is not depressed below the surrounding plain. One type of the class has low walls that are discontinuous and present a "ruinous" or broken-down condition of these "ramparts" indicating probably they were once intact but have since suffered erosion, from either volcanic, meteoric, or other activity.

The *mountain-ringed plains* are the most numerous; they are from 10 to 60 miles in diameter. They have practically circular ramparts, with walls commonly broad, and steep inner slopes, which are terraced with wide peculiarly eroded ravines. The moon's face is literally almost covered with these formations, which are, as in the case of other details except the bright rays, seen best when on the terminator.

In all the ring-plains, the floors are considerably depressed below the level of the surrounding wall. Most of the mountain-ringed plains, like Theophilus, Copernicus, Tycho, have large central peaks. The peak is ordinarily a composite rather than a single mass, so that the crater floors are rarely smooth.

Central peaks are often found even when the entire "crater" is small, as with Herschel. This object, located just north of the great enclosure Ptolemaeus, is only about 23 miles in diameter. When the terminator—either the sunrise or sunset line—is passing by this crater, the latter is thrown into greatest relief and can be clearly seen with 18× binoculars. With a telescope giving much greater magnification, it has "high, regular, circular walls, much terraced, and a fine central mountain on the summit of which Schmidt shows a craterlet, also a double crater and a craterlet on the crest of the north wall" (Goodacre). Such is a fragment of typical description of lunar formations.

It is plain from observation that not all the craters have central peaks; why some do, and others do not, cannot be explained. It is thought that in many cases the absence of peak has been brought about by erosion, for very often vestiges can still be observed; but in some, like Longomontanus and Clavius, there is definitely no central cone.

Crater-rings are a third type of round formations. They are from 3 to 10 miles across, approximately. They are circular, with walls only slightly elevated over the outside surface while the inside is well depressed. Thousands of these small objects are scattered over the moon's surface with no systematic arrangement. Too small to appear on our moon chart, they can be detected on photographs. One of these, Linné, is said to have shown distinct changes.

Craterlets are of the same nature as the crater-rings only smaller, and are scattered indiscriminately over the surface. They are indeed so numerous as to render impossible an estimate of their number, for inasmuch as they are very small they become more and more evident the higher the telescopic power used. Similarly, *crater-pits* cover the surface in large numbers, being shallow depressions with ordinarily no surrounding rims.

Crater-chains and *chains of walled plains* attract considerable attention, like the group starting with Herschel and Ptolemaeus and extending southward. Such are used as arguments both for and against the opposing theories of the moon's origin. *Ruined ring-plains* are almost surely an effect of erosion. Fracastorius is an excellent example—a great ring-plain in which the "seaward rampart"—as it were—has been leveled to a chain of low hills with wide passes between them, on the place where the original wall once existed. Many others show this effect in parts of the walls, such as Pitatus and Posidonius. Other minor features include *twin craters*, *multiple craters*, *hilltop craters*. The latter are the most nearly like our terrestrial volcanic craters. They are not common however and need high magnification. They can be found on the tops of the central peaks of Walter and Arzachel.

When the moon's crust cooled—so runs the idea held by some though not all astronomers—it shrank and cracked. Whether this is true or not, there are various *rills* or *clefts* found on the surface. Some are flat and broad and others narrow and deep, as on the floor of Alphonsus. The one most clearly visible is the large winding valley known as Schroeter Valley, at the north end of Herodotus. Ordinarily it takes high optical magnification to see the rills, and various selenographers of note have identified hundreds of rills, especially under oblique lighting.

True, well-defined lunar *valleys* are not very numerous. The best examples are the great Alpine Valley and the Rheita Valley. The Alpine Valley cuts directly into the Alps. Straight and wide, with steep cliffs, it is possible that it may have been caused by a huge meteor striking at a very acute angle. The Rheita Valley is about 15 miles wide and extends for 100 miles; it can be found northwest of the formation Fabricius. It is noticeably curved, and the origin is probably very different from that of the Alpine Valley; possibly subsidence of the land is responsible for the Rheita Valley. East of Ptolemaeus, in the Mare Nubium, is one of the largest valleys on the moon; another lies to the west of Herschel; still other types of valleys are found on the ramparts of the mountain-walled enclosures, as in Gassendi.

Perhaps more mystery surrounds the nature of the *bright rays* than any other single feature of the moon, for although they are clearly in evidence even in a small glass, their nature and origin are obscure. They consist of brilliant, narrow, white streaks always emanating from some crater formation. At least 100 of them are known. Some extend for hundreds of miles over the surface before becoming finally lost. Evidently they are surface formations only and are probably never found on high elevations. They seem to proceed without regard to changes of level over which they pass. It is also clear that the rays manifest no change that can be detected.

Some of the largest of the bright ray systems are to be seen extending from Tycho, Copernicus, Kepler, and Aristarchus. Rays from Tycho are the largest and finest of all, some going as far as the outer boundary of Mare Nectaris. Crater-floors in the path of Tycho's rays show that the rays cross the crater formations; hence we infer that the rays must have been formed after the craters. When they cross the maria, however, they invariably lose in brightness. Some of the ray systems are composed of much shorter rays.

No one knows the origin of these brilliant streaks. Perhaps they were occasioned by the deposition of crystalline dust on either side of invisible surface cracks.

A long range of light shadings, from heavy, black, detailless shadows to a dazzling white, exists on the moon, although the average reflective power is that of dark rock. Aristarchus is the brightest spot on the moon, and Mare Humorum the darkest "sea".

Our satellite seems generally to be composed of shades of yellow and gray, yet a few observers see other colors. Tints of green have been distinguished on the Maria Humorum, Crisium, and Serenitatis. It is also said that the Palus Somnii shows a golden-yellow to light brown hue, that Mare Frigoris is dull yellow-green, and most remarkable of all, a dull reddish area is supposed to have been seen once in a small crater. Naturally, perfect optical equipment is necessary to distinguish the colors correctly—either a reflecting telescope or a highly corrected objective—as well as good seeing conditions of the atmosphere and a good eye. Moreover, terrestrial atmospheric effects must not be confused with intrinsic lunar colors, nor must we be confounded with "penumbral" shadow effects on the moon at certain times. Many expert observers never see any special colors on the moon.

No one knows yet how the moon's topographic features originated. The two leading theories that attempt to account for their origin are the volcanic idea (in which all the crater-like objects were formerly volcanic centers, and the gray plains volcanic extrusions) and the meteoric hypothesis (wherein such formations resulted from the impact of meteorites that fell to the moon's surface eons ago, during the formative stages of the lunar globe).

The commonest opinion held formerly was the volcanic idea; but later Proctor argued that meteorites were responsible. At present opinion is probably about evenly divided between the two notions. An immense amount of discussion has taken place, with arguments and objections on each side. Against the volcanic theory is the objection of the form of a typical lunar crater, which differs notably from a terrestrial volcano, the craters on the moon being hollow with no conical mountain mass. Also it is almost inconceivable that vulcanism could nearly cover the surface of the moon, as it seems to have done, with 30,000 craters on our side of the surface, and with the maria, whose forms are similar to the mountain-walled plains and so may have the same origin. Again, the craters are distributed indiscriminately, not following lines of crustal weakness as on the earth.

Goodacre claims that the presence of a large number of bright spots on the surface, of the type of the Linné crater, is the best evidence of volcanic origin. At the center is a small crater from which it *appears* as if the white material composing the rays has been ejected. Radiating ridges, as from Tycho, also help in this idea.

Objections to the meteoric idea include the following arguments: since the earth and moon have probably been

traveling together in the solar system since the "beginning", meteors should have fallen on each body alike, or
rather, they should have fallen correspondingly more on
the earth than the moon, because of the larger size of the
former. Yet only a comparatively few meteoric gashes have
been found on earth, of which Meteor Crater is the largest.
And there seem to have been no traces left in the rocks
to indicate "fossil" falls, or those antedating the present
geologic era. Yet the presence of the earth's atmosphere
would consume most meteors and hence they would not
produce craters. Gigantic size and number of craters on
the moon indicate that the meteors would have been larger
and more numerous than is held likely.

The *explosive meteoric theory* is a rather new form of the
meteoric idea and possibly has more in its favor than any
of the other ones. According to the calculations of physics, a
meteor moving at great velocity has so much kinetic energy
that, when suddenly stopped, it explodes with unparalleled
violence. At 40 miles per second, according to Gifford, it
has 400 times the energy of dynamite, and many of the
meteors come in with greater velocities than that. The
question is, why is there not a continued bombardment
now, like the ones which seemingly occurred in the past? If
the number of meteors still coming to the earth's atmosphere, after many millions of years is as great as is proved,
what must the colossal "harvest" have been in the early
eras, it is asked. Very probably the larger masses were all
gathered up soon in the life history of the solar system, so
that only the small ones are now being drawn in—which
appears reasonable, as we seldom have large ones striking
the earth, although here it is partly because they are con-
sumed in the atmosphere.

It is held that if a meteor at 40 miles a second strikes the
moon's surface (of lesser density than the earth's, and with
no atmosphere to resist the flight) and has its motion
stopped in $\frac{1}{10}$ second by the resistance of the globe, it will

penetrate about 2 miles below the surface. In the $\frac{1}{10}$ second its "energy of translation" is transformed into molecular agitation. The energy necessary to vaporize the meteorite is but a small part of its total energy, and the surplus energy after vaporizing the meteorite is still over 400 times the energy of dynamite, with a resulting prodigious explosion. There is no time for conduction of heat, and little time for melting, but instead, the materials surrounding will be instantaneously pulverized by the shock, like the "star dust" of Meteor Crater. The lesser gravity on the moon would have the effect that for a certain velocity of meteor, a surprizingly larger crater would be formed.

This idea of penetration of a meteorite below the surface, and the explosion and vaporization of the greater part of the mass is in accord with the views of Moulton, who claims that to be the reason why more of the supposedly hidden iron masses are not found in meteor craters. The great extent of explosion does not seem to be appreciated by scientists in general. The explosive meteor idea also explains best the great lunar maria, where a larger meteor, or perhaps a swarm of these bodies, broke the crust. Mare Imbrium, it is believed, might have been produced by a 4-mile-in-diameter meteor if going at 40 miles a second.

The dark color of the lunar seas is also best explained by this theory. And lastly the vexing question of the bright rays seems to be more logically solved. Explosion by a meteor passing into the solid crust, perhaps in the subsurface liquid material, first caused a cracked surface and then a wave of hydrostatic pressure in the liquid that forced some of the material into the cracks to condense around them at the surface.

The moon is our nearest planetary neighbor to remain always a certain distance from the earth. From observations it has been determined that the mean distance of the moon from the earth is 238,857 miles; but the eccentricity of the orbit, or ratio by which it differs from a perfect circle, causes the distance to vary from 222,000 to 253,000 miles. This means that *the moon is distant about* 60 *earth-radii.* This true scale should be remembered, rather than the usual models showing the moon close to the earth. After the size and shape of the orbit are determined, it is not difficult to calculate the velocity of motion. This is about 2300 miles an hour in its orbit, and equal to the muzzle velocity of very high-power guns. The distance of the moon is such that the average *angular* velocity as seen from the earth is about 33′ per hour, so that the satellite moves over a space just a bit more than its own diameter every hour.

As the distance of the moon can be found by triangulation methods of surveyors, and as the diameter can be measured in the telescope, the size of the moon is easily derived. The diameter is about 2160 miles or over $\frac{1}{4}$ that of the earth, the surface area about $\frac{1}{14}$ of the earth's, and the volume $\frac{1}{49}$. Although some of the other satellites in the solar system are larger than our moon, none is as large as our moon compared to its primary—the planet around which it revolves. The moon's density is 0.6 the earth's, or $3\frac{1}{3}$ times the density of water. The gravity at the surface is $\frac{1}{6}$ that of the earth, so that a man weighing 175 pounds on the earth would weigh $29\frac{1}{6}$ pounds on the moon (if weighed by a spring balance). Contrary to the usual opinion, he could not jump six times as far in actual height, but could lift his center of gravity six times as high. Also an object thrown by one on the moon would go six times as far—and probably farther, there being no wind resistance. Many curious phenomena would be observed in connection with such a small surface gravity.

Of course all the light of our moon is reflected sunlight; there are no incandescent areas where it could be shining by its own light. The easiest method of proving this is to look at the dark invisible limb of the moon, which is in shadow. When it is not illuminated by earthshine we see

MARE IMBRIUM REGION ON THE MOON

A portion of one of the finest lunar photographs made, this magnificent picture shows Mare Imbrium, the Sea of Showers. Below or north of Plato is a dark, area, Mare Frigoris. (*Original, Mt. Wilson Observatory.*)

1 Plato	14 Carlini	27 Timocharis	D Sinus Iridum
2 Pico	15 C. Herschel	28 Archimedes	E Prom. Heraclides
3 Condamine	16 Lahire	29 Autolychus	F Carpathian Mts.
4 Maupertius	17 Lambert	30 Aristillus	G Apennines
5 Bianchini	18 Euler	31 Thaetetus	H Palus Putredinis
6 Bouguer	19 Pytheas	32 Cassini	I Caucasus Mts.
7 Foucault	20 Gay Lussac	33 Piton	J Palus Nebularum
8 Harpalus	21 Eratosthenes	34 P. Smyth	K Alps
9 Sharp	22 Wolf	35 Mt. Blanc	L Alpine Valley
10 Louville	23 Mt. Huygens	36 Kirch	M Sinus Roris
11 Mairan	24 Mt. Bradley	A Teneriffe Mts.	N System of clefts south-west of Archimedes
12 Leverrier	25 Conon	B Straight Range	
13 Helicon	26 Mt. Hadley	C Prom. Laplace	O Rays extending from Co-pernicus

Chart of the Moon

1 Schickard	24 Alphonsus	47 Aristoteles	C Altai Mts.
2 Schiller	25 Ptolemaeus	48 Eudoxus	D Pyrenees Mts.
3 Scheiner	26 Hipparchus	49 Cassini	E Mare Smythii
4 Longomontanus	27 Albategnius	50 Plato	F Palus Somnii
5 Wilhelm I	28 Abulfeda	51 Aristillus	G Mare Humboldtianum
6 Tycho	29 Catharina	52 Autolychus	H Haemus Mts.
7 Maginus	30 Cyrillus	53 Archimedes	I Caucasus Mts.
8 Clavius	31 Theophilus	54 Timocharis	J Apennines
9 Newton	32 Fracastorius	55 Eratosthenes	K Carpathian Mts.
10 Cuvier	33 Santbech	56 Copernicus	L Straight Range
11 Stöfler	34 Petavius	57 Aristarchus	M Promontory Laplace
12 Maurolycus	35 Phillips	58 Herodotus	N Sinus Iridum
13 Pitiscus	36 W.Humboldt	59 Kepler	O Prom. Heraclides
14 Vlaco	37 Vendelinus	60 Encke	P Alps
15 Janssen	38 Langrenus	61 Herschel	Q Alpine Valley
16 Fabricius	39 Macrobius	62 Hevel	R Riphaen Mts.
17 Zagul	40 Cleomedes	63 Riccioli	S Straight Wall
18 Piccolomini	41 Gauss	64 Grimaldi	T Palus Putredinis
19 Furnerius	42 Posidonius	65 Gassendi	U Palus Nebularum
20 Walter	43 Hercules	66 Mersenius	V Cordilleras
21 Regiomontanus	44 Atlas	67 Pitatus	W Dörfel Mts.
22 Purbach	45 Endymion	A Leibnitz Mts.	X Lacus Mortis
23 Arzachel	46 Goldschmidt	B Mare Australe	

nothing of the surface. Besides this, an observation with the spectrograph shows that the light of the moon is similar in spectral characteristics to sunlight, and this proves its nature.

Astronomers are often asked how our satellite compares with the sun in brightness. It is not an easy matter to measure this ratio, but the moon is weaker than most of us would guess. The average of the best photometer measurements shows that the full moon gives $\frac{1}{465\,000}$ of the sun's brilliance. More sunlight comes to the earth in a few seconds than moonlight for one year. At the quarter phases, the earth receives only about $\frac{1}{1\,000\,000}$ as much light from the moon as from the sun. Photographs prove that the moon is *yellower than sunlight*—contrary to popular ideas. It would take five skies entirely filled with full moons to equal the sun's light.

It is comparatively easy for anyone to get a good idea of the general movements of the moon in the heavens, as these movements appear to us, that is, the apparent motions. After the diurnal motion, the apparent motion easiest to observe is the constant eastward motion against the background of distant stars. When the moon is apparently near a planet or bright star, its motion can be detected with the unaided eye, sometimes in an hour's time. The eastward motion is also detected by the noticeable retardation of rising each night, for it rises perceptibly later every night (or day).

The eastward motion is evidence that the moon goes entirely around the earth in about a month. The *sidereal period* is the time taken to pass from a certain star around the heavens and back to the same star. Its average is $27^d7^h43^m11^s.5$, and is used as the sidereal month. The *mean* daily motion is $13°10'.58$. Another revolution time of the moon is the *synodic period*, or the time taken in moving from a certain position with respect to the sun, around to the same relative position again, as between two successive full moons. This interval, the synodic month, is $29^d12^h44^m2^s.8$; it is the one most closely corresponding to our calendar month.

Of course, the times of rising and setting of the moon are of importance to everyone interested in this heavenly body. Phenomena of rising and setting are complicated because of the fast eastward "drift" among the constellations and the variation in declination of the moon from day to day (caused by the inclination of the moon's orbit to the equator).

The moon in a month's time is now north of the equator and now south—racing among the constellations at the rate of about one constellation in 2 days. The first effect gives it a change in declination. If we are in the northern hemisphere, as the north declination increases, the moon goes nearer the north celestial pole. Then the length of time it stays above the horizon becomes longer. Hence a greater declination makes for an earlier rising and a later setting (for the observer of the corresponding hemisphere) than otherwise. And if the observer be in the opposite hemisphere of the earth from where the moon is, so to speak, he has correspondingly less moonlight per day.

Although the daily motion of the stars and celestial objects is westward, the moon is also moving more slowly in the other direction (eastward), so that it takes longer than just a day between two successive moonrises, or two transits over the meridian, or two moonsets. This is the *daily retardation*. The combined effect of the two motions is this: the retardation causes the moon to rise, on the average, about 50 minutes later every night; and this retardation itself fluctuates with change of declination of the moon.

When the moon is near the vernal equinox, the increasing declination day by day tends to lessen the normal retardation in the rising time (for the northern hemisphere); but the retardation at setting is increased. In the southern hemisphere the effects are the opposite. Similarly, when the moon is near the autumnal equinox, the moonrise is later and later each day by a large amount, but moonset is later each day by the minimum difference—in the northern hemisphere; and the opposite in the other hemisphere.

The above phenomena of changing retardation of rising and setting moon occur each month and are most noticeable in the autumn with the full moon at the vernal equinox. Moonrise takes place nearly simultaneously with sunset. The moon's apparent path is now more nearly parallel to the horizon than at other times, so that *at the same hour each evening*, it can be successively farther eastward in its longitude, yet will be comparatively near the horizon for several days in succession. This is the *harvest moon* and gives us glorious moonlight evenings—the nearest full moon to the time when the sun is at the autumnal equinox of September. The next full moon is nearly the same, and goes by the appellation of *hunter's moon*. In high latitudes the effect of the harvest and hunter's moons is most pronounced.

In case the moon's ascending node corresponds with the vernal equinox, the moon's path (when the node is rising at the eastern horizon) lies more nearly parallel yet with the horizon, and thus extreme conditions prevail. In latitudes south of the earth's equator, the harvest-moon conditions occur at the vernal-equinox times, or spring in the northern hemisphere, but autumn in the southern latitudes.

Strangely enough, our satellite always presents nearly the same face to the earth, wherever it is in its orbit or whatever the phase. It rotates on its axis in exactly the same period as its sidereal period around the earth, and rotation is in the same direction as the revolution. At first it seems to be difficult to understand that the moon can rotate at all, while always turning one face to the earth, but if you walk around the room in a circle, always facing the center of the room, you will find that you have been facing every direction of the compass during the circuit, and have performed a rotation. The same situation holds with the moon;

if the moon did not rotate on its axis, it would have to face always the same direction in space, and would then *seem* to us to turn, presenting all of its "sides" to us in the course of a revolution.

Actually though, a considerable portion of the moon's surface at the edges is alternately visible and then turned away. Because of these "libration" effects of the moon, it does not always show precisely the same face to us but has certain oscillations back and forth from a mean. Because of *libration in latitude*, the observer from the earth sees 6°41' beyond one of the poles, and then half a lunar month later, he sees beyond the opposite pole by a similar amount.

Libration in longitude allows us to see around the eastern or western limb alternately, about 7°45' farther than the mean, this motion putting into view at times certain plains like Mare Smythii and Mare Humboldtianum, that lie on the extreme edge. At the opposite periods during the lunar month, each region can scarcely if at all be seen. For the moon's angular motion in orbit is variable, because of orbital ellipticity, while the rate of rotation is uniform. Near perigee, its closest approach to the earth, it revolves faster than average and accomplishes 90° in angular measure, or one-fourth of a revolution, in less than one-fourth of the time of its period of revolution.

Besides exploration of the moon's surface, certain special telescopic observations of interest may be made of other phenomena involving the moon, such as occultations and eclipses. Moving along its prescribed path against the starry background, the moon frequently glides in front of a star or planet, hiding one of them from view. Inasmuch as the moon always moves (nearly) eastward in the sky, the occulted object disappears behind the limb of the eastern hemisphere at immersion, and reappears on the western limb at emersion. A telescope is needed, even for bright planets occulted, for the glare of the moon prevents the eye from noting the exact moment of disappearance or reappearance. And it must be remembered that an astronomical (inverting) telescope reverses the image, top and bottom as well as side for side, so that a star appearing at the left of the moon to the naked eye will seem to be at the right in the telescopic field.

Occultations give spectacular proof of the absence of lunar atmosphere, for the disappearance of a star is instantaneous; no gradual diminution of light occurs: it suddenly is invisible. Similarly, at the calculated time the reappearance takes place in an equally startling manner. Good observations made with proper timing are of value to certain professional astronomers, who encourage the work and who use the results for improving the data of celestial mechanics.

Time of immersion or emersion in good occultation work must be known accurately within 1 second. Radio time signals from the Naval Observatory station, an electric clock, experience, and ingenuity are essentials. A list of predicted oppositions for one's own latitude and longitude can be found in the *American Ephemeris* and some other professional periodicals, notably the *Nautical Almanac* (London). To get the exact predicted time for a particular locality, a small amount of computation has to be made with the given data, to fit the observer's station. Occultation work is more interesting than one would think, and observers become highly enthusiastic over it.

Eclipses of the moon are never missed by the enthusiastic astronomer. Sufficient data are always given in the professional ephemerides. Commonly, each eclipse presents features different from the average. As the moon enters the earth's shadow, the stages are timed, and found to run close to prediction. The spectacle is often more beautiful and interesting than one would think. The color of the moon at different stages of the eclipse varies: typically there is a real copper color cast over the moon at and near total. During mid-eclipse the surface may be more or less visible, from sunlight refracted and reflected from the atmosphere

THE MOON IN ECLIPSE

One proof of the earth's general spherical form is presented in this photograph of our planet's circular shadow as cast on the moon during a total lunar eclipse. The deep shadow is the umbra. (*Photograph by Irving L. Meyer.*)

around the disc of the earth. Yet in some lunar eclipses the moon at mid-totality is so dark as to be invisible.

The curved shadow of the earth on our satellite constitutes a partial proof of the general spherical form of our planet. One such eclipse is no proof, because any object of circular cross-section might cast such a shadow. But if under every circumstance covering many eclipses, the shadow be observed as circular, the evidence is highly conclusive for sphericity of our globe.

When an eclipse of the moon begins we have first the event *moon enters penumbra,* which always occurs near the eastern limb of the moon, whereas solar eclipses begin at the western limb of the sun. This penumbral, or outer, region of faint partial shadow can scarcely be detected near the beginning of eclipse; but as the eclipse progresses, it gradually becomes evident that the penumbral region is darkening as it nears the central section of the earth's shadow—the umbra.

This umbra is the full shadow and is quite dark. The unaided eye from the earth sees the umbra with sharp clear edges; but with low-power glasses the shadow appears somewhat diffuse, and high magnification prevents us en-

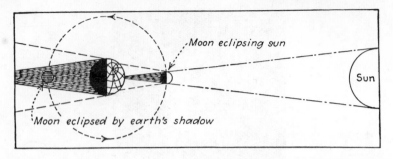

Moon eclipsing sun

Sun

Moon eclipsed by earth's shadow

tirely from defining the exact edge of the dark shadow. Duration of totality may be from nothing at all, where the eclipse is only partial, or may range up to a maximum of 1^h40^m. As to the duration of events, the moon may be in the first part of the penumbra an hour, in the deep shadow 1^h40^m, in the last part of the penumbra as long as an hour, giving an entire maximum period of about 3^h40^m for the phenomena.

Moon eclipses can be seen over half of the earth simultaneously although clocks in different time-zones read different hours. Not only are the events visible wherever the moon is above the horizon, but on account of rotation of the earth, actually more than half of the globe is subject to a lunar eclipse. The whole half of the earth in moonlight is simply darkened during eclipse. The mechanics of solar eclipses are different, and the path of totality is a small strip across one part of the earth.

Eclipses of the moon are not nearly as important as those of the sun. The main value of lunar eclipses lies in the partial proof of the earth's form, the opportunity for study of heat radiation at the moon's surface when eclipsed, and the spectacular effect. It touches one's general astronomical interest to note the differences between various eclipses. They may be darker or lighter than the average, depending upon the atmosphere around the earth's edge as seen from the moon; and there are apt to be phenomena of lighting effects near the limb, which are always unpredictable.

The Sun

Between the sun and the earth are some 93,000,000 miles of nearly empty space, with the temperature close to the absolute zero of −459°F. But should you carelessly turn even a small telescope on the sun without using a darkened sun-glass, it would burn your eye severely.

Which is in the nature both of a warning and of a commentary on the size and heat of this comparatively small star which makes life possible upon the earth. The sun is a huge globe of incandescent gases, measuring 865,380 miles in diameter. It would take a line of 109 earths to reach across its diameter (and more than 1,000,000 to equal its bulk).

But the planets wouldn't remain there long. They would melt into the body of the sun almost instantly, unable to withstand the surface temperature of 11,000°F. The heat at the interior of the star, incidentally, has been estimated at as much as 40,000,000°. Under the conditions of heat and pressure at the sun's core, it is believed, atoms are unable to remain in what is to us their normal state.

These tiny building-blocks of matter are broken down, according to a popular version of one of the current theories. The electrons that revolve about the central nucleus, as the planets do about the sun, are stripped away, and the nuclei are subjected to terrific mutual collisions. It is violent processes of this type, some astronomers believe, that supply the sun with the heat and energy it pours out into space.

As it releases this energy, the sun is at the same time giving away of its own mass and body. Every second over 4,000,000 tons of the star are poured off into the void, and so big is the source of life that scientists estimate it can continue at this rate for several billions of years—even if its resources are not supplemented in some manner from the outside.

The earth receives the tiniest portion of this energy, and yet, as every schoolboy sooner or later discovers, the small amount falling on the surface of a magnifying glass is sufficient to burn wood or start a fire when concentrated at the focus.

The surface of the sun (that which we see when observing it with field-glasses or a telescope) is known as the photosphere. It's the first of four outer layers, and directly above it is the reversing layer, surrounded by the chromosphere, which in turn is enveloped by the sun's corona.

Down on the photosphere are the sun-spots. On some days, especially during the time of a sun-spot maximum, there are sun-spots large enough to be seen with the naked eye. These are the big ones, running perhaps from 50,000 to 150,000 miles in diameter over-all, into which a handful of earths could easily disappear. Almost any day during the maximum season as many as 25 smaller ones—still large enough to swallow our entire world—are visible in a 2- or 3-inch telescope, or even with a smaller glass.

The spots frequently swim through the sea of incandescent gases in pairs or clusters, and seem to move across the disc as the sun turns on its axis. They prefer solar latitudes between 5° and 40°, both north and south, and most live for only a few days.

Some, however, do stay longer and may even last through a full solar rotation of 25 days and still be "going strong". Under higher magnification, the spots show a dark center known as the umbra and a lighter surrounding area called the penumbra. Umbras generally run from a few thousand

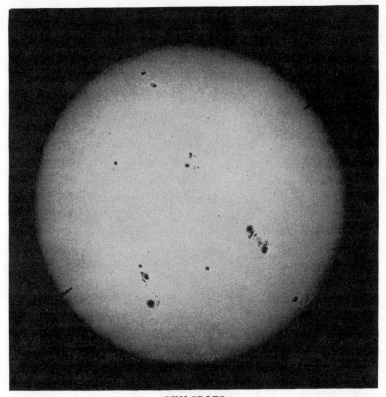

SUN-SPOTS

The solar disc as it appeared at the time of the April, 1939, sun-spot maximum. The largest spots, which often occur in groups, were each huge enough to engulf many earths. (*Mt. Wilson Observatory.*)

to 50,000 miles in diameter, while the penumbras sometimes reach 150,000. The entire spot appears black against the background of the sun, but if it were not seen against the surrounding photosphere it would seem to be white hot, as it really is.

Scientists constantly discuss pro and con the possible effects of these sun-spots on daily life here on the earth. And although the precise effects may be debatable, there seems little doubt that the appearance of great numbers of sun-spots in the course of the primary cycle of 11 years does have some influence on the weather, auroras, magnetic poles, radio reception, and perhaps even upon the normal course of human behavior.

What then is the nature of these spots which have so much to do with life on the earth? They seem to be magnetic storms on the surface of the sun, whirling about a center in a manner similar to cyclones on the earth, although they are quite different. They are apparently associated with streaks of extreme brightness known as faculae which are also located in the photosphere and are frequently observed in the vicinity of spots.

These faculae are visible in high-power binoculars, or in a 2-inch telescope, especially when observed near the edge of the sun, where the photosphere seems to be darker. They commonly seem to have longer lives than the associated spots, and often new spots can be seen growing among them in places where old ones have died.

Three methods of observing the sun-spots and faculae are available to the amateur astronomer. The first, of course, is by looking directly at the sun with a telescope, *when extreme care must be taken to use a sun-glass, a dense ray filter, or some other means of protecting the eyes.*

It is more interesting, though, to project the solar image on a piece of paper. It eliminates all danger to the eyes, permits simultaneous observation by a number of people, and also allows the accurate charting of spots. Using a telescope, rack out the eyepiece a little farther than necessary for normal visual observation, and then move the paper screen back and forth until the image thrown on it becomes sharp and clear. A wire frame can be rigged to hold the paper at the correct distance, and it might be worth while to drape a piece of black cloth over the wire framework to keep out some of the extraneous light and give a more distinct image.

Another aid in this direction is a piece of cardboard, with a hole at the center, placed on the telescope tube near the

eyepiece. The diagram on page 288 is designed to suggest the best method for assembling the accessories, and
they can be adapted to even a small telescope without
a mounting.

By tracing the images projected in this manner, estimating the size of sun-spots is easy. Suppose, for instance, that
the diameter of the sun's disc is 4 inches, and that the
diameter of the spot under observation is $\frac{1}{16}$ inch—or $\frac{1}{64}$
of the sun's disc, in other words. That 4 inches represents,
of course, the sun's true diameter of 865,380 miles, and
the spot then is 13,500 miles in diameter. Just average!

Also, from the projected images one can make charts of
the spot-positions, their number, speed of rotation, and
duration. The other methods of observing the sun offer no
such facility. The third method, for instance, is little more
than a variation (and a highly expensive one) of the first. A
solar eyepiece is fitted to the telescope, equipped with a
prism that eliminates most of the sunlight and permits a
direct view of the sun with least danger. Serious observers
prefer direct observation with this "Herschel solar prism"
because it permits more accurate study of details in the
various solar features.

The third characteristic of the photosphere is out of
reach of the small telescopes we have been considering so
far, but seen through instruments of considerably greater
power it is quite absorbing. All over the solar image there
is a granular structure that characterizes the surface. It
consists of light nuclei, which brighten the entire sphere,
set against a dark background. The nuclei are usually
round, but in the vicinity of sun-spots, because of some pull
or pressure exerted upon them, they may be oblong.

These "rice grains" are separated from each other by
about 500 miles, a distance that is equal to their diameters,
and they do not retain their form constantly. Rather they
appear and disappear, or change their shape, continually.

The reversing layer is a mass of vapors, entirely of the

earthly elements, that stretches some 1200 miles above the photosphere. It is cooler than the surface, and as a result the gases in it absorb light coming from below causing certain dark lines to appear in the solar spectrum. During a total solar eclipse, as the moon covers the surface layers at the edge of the sun, the background of brighter spectral lines is removed and for an instant these dark lines appear as they really are—brilliant in themselves. The split-second reversal of the spectrum, of course, gives the reversing layer its name.

Outside of the reversing layer are several thousand miles of lighter gases—hydrogen, helium (first discovered in the sun, then sought on earth), and perhaps calcium—which compose the chromosphere. Here, in this third layer of the sun's atmosphere, originate the hydrogen prominences that rise like clouds of luminous smoke thousands and hundreds of thousands of miles. Some have been measured as climbing 1,000,000 miles above the solar surface, and they travel at amazing speeds. Here, too, lie the flocculi, which are incandescent masses of hydrogen or calcium, probably associated with the prominences.

The nature of the corona is a mystery. It extends all around the sun and is so tenuous that comets have been immersed in it without slowing down. The form varies with the sun-spot cycle; when the spots are minimal, equatorial streamers extend to several diameters, whereas at maximum the corona is essentially spherical. Evidence points to coronal temperatures of 1,800,000°F.

For the corona we need a total solar eclipse, but these are rare for any one spot on the earth. Though they are more frequent than those of the moon (which almost everyone has seen at some time or another), they are visible in very small areas while lunar eclipses are visible over half the earth. In New York, for instance, there was a total eclipse of the sun visible on January 24, 1925. There had not been one over Manhattan Island since the fifteenth century, and there will be no other visible from that location until October 26, 2144.

But sometime we may have an opportunity to see a total eclipse of the sun without traveling too far from home, and it is quite probable that should such a chance come we'll take advantage of it. For, aside from the fact that it may well be our only hope of seeing the prominences and corona, a solar eclipse is beyond a doubt the most beautiful and impressive of all the sights in nature.

It begins quietly enough, with a small nick appearing on the western edge of the sun. As the minutes pass by, that little nick grows larger, and the visible portion of the sun becomes smaller. Toward the end, just before totality, the sky is noticeably darkened, and an ominous silence settles over the earth. Birds flutter to their nests, animals slink home, the temperature dips. Then, after a last thinning crescent, the sun disappears completely behind the moon, and a pearly corona glows softly in the sky around a black disc. A few stars come out, night birds wheel in the air, and night insects begin to chirp. Everything else is still, and there is an eerie orange glow at the horizon.

It is so quick! Already we have seen the Baily's beads. They came just before totality. The last rays of the sun, shining through the jagged valleys along the edge of the moon, were a few dazzling spots of light at the rim of a black disc. Just for an instant; then they were gone.

Now the sun is completely hidden. All that is left is the corona, irregular in shape, glowing in the heavens. Its arms reach off one, two, even six million, miles into space. We see it first as a small circlet of soft light. Turn the field-glasses on it, and arching over the sun's north and south poles we see intensified lines of light—polar brushes—following the lines of the sun's tremendous magnetic force.

With the glasses scan the edge of the moon—quickly, for time is short. There are red and orange jets along the curve, lacing into the inner corona. The prominences! They fade suddenly. The corona is gone. The crescent sun is shining again on the other limb of the moon. Totality is over.

Did we forget to look on the ground for the strange, flickering shadow-bands—weird atmospheric effects that are so hard to photograph? And did we overlook the sun's crescent image, projected a thousand times on the ground and the sides of houses by space between the leaves of trees? They are pinhole images similar to those formed by a simple camera. Did we miss seeing the "flash spectrum" with a direct-vision spectroscope? The ordinary spectrum vanished, for a split second, and what had formerly been dark lines stood out in sharp color. It will be a long time before we have another chance to see these things, unless we travel far.

Perhaps, with our attention focused too long on the prominences, we may have missed the diamond ring. That came when the outer corona was blotted out, just before the reappearance of the sun, and while the inner corona was still visible. As the first speck of the sun returned to view, irradiation made it seem larger than it really was. The resultant effect was the formation of a diamond ring, with the speck of the sun as the diamond and the inner corona as the ring.

We would have had less to worry about, and far less to see, had we seen the eclipse simply as a partial one. For then it would have been a case of watching the moon move across the face of the sun, never reaching a point where it covered it completely. Just about all the amateur can do during a partial eclipse is to time first contact, the instant the moon first nicks the sun's edge, and last contact, when the moon leaves the disc. At intervals he can estimate the percentage of the surface covered, measure the drop in temperature, watch the crescents projected by spaces between leaves, and take photographs. The spectacle does not compare with that of a total eclipse but, as if in compensation, partial eclipses may be seen much more frequently.

Any solar eclipse in which the center of the moon passes

ANNULAR ECLIPSE OF THE SUN

Annular eclipse of the sun, April 7, 1940, showing moon's disc surrounded by outer edge of the sun. (*Photograph taken at* 13,000 *feet by Peter A. Leavens, in collaboration with Dr. Clyde Fisher.*)

over the center of the sun is known as a central eclipse, and only when the eclipse is central can it be total. It could, however, be central and still *not* be total, for if the moon were so far from the earth at the time that it did not appear as big as the sun, it would not cover the latter completely. At the moment of maximum eclipse, there would be a ring of sunlight surrounding the moon's disc, and no corona would be visible, nor would the darkness of the heavens approach that during a total eclipse. This phenomenon is known as an "annular" or "ring" eclipse, and while it is a striking spectacle, the practical observations for the amateur are substantially the same as those during a partial eclipse.

When the phenomenon is total, of course, he can do these

[115]

CELESTIAL DECEPTION!

This unusual photograph simulates the appearance of an annular eclipse. It was made during the central eclipse of April 28, 1930, and the camera was at a point in the path of totality where the silhouette of the moon was nearly coincident with the solar disc. The "annular" effect is not a true one because the solar ring was formed by the sun's chromosphere, not its true disc. Baily's beads can also be seen. (*Photograph by Dr. W. F. Meyer, University of California.*)

same things and more. A total eclipse has two more "contacts" than has a partial one—second contact being when totality begins, third when it ends. The amateur can count and identify the stars that become visible; he should note the shape, position, and number of prominences, the outline and color of the corona, the number of Baily's beads, the width, speed, and direction of the shadow-bands. And always there is the possibility of a comet (otherwise invisible) appearing as the sky is darkened. The loss of light in the sky, incidentally, can be recorded with so simple an instrument as a photographer's photometer.

Thus the sun, which is visible every day and therefore offers the possibilities of observing its varying seasonal position, and which provides opportunities for daily telescopic observation, offers too one of the greatest spectacles that man can ever witness.

[116]

9

The Comets

M ORE excitement has been caused by comets than by any other objects that appear in the sky. Battles have been stopped in mid-career, proclamations have been issued, whole populations have been thrown into a panic, kings have abdicated from their thrones, men have died of fear. Comets were considered for centuries as omens of death and destruction. People actually wore charms against them.

But all this is no wonder when you consider some of the spectacular comets that have been seen. There was one in 344 B.C. that was likened to a flaming torch; in 146 B.C. one was as bright as the sun. In 530 A.D. a comet reached from horizon to zenith. The second comet to appear in 1811 possessed a head nearly 1,000,000 miles in diameter, a tail 130,000,000 miles in length. The comet of 1744 had six tails in a great fan, and the Great Comet of 1843 had a tail 200,000,000 miles in length.

It is not only their spectacular appearance that attracts attention, but also their frequent occurrence. At least 15 to 20 comets per century are visible to the casual observer, and, on an average, four wondrous ones appear every 100 years. In a lifetime one may see several great comets and perhaps a dozen others if he makes any effort to find them. In fact, sometimes as many as five come into telescopic view in one year, and often one of these is visible to the unaided eye. Many have been as brilliant as Venus and a few bright enough to be seen in the daytime.

AN AMATEUR'S COMET

Peltier's Comet of 1936, discovered and photographed by amateur astronomer L. C. Peltier, of Delphos, Ohio. The astronomical world is indebted to such observers who indefatigably scan the heavens.

Amateur astronomers find real enjoyment in keeping watch for comets, occasionally even discovering them and following them as long as they can be seen. The finding of a comet is a certain road to fame, for comets are named after their discoverers. Find a comet, and you have made your place in astronomical history. Pons found 27; Messier, Swift, Barnard, Brooks, Perrine, and Giacobini have each found 11 to 20 comets. In July of 1937 Finsler's Comet attracted wide attention. In 1936 amateur astronomer Peltier found his fourth comet, in 1939 his fifth. Although professional astronomers with their telescopes are better equipped for comet discoveries, the amateurs with more time for "comet-sweeping" have a surprizing total to their credit.

Of course, most comet-discoverers have used telescopes, yet three railroad workmen in Africa were the first to see and report the great Daylight Comet of 1910. Surely there is nothing to equal the great satisfaction of being the first to see one of these visitors from outer space, but it is also interesting to keep track of comets once they have been found.

Almost every month of the year there is some comet within reach of a telescope. Although the number per year may be small, perhaps three, some comets can be followed for 2 months or more. The *Handbook of the British Astronomical Association* annually lists search ephemerides for all comets scheduled to return during the year. The Harvard College Observatory *Announcement Cards* publish the positions for all comets. *Sky and Telescope* usually has current news on observable comets. An authority on comets writes the monthly "Comet Notes" in *Popular Astronomy*. Almost every year a comet assumes naked-eye brilliance, and usually before this happens considerable publicity has been given it so that even the newspapers carry directions for finding it.

About every 25 years on the average, one of the spectacular comets returns. These cause so much excitement that it is hard to escape notice of them. The Great Comet of 1811 attracted so much attention that a vintage of wine was named for it. It was so huge and so threatening that it was rumored among superstitious people that it might have caused the Great Lakes of America and the fiords of Norway on some previous visit. Of course these geographic features were caused by other agents.

Most comets do return again and again. Many of them are regular members of the solar system and move in definite paths which focus around the sun. Some, with small orbits, return frequently. Encke's Comet, with its nearly circular path, returns every $3\frac{1}{3}$ years. On the other hand, Halley's

HALLEY'S COMET

Halley's, one of the largest of the naked-eye comets, had a proportionally large nucleus, as shown in this photograph. Last seen in 1910, this comet will not return to the earth again until 1986. (*Photograph by Perrine, Observatorio Astronomico, Córdoba, Argentina.*)

Comet moves in such a large and elongated ellipse that it averages about 76 years before coming back near the sun. When a comet reaches its nearest point to the sun, perihelion, it then starts out upon a journey that may carry it far beyond the most distant planet. Some 50 comets are known to have periods less than 100 years, while the comet of 1811 may take 3000 years to return, and Comet 1864 II, is estimated to require over 2,000,000 years to cover the vast extent of its orbit!

Some of the greater comets seem to appear from the depths of space, make one circuit of the sun on hairpin curves, then travel away again along almost straight paths for centuries, perhaps never to return again. Parabolic orbits have been ascribed to many of these for which but one perihelion visit has been recorded in thousands of years. Other famous comets appear to have traveled in toward perihelion on the spreading arc of a hyperbola, a slightly different form of curve. It has been suggested that such comets as these move in a great open curve, only a small part of which passes through the solar system, and that they may not belong to the system at all. Where these comets come from and whence they are bound no one can say. They are not like the short-period comets with the latter's elliptical paths that are obvious members of the solar system.

Certainly our understanding is limited by our lack of knowledge of these celestial visitors. Were our life span longer, or even man's historic stay upon this planet of a greater period, then we might have other records of the comets which we now imagine to have made but one visit to our star. In fact, recent studies have taken many comet paths from the parabolic and hyperbolic group (which would indicate that they are not members of the solar system) and added them to the elliptical one. No doubt many more of the exceptional comet paths will be established as ellipses as the years go on, for many comets that we once considered visitors from elsewhere have proved to be regular members of the system.

And right here is the important reason for the rigorous nightly observation of comets, and the year-by-year check of comet paths. For only by the most exhaustive study of each comet that comes our way shall we be able to understand the true relation of these wandering visitors to the sun and the solar family. The amateur can make substantial contributions to comet fact and theory by doing his part in

TEBBUTT'S COMET

The Great Comet of 1881, discovered with the naked eye by John Tebbutt of New South Wales, an assiduous comet observer. It exhibited a star-like nucleus, typical coma, and a brilliant, bifurcated tail. Pastel by Trouvelot. (*Charles Scribner's Sons.*)

this night patrol. Day-by-day charts of the comet's position, its changing place among the stars, sketches and measurements of head and tail, and photographs are important.

Even though some comets are accredited members of the solar family they have many characteristics that are quite different from other members of the group. Their forms are irregular and changing, while planets are constant. Comets shine partly by their own light and partly by reflected sunlight, while planets are illuminated only by sunlight.

The orbits of most periodic comets are greatly elongated, while the planets move in almost perfect circles. Comets may come from any direction and any angle to go round the sun, while the major planets all move in nearly the same plane in space, and go around the sun in the same direction.

Each of these differences has its effect on the appearance of the comet as we see it in the sky. Usually, when the comet first appears it is a hazy patch, with no well-defined feature except the head or coma. Coma is the Latin word for *hair*, and comets in both early and late stages correspond well to the name. The coma of a comet is the roundish nebulous region. The head region includes not only the coma, sheaths, and envelopes but also the nucleus if present. The heads have been observed to be 30,000 to 1,000,000 miles in diameter.

As the comet comes within about 250,000,000 miles of the sun, it seems to undergo some excitation. It suffers the first of sometimes endless and startling changes. The coma brightens, and in most comets a brilliant nucleus appears within it. Then the coma expands, and its material often streams back away from the sun to form a tail. Probably it is the radiation pressure of the sun that drives the coma material back. There are comets that never go through these changes under our observation and never show more than a fuzzy head. There are others, though, that produce jets and streamers from the coma and throw off sheath after sheath from the head. Sometimes the head seems surrounded by luminous envelopes. Coggia's Comet displayed magnificent envelopes. The light from a comet's nucleus is reflected sunlight, whereas the coma and tail are probably sunlight absorbed and then re-emitted by gaseous molecules.

In certain comets the changes have followed in great numbers and with amazing rapidity. Donati's Comet, for instance, threw off seven envelopes in just a few days. Tebbutt's Comet of 1861 shed 11 envelopes in 2 weeks.

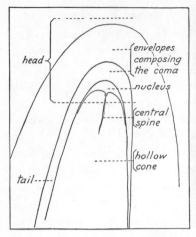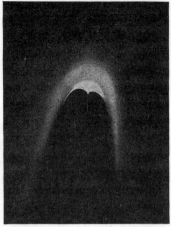

PARTS OF A COMET

are illustrated here by the Great Comet of 1861, shown in diagram and photograph. This comet, discovered by Tebbutt, was an extraordinary object; it threw off 11 envelopes in 17 days. On June 30, it is supposed the earth passed through the tail; peculiar atmospheric effects were observed. (*Photograph by Warren de la Rue. From Guillemin, Le Ciel.*)

Morehouse's Comet in 1908 is the comet most famous for the changes in its coma and tail. It seemed to require but a few hours to release huge clouds of material.

Not all comets have nuclei, but a great many of them do. Sometimes the comet's nucleus is less than 100 miles wide, but the one of 1882 was 50,000 miles in diameter. Most nuclei appear as a single brilliant star-like center in the head, but in the comet of 1882 there were six or eight "knots" of luminous material. Very often the nucleus appears to contract and grow brighter just before the appearance of envelopes. This change was noted in Donati's Comet some 4 to 7 days before the sheaths appeared and in Morehouse's but a few hours preceding. Here is where the amateur can render his greatest service—in keeping records of all changes that may come from hour to hour and day to day.

Normally, then, a comet first appears with only the coma

in view. Within this by careful observation one may frequently but not always be able to discover a nucleus. Watching the nucleus he may find variations in its brightness and its size. These may be warnings of even greater changes to come. A few hours or a few days thereafter nebulosity may develop; tenuous envelopes may appear to issue from the coma and then drift back to form the tail.

The tail is by far the most spectacular of the comet's features. It may be millions of miles in length and extend over a larger area than any other celestial body except a super-giant star, a star cluster, or an entire galaxy. Comet 1861 II possessed a tail 24,000,000 miles in length, stretching 105° across the sky. Donati's Comet had a tail nearly twice that length, and the Great Comet of 1843 possessed a tail (as mentioned before) of nearly 200,000,000 miles. In 1882 the Great Comet of that year had a tail only second to that of 1843.

The tails of comets are curious phenomena. Often the brighter stars visible to the naked eye have been mentioned as visible through a comet. On one photographic plate Van Biesbroeck counted 73 stars of twelfth and thirteenth magnitude visible through the tail of the Pons-Winnecke Comet. Comets must be extremely tenuous in nature and, despite their tremendous size, not massive at all. Probably the heads of comets are loose meteoric particles, the outer regions of which are whirled out by excitation, forced back by radiation pressure of the sun, and dissipated into microscopic fragments to form the tail. Scattered over a tremendous area the tiny particles hang perhaps a mile apart, so that a comet's tail is almost a vacuum, more tenuous than the air. It has been suggested that the carbonized and ultra-rarefied gases that comets contain and the tiny particles that compose the tails are probably illuminated by the shock of electrons from the sun. The tails themselves may actually be hollow cylinders, the envelopes trailing

DE CHÉSEAUX'S COMET

De Chéseaux's comet, a unique, six-tailed visitant that appeared in the heavens in 1744. is shown rising before the sun. (*Drawing from Guillemin. Le Ciel. 1885.*)

back like a shepherd's horn, and the tail-material is lost to the comet forever.

Tails of comets have assumed the greatest variety of forms. Some are short and stubby and some, as already suggested, unbelievably long. The great comet of 1744, De Chéseaux's, had six tails visible to the naked eye; Borelly's of 1903 had nine tails barely distinguishable on the photographic plate. Four well-defined tails followed the comet of 1861, enclosing within them some 23 separate rays. In 1823 a comet had two tails separated by 160°.

Strangely enough the tails, although they follow the comets on their sunward journey, wheel about at perihelion —the closest approach to the sun—so that a line from the sun to the comet runs almost through the tail. Then, however, the tail seems to gain on the comet and after perihelion, leads as the comet leaves the sun and starts toward outer regions. There is a slight lag, so the tail is seldom exactly on a straight line from sun to comet head except when far away from the sun. As the comet approaches the sun, the tail is a little behind the straight line; as the comet leaves, it is still behind this radius vector—although now it begins to precede the comet head.

Once in a while comets come extremely close to the earth or the sun. In 1680, Newton's Comet went within the very corona of the sun, 147,000 miles from the surface. In 1882 a great comet went directly between the earth and the sun in transit. The earth, on the other hand, went right through the tail of Tebbutt's Comet on June 30, 1861. Observers on the watch for any strange sight, as our planet passed through the comet's tail, reported a peculiar glow in the sky like a faint phosphorescence. And again, on May 19, 1910, the earth passed right through the outer regions of the tail of Halley's Comet. Knowing this, a number of astronomers made careful observations and measurements throughout the night. On this occasion they saw nothing, heard nothing, measured nothing, felt nothing to indicate the presence of the comet.

Evidently a comet's tail can do the earth no harm. The solid meteoric particles of a comet's head might produce a minor earthquake or actually dig a great hole if it should strike the surface of the planet, or a "tidal wave" if it struck the sea. It is thought that the huge meteor crater in Arizona was caused by an encounter with a small comet, the nucleus (of separate fragments) being 400 feet across.

Comet-observing is, in the main, of two types. First is comet-seeking, a deliberate attempt of the telescope-user to discover new comets. No one knows when a new one may appear in the sky, even a great comet. Many hours are wasted without results; nevertheless, many comets have been discovered by patient comet-hunting.

For comet-seeking, small areas of the sky are examined with utmost care, noting and checking on every star cluster, nebula, and hazy object. The greatest chance of finding one lies near the ecliptic, and in the evening sky after sunset, and also in the morning sky before sunrise. An aperture of 4 to 10 inches is preferable, with magnification of about 30 diameters, and a fairly wide field. Examine the sky minutely, studying every suspicious object, inasmuch as some of the faintest visual comets discovered were first but a "stain" on the background of the sky. Great observers advise that it is better to examine a small region closely than a larger area hurriedly.

When a comet first appears it looks like a hazy patch of light. At first glance one could take it for a star cluster or a nebula. That is the time to get out an atlas and compare the new object's position with that of known objects on the chart. Any star atlas, like Norton or Schurig, will include the clusters and nebulae down to about ninth magnitude, and for advanced work Dryer's *New General Catalogue* together with the *Index Catalogue* is really the last word. If your suspicious patch of light is not on any of the star fields, the chances are that you have found a comet.

Careful observation for another night and accurate study of its position each time will help to eliminate doubt. Plot its location with extreme care and estimate its magnitude by comparison with some neighboring cluster. If the supposed comet has shifted its position you need doubt no longer. If there is an observatory near where you live, or some person who is especially interested in comets, you might take one added precaution. The staff at the observatory might know whether the comet is a new one as yet unknown, or an old one returning and already under observation. If the comet should be unknown to them, waste no more time. Send a telegram to Harvard College Observatory, describing its location and brightness, and claim credit for the discovery of a comet.

The second type of comet-observing is the picking up of comets already discovered. Here the comets can be found without delay, if the sky conditions are suitable and if the magnitude of the comet be within the power of the instrument. The principal tool needed besides the telescope is an ephemeris, giving positions of the object at definite times. When the comet's magnitude is 6 or brighter, the positions may be plotted at once on a star chart of visible stars, and it can then be located with ease. For fainter comets, proceed just as in the case of finding asteroids (as described in the asteroid chapter).

Because of the very nature of comets, they seem brighter to the unaided eye than in the glass and appear less diffused than in binoculars and telescopes, for the same amount of light intensity is spread over a lesser area. Sometimes, therefore, naked-eye observations are surprizingly satisfactory, and binoculars are adequate to detect the nucleus, head, and straggling tails of most comets. With the telescope, it is usually best to use low powers and wide field. The greater the light-gathering power, the more details observable in the coma, tail, and faint envelopes. Just as one can see more stars in a 10-inch than in a 3-inch telescope, so one finds more light in comet images when he uses greater aperture.

There are really many things that one can observe when a comet appears: its position day by day, brightness, shape, size of head, nucleus, appearance of coma, number of envelopes, changes in the tail, number of tails, color, any features unique for that comet, and change of velocity as it approaches and then leaves the vicinity of the sun.

Often when a comet is first observed its passage is a very slow and serene one. It takes careful observation to detect any change in its location from night to night. As the comet approaches perihelion its rate of travel increases. Just as the earth moves most rapidly when nearest to the sun, and the moon most swiftly when nearest to the earth, so comets, following the same laws of gravitation, speed up as they come close to the sun.

Any comet that is brilliant and spectacular is commonly

known by the name of its discoverer. It always bears another name, too, to indicate the comet's place in order of discovery for the year or the time of its perihelion passage among all the comets of that year. Thus Donati's Comet in 1858 is also called Comet 1858 f for the order of its discovery, and Comet 1858 VI for the order of its perihelion passage. There are also Di Vico's (1846 IV), Coggia's (1874 III), Swift's (1899 I), Kopff's (1906 IV), and numerous others.

Occasionally there comes a comet like Morehouse's of 1908, which changed so rapidly from night to night that one could hardly imagine it the same object. Now and then a comet like the Great Comet of 1882 will arrive, which was visible for 9 months and was known to transit the sun. Once in a while we may see another like the Great Comet of 1861 which threw off 11 envelopes from its tail. Surely there will be others visible in the daytime and about four times a century one brilliant enough to attract observers all over the world.

There may be another like Biela's which split in two before the eyes of an observer in 1845. Seven years later the twin sections returned still farther apart but still traveling in the old orbit. Then, when the next approach was eagerly anticipated, the comet could not be found at all. In its place, however, appeared a shower of meteors. Since that time other meteoric showers have been associated with the periods and orbits of old comets which have disappeared.

There are the cases of Tempel's Comet of 1866 and the Leonids of November, Tuttle's Comet of 1862 and the Perseids of August, Biela's Comet and the Andromedes of November. It would appear that comets do represent an aggregate of meteoric materials which, disintegrating, often give rise to a periodic shower of shooting stars.

10

The Meteors

THROUGHOUT interplanetary space there are countless pieces of stone and iron, most of them wheeling about the sun in long elliptical paths and some apparently sweeping into the solar system from the depths of interstellar space. On an average, they are no bigger than a few grains of sand, but there are those that are immense and weigh tons.

More than 100,000,000 of them bombard the earth every day, pouring down on the atmosphere in a constant stream, and were it not for our surrounding blanket of air they would pepper the ground in a ceaseless barrage. As it is, these meteors, as they are called, are vaporized or burned to a fine ash by heat resulting from *friction with the air* and settle imperceptibly through the atmosphere to add themselves to the vast bulk of the earth. We see them usually for only a brief instant, when the heat has vaporized their surfaces into gaseous light-emitting envelopes that appear much larger and more brilliant than the original object. Almost immediately, after that fleeting glimpse, the average meteor is gone and we have seen a "shooting star".

But we see only a few, perhaps a half-dozen per hour in an ordinary night's watching by one person. The rest are never known because they fall over the oceans and deserts and other uninhabited areas that take up so much of the earth's surface. Or because they come in the daytime, or are hidden by clouds, and so escape notice. Only the brighter

BIRTH OF A METEOR?

As a comet "grows old" and disintegrates, it leaves behind it widely scattered meteoric material which becomes distributed along the orbit. When the earth intercepts a swarm of this material, a "meteor shower" results.

ones are visible to the unaided eye, of course, and one observer in one location will see only a small portion of those striking the earth at any one time—which are additional factors accounting for the comparatively small number seen.

Occasionally one is bright enough to be seen in the daytime, and may even explode somewhere in its path. Such an appearance as this, whether it comes during the night or day, is usually called a fire-ball, and in fact any "shooting star" that ranges in brightness from that of Jupiter or Venus to something many times larger and brighter than the full moon is classified generally as a fire-ball. The term "bolide" usually indicates an exploding meteor. The phenomenon is termed simply a meteor if the brightness ranges from the lower limit of naked-eye visibility up to

that of Jupiter and Venus. Fainter ones, streaking across
the telescopic field, are known as telescopic meteors. Should
any fragments of either a meteor or a fire-ball reach the
earth, the name changes again and they are known as
meteorites.

Billions of these meteors appear to travel together in
space along orbits that, in a number of cases, have been
identified with the orbits of certain comets. The comets
either may or may not still exist, but there is evidence
that the meteors of these groups are simply the remnants
of comets which have disintegrated or are now in the process
of breaking up and that the scattered comet-material thus
formed is distributed about the comet's orbit.

At any rate, when the earth, as it frequently does, cuts
into the orbit of one of these meteor swarms, thousands of
the tiny objects are pulled down into the atmosphere within
a short space of time, resulting in what astronomers call a
meteor shower. The most famous example in modern times
is that shower which, in November, 1833, shot so many
meteors through the heavens that 250,000 were counted at
one station between midnight and dawn.

When the paths of the shooting stars in such a display
are marked on a star map and traced backward, nearly all
seem to emanate from the same section of the sky. The
shower takes its name, usually, from the constellation in or
near which this "radiant point" seems to lie, and the
swarm of 1833, which apparently diverged from the constellation of Leo, is known as the Leonid shower.

This radiation effect, by which the meteors of a shower
seem to emanate from a point, is only an optical illusion, an
apparent radiation that has no connection whatever with
the stars that lie about it. The meteors appear in the atmosphere at heights that average from 60 to 80 miles, while the
stars are trillions of miles away from us. The impression
that there is a radiant, then, is the effect we obtain when we
view these meteors traveling toward us in parallel paths.

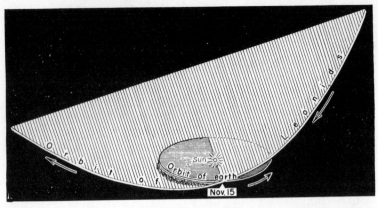

METEOR SWARM

The Leonid meteor group, as pictured in a three-dimensional diagram which is correctly drawn according to orbital characteristics of the swarm. Inclination of the Leonid orbit to that of the earth is about 163°, so that in effect the meteor swarm moves in a direction opposite to that of the earth. The actual orbit of the Leonids practically coincides with that of earth on November 15 each year giving annual display.

Just as, when we stand between railroad tracks and look off in the distance, the tracks seem to come together, so do these parallel meteor paths, traced backward, seem to come together in a radiant point.

In the case of the Leonids, and they are fairly typical, there is an unusual display of shooting stars every year in November, which occurs as the earth travels through the portion of its orbit that intersects the path of the meteor group. But every 33 years the main body of the meteors is at the intersection and a major shower occurs. The meteors, obviously, are not distributed evenly along their orbit, and even the main swarm may vary in its date of appearance because of changes induced in its path by the gravitational attraction of other planets. The Leonids, for instance, have failed in their last two "major" appearances to produce anything remotely resembling the fine spectacles of 1833 and 1866, even though the showers of 1931 and 1932 produced results far beyond the annual average for "off years".

The other meteor showers, similar in nature to the above, have never, within recorded history of such events, produced such celestial shows as have the Leonids, but there are a number that offer annual spectacles during which the observer may see several hundred meteors in the course of a night. Perhaps the richest and most consistent of these is the Perseid swarm which appears to visit the earth, during a full month, from July 15 onward. It reaches its peak about August 10 to 13, when perhaps 50 to 100 meteors an hour may be seen after midnight, apparently emanating from the constellation of Perseus.

But we don't have to wait for meteor showers to watch these visitors from interplanetary—and interstellar—space flash across our skies. They are constantly arriving, and an hour's watch on the sky will almost always result in seeing a few. The latter half of the year, from July onward, seems to be the best time to look for them, for during that time the average number of meteors visible (10 to 15 an hour near midnight) is nearly double the average number per observer per hour of the first 6 months (5 to 8 an hour near midnight). And in addition, an observer will see twice as many shooting stars from midnight to 6 a.m. as he will from 6 p.m. to midnight.

The latter fact is easily explained, for in the evening we are on the rear of the earth as it speeds in its orbit around the sun. But in the morning, we have been spun around so that we are on the front, or advancing half, of the planet. Meteors we see in the evening have to catch up with us, but those we see in the morning we meet head on. There are not only more of these, then, but when they are in the atmosphere they are traveling much faster than those of the evening skies. And since velocity is an important factor in determining the brightness of a meteor, those seen in the morning will naturally be brighter than the ones seen earlier in the night.

In the atmosphere, the speeds of meteors range from 9 to

49 miles per second, and what happens at this speed happens in an instant. The friction of the air with moving objects within our normal experience has little effect other than to reduce speed. But at the velocity of a meteor it is sufficient to raise the surface temperature of the object to white heat. The brilliance of the tiny objects is explained by the fact that the surface is vaporized, forming a luminous gaseous envelope which stands out against the dark sky. Since meteors are usually small, most of them are burnt out miles above the ground.

Most meteors disappear at an altitude of 40 miles, having first become visible at from 60 to 80 miles (30 to 100 miles for fire-balls). This is true even if the object has not been burned away, for the air retards its speed steadily so that if the meteor is large enough to reach the earth it does so, usually, with merely the speed of an object falling freely from a considerable height. It probably will not be glowing as it drops to the ground, and it may even be cool to the touch immediately afterward—because the friction-generated heat affects only a thin layer of the outer surface which can cool rapidly. The interior of the stone is deadly cold, and there is not time for the subsurface layers to become hot.

Because a meteor ceases to be visible at an average height of 40 miles, it is unlikely that you will ever see a flaming stone crash to the earth a short distance away. You may think it has done so, but more probably it will have simply vanished below the horizon—not into the soil.

Amateurs can be of considerable assistance to the science of astronomy in recording their observations of meteors, even should the records they make be only of an occasional but unusual meteor; for some other amateur, in some other location, may have seen the same object. By putting the two reports together scientists can tell a good deal about the phenomenon.

One of the best and most valuable methods of observation

METEOR CRATER

From the south rim of Meteor Crater, near Canyon Diablo, Arizona, the camera looks nearly a mile across to the depression in the northern rampart which is believed to have resulted from the north-south angle of descent of the meteor or small comet that caused the earth-scar. The bottom of the crater is about 500 feet below the northern rim. In the background looms the snow-capped San Francisco peak, highest in Arizona. (*Photograph by Hubert J. Bernhard.*)

[137]

is that in which two observers take up positions miles apart and watch the same section of the sky. Adequate observations from two such separated points will enable astronomers to compute the height and path of meteors seen by both persons. The work, naturally, presupposes a good knowledge of the constellations.

The two observers should be stationed not less than 20 miles apart, to provide a good base-line for computations. Nor should they be more than 100 miles distant from each other; Dr. Charles P. Olivier, one of the world's foremost authorities on meteoric astronomy, recommends a base-line of from 40 to 60 miles. The necessary equipment consists of an accurate timepiece and a celestial globe or a good set of star charts. A ruler will prove very useful.

What is most desired in such observations is the path of the meteor across the heavens, timed as accurately as possible to the hour, minute, and, if practicable, the second. The ruler, held at arm's length, will help in trying to fix exactly the path of the meteor among the stars after it has vanished.

It is of great importance to determine as exactly as possible the point at which the meteor was first seen and the point at which it disappeared. This can be done, of course, in relation to the stars near which it passed, and the terminal points of the path indicated in distance (in degrees) from or between certain stars or star configurations. It will always prove easier to determine the end of the path than the beginning, since the sudden appearance of a meteor at any particular point is unpredictable.

To make the observations of the greatest possible value, the meteor paths should be marked accurately on a star chart, together with an arrow indicating direction of flight, and the paths should be numbered. With this record should be kept a tabulation, giving the number of the meteor on the chart, the points near which it began and ended, its direction, brightness, color, speed (fast, medium, or slow), and comments concerning any train it might have left in its wake and how long it lasted, together with remarks about any other unusual characteristic the meteor may have displayed, such as an explosion or other sounds. It is more than worth while, too, for the observer to note sky conditions at the time, together with a candid statement as to how accurately he feels he has made his observations.

But this is far from the only way in which the amateur may make useful records for the professional, even though it is perhaps the most difficult and exacting method. Observations made by one or two persons working together and simply charting the paths of the meteors of a particular shower or of an evening are valuable in helping to study radiants. Not all meteor radiants remain in one fixed position among the stars, and research on the slight shifts occurring in that of a particular shower may reveal extremely interesting facts about meteor distribution.

In working to determine the radiant of a meteor display, the precise direction of the paths of meteors in the swarm is needed above everything else. A slight error in indicating the beginning and ending points in the meteor paths will not alter the determination of the radiant, but the paths should be charted accurately, and with an arrow-head indicating the direction of fall.

The whole process, including a tabulation containing the material listed above, can be run through for each meteor, experts find, in about a minute.

If all this seems too much, or beyond your knowledge of the constellations (which such work will inevitably improve, by the way), then you can still be of help to science. For merely counting the number of meteors seen per hour is of value in aiding the determination of the density of the meteor stream. Better work might be done perhaps by counting the number seen at 5-minute intervals over a considerable period of time.

It will always prove of value to observe as carefully as

PATH OF A METEOR

This rare photograph shows the luminous train left behind after passage of a large meteor through the atmosphere. It is believed that the object's terrific speed causes ionization of the air through which it passes, resulting in such a glow as seen here. Long-lasting trains of this sort are seen in comparatively few instances. (*Photograph by C. R. West of Timpas, Colo.*)

possible the trains left by brilliant meteors. Estimates of the brilliance, colors, duration, direction, width, and drift through the air can be made. And field-glasses or binoculars will enable the watcher to follow the train for an appreciable length of time after it has become invisible to the naked eye. The train, also known as the "afterglow", is a luminous trail in the path of the meteor, generally presumed to be an electrical phenomenon resulting from ionization of the air through which the burning body has passed.

When a rare daylight meteor bursts into view, fix its path as accurately as possible in relation to near-by houses, poles, or trees, and mark the spot at which you are standing. Then measure the path later in altitude and azimuth, using a quadrant or protractor, and note any other details. Such

[140]

records will help in fixing the path of the meteor in the air, and perhaps, in space. Don't forget to include time, direction, and an estimate of brightness, as usual.

The American Meteor Society, with headquarters at the Flower Observatory, Upper Darby, Pa., supplies maps and charts to interested observers, and will in addition offer more detailed information upon request. Completed observations may be sent to the society, where they will be studied carefully. For English observers, the meteor-observing section of the British Astronomical Association (London) takes meteor reports.

Since meteors which actually reach the surface of the earth are the only celestial objects we can touch and analyze in laboratories, they are important. They show elements similar to those of the earth and furnish clues to the condition of outer space. In other words, they are well worth finding.

So looking for meteorites is actually another field of observation—one that requires one's every-day powers of observation, rather than the watching of the heavens. Frequently amateurs find unusual pieces of stone which they take to be meteorites and excitedly proclaim as such. Be cautious and examine the object for certain characteristics before rushing to a laboratory—which is the only place where a final decision can be made.

The first consideration should be to compare it with the rocks of the region. Often the supposed meteorite can be immediately eliminated on this basis. Iron meteorites, because of their unusual weight, instantly distinguish themselves; but don't be fooled by a piece of slag or waste iron. Meteorites are deceptive because some are predominantly iron while others are largely stone, and a third type combines the two materials. Because the iron ones are easier to recognize they are most frequently found. But a bolide, exploding with a loud detonation, is apt to scatter dozens of stony fragments within a small area.

WHAT'S LEFT!

A small meteorite, showing glazed surface and effects of unequal melting during passage through the earth's atmosphere. Meteorites like this one commonly show a crystalline structure, from which we infer they were once in a liquid condition and have since solidified. (*Photograph from American Museum of Natural History.*)

[142]

Meteorites usually have a coating on the surface which results from melting as they pass through the atmosphere. This coating, which is extremely thin, has the appearance of a black crust or varnish, and is sometimes dull or grayish in color. The surfaces of most meteorites, moreover, show cavities or pittings that result from unequal melting of the surface in that same passage through the air. Those cavities on the front (as the meteor traveled) are small and deep, while those on the rear are broad and shallow. Eventually the weathering effects of rain and wind cause the pits to become deeper and the crust to disappear with the formation of iron oxide, or rust.

Often meteorites are found on the surface of the ground, or only partly buried, because they have lost so much of their velocity in passing through the air. But there are, of course, exceptional instances where they have buried themselves deeply in the earth.

Meteor Showers for the Year

We give herewith a table of the principal meteor displays that are known to occur, more or less, each year. The leading ones, which are quite dependable, are indicated with asterisks before the respective dates. The others are sometimes conspicuous but are quite uncertain, so that the observer may or may not see many meteors. According to Prof. C. P. Olivier, president of the American Meteor Society, the lesser-known (unstarred) meteor streams "probably exist, but there are hundreds of minor radiants, some doubtless detectable one year and not perhaps for several more. As a rule, an observer will not get such a radiant unless he observes all night . . . "—or at least for several hours. Nevertheless, many meteors in the lesser-known showers have been observed.

Our list of showers is based upon the most important ones in much longer lists by the famous English observer, W. F. Denning. The data as given for the nine main showers are up-to-date, having been checked by Prof. Olivier (1945). Besides this, the data of the Meteor Observing Section of the British Astronomical Association are taken into consideration. The latter society would have us note three of the unstarred showers: the Pons-Winnecke meteors, the Taurids, and the Andromedes. In looking for the meteors, consider the late night of the days marked, together with the following morning hours.

— Date	Meteor stream	Radiant R.A.	Dec.
		h m	°
* Jan. 1–4...................	Quadrantids	15 20	+52
Jan. 17......................	κ Cygnids	19 40	+53
Feb. 5–10..................	α Aurigids	5 0	+41
Mar. 10–12................	ζ Boötids	14 32	+12
* Apr. 19–23...............	Lyrids[1]	18 4	+33
* May 1–6..................	May Aquarids[2]	22 16	− 2
May 11–24.................	ζ Herculids	16 28	+28
May 30.....................	η Pegasids	22 0	+28
June 2–17..................	α Scorpiids	16 48	−23
June 27–30.................	Pons-Winnecke meteors[3]	15 12	+58
July 14.....................	α Cygnids	20 56	+47
July 18–30.................	α Capricornids[4]	20 16	−12
July 25–Aug. 4............	α-β Perseids	3 12	+43
* July 26–31...............	δ Aquarids	22 36	−11
* Aug. 10–14..............	Perseids[5]	3 8	+58
Aug. 10–20................	κ Cygnids	19 20	+52
Aug. 21–23................	o Draconids	19 24	+60
Aug. 21–31................	ζ Draconids	17 28	+63
Sept. 7–15.................	ε Perseids	4 4	+36
Sept. 22...................	α Aurigids	4 56	+42
Oct. 2......................	Quadrantids	15 20	+52
* Oct. 9....................	Giacobinids[6]	17 40	+55
Oct. 12–23.................	ε Arietids	2 48	+21
* Oct. 18–23...............	Orionids[7]	6 8	+15
Oct. 31–Nov. 6............	Taurids	3 40	+15
* Nov. 14–18..............	Leonids	10 0	+22
Nov. 26–Dec. 4............	Andromedes[8]	1 40	+45
* Dec. 10–13..............	Geminids	7 32	+32

[1] Associated with the orbit of Comet 1861 I.　　[2] Associated with the orbit of Halley's Comet.
[3] Associated with the orbit of Comet Pons-Winnecke.
[4] Associated with the orbit of Comet 1881 V.　　[5] Begin by July 20.
[6] Associated with the orbit of Comet Giacobini-Zinner, 1933 III. Great showers in 1933 and 1946.
[7] Continue until Oct. 31.
[8] Also called *Bielids;* this important meteor stream has been "lost" for years, its narrow stream having been diverted by planetary perturbations; but the meteors may appear again.

11

The Asteroids

IN A great broad zone between the orbits of Mars and Jupiter, and perpetually circling about the sun in giant ellipses, there are thousands of diminutive bodies—each a world by itself. These are the asteroids, known also as minor planets.

The asteroids are likely barren worlds, without water, air, heat, or living things. Why no water? If there had been any, it would have evaporated into space; and there can be no atmosphere on these planets, for they are so diminutive that their gravity is far too small to hold it. The smallest asteroids visible are less than a mile through, as in the case of Adonis. Even on Ceres, the largest, a man weighing 175 pounds on the earth would weigh only about 6 pounds! On still smaller ones the force of gravity is so weak that he would weigh but a fraction of an ounce and naturally would have considerable difficulty staying on the ground.

The amount of heat and light received from the sun by asteroids is governed by distance from that source at the moment, and on the average varies between that received by Mars and that by Jupiter. The light and heat are not absorbed by clouds, as in the case of Venus and Jupiter, two cloud-covered worlds; and although some heat is received, there is no atmosphere to hold it and keep it from radiating away, so that the temperature must be near the absolute zero of interplanetary space. It is scarcely conceivable that the asteroids can be the abode of any life.

Asteroids are forever beyond the range of the naked eye, with the exception that one of them can just be seen under most favorable conditions and at critical times. Yet it is not difficult to locate a few of them with low telescopic power—even binoculars—and follow them, night after night, during an entire apparition or "season" of visibility. Usually at least one can be seen with field-glasses, and as the size of the glass is increased, a greater and greater number become available.

The immense zone containing nearly all these numerous planets of the solar system is a great ring-shaped belt over 340,000,000 miles from the inner to the outer part of the ring. While the orbits of most of the asteroids are confined to this area, yet an occasional one is found that goes beyond the outermost boundary or within the innermost limit.

Ceres, the first asteroid, was found in 1801; since that time one or more new ones have been discovered nearly every year, and often several during one year. The method of search for new ones is now exclusively photographic and is performed only with an equatorial mounting of telescope, with camera rigidly attached. In such a mounting, one of the axes is lined up with the earth's axis, and the other is at right angles, so that with this arrangement a planet or star can be held relatively motionless in the field of view.

The observer exposes a plate for an hour or two on a star field near the ecliptic; with extreme patience he holds the stars exactly at the same place every moment. The negative when developed gives a field of view of many stars, and if a minor planet be among them, it appears as a short streak among stellar points, the trail being produced by the apparent movement of the planet with respect to the background of remote stars. An alternate method is to give the plate an additional motion in accordance with the average hourly motion of the planets for that particular region of the sky. In this case, the asteroid has its light accumulated so that the image (now a point) is stronger than if a trail. This time, the stellar images trail as in comet exposures, and a fainter asteroid can sometimes be found this way.

The first four asteroids discovered are sometimes called the Big Four, as they are the largest and brightest. Observers with even small telescopes can actually locate any of these four when in the night sky. Of the Big Four, Ceres, the giant among the planetoids, was discovered by Piazzi in 1801. Its diameter of 480 miles places it above all others in size. The *albedo* is 0.06 (that is, $\frac{6}{100}$ of the light received from the sun is reflected from the surface), and the average magnitude at opposition is 7.4.

In 1802 Olbers found the second one, Pallas. It ranks next after Ceres, with diameter 304 miles; the albedo is 0.07 and the opposition magnitude 8.0. Juno was third in 1804, and was discovered by Harding. Its diameter of 120 miles makes it the smallest of the Big Four. The albedo is 0.12 and the magnitude at opposition 8.7. Olbers again, in 1807, found Vesta. Its diameter of 240 miles makes it larger than Juno, and the albedo is the highest of all, 0.26, so that it reflects the most light per unit area, and the average magnitude at opposition is 6.5. Vesta becomes considerably brighter than this (say 5.9) at a favorable opposition, however.

It is remarkable that Vesta is so bright, for it is considerably smaller than Ceres and Pallas; apparently this asteroid has surface material lighter in tone than the others. Relatively few astronomers ever see Vesta with the naked eye, but it can be done during apparitions when the opposition magnitude is around 6. Juno at times is fainter than magnitude 9, and needs high-power binoculars or a 2-inch telescope. Always the magnitudes are continually varying, on account of the relation of the asteroid to the sun and to us.

Astronomically the magnitudes are important: first, they designate the brightness as seen by us and thus indicate

what telescope aperture is needed. Second, they are a basis
for determination of size of the minor planet. All but the
largest are too small for direct measurement in the telescope.
So a mean reflecting power of surface is assumed, which
may or may not be true, but which gives a working basis
on which to proceed. Then from a knowledge of the orbit
and the apparent brightness at opposition, the approximate
diameter is computed.

Actually, there is an immense and unknown number of
minor planets. The greatest number of known ones occurs in
magnitudes 13 and 14, of which there are about 400 each,
this number decreasing toward the brighter and toward
the fainter side. There are about 1600 asteroids whose
orbital elements are sufficiently well known that positions
in right ascension and declination are computed for each
opposition, by various institutions assigned by the International Astronomical Union. These 1600 minor planets
might be called the well-known asteroids. Besides these, it
is estimated that 5000 have been observed at one time or
other, many of which have been lost or have gone adrift, so
to speak, as insufficient observations were secured at the
time of appearance for a good set of data to be made, even
by the best computers. Leuschner estimates there must be
a total of some 50,000 of these spheroids in existence. The
vast majority are probably but a mile (more or less) in
diameter.

Most of the features of asteroids are of special interest
to workers in mathematical astronomy, because they con-
cern orbital characteristics. Because we do not know much
about the physical nature of the tiny bodies, our knowledge
is mostly confined to their motions, and to what possible
significance they may have in the evolution of the solar
system.

The orbits as a whole are much less uniform than those
of major planets. The asteroid 944 Hidalgo has a very exceptional orbit. Eccentricity is a numerical relation defining

the shape of an ellipse. The nearer it approaches 1.00, the more elongated is the ellipse, and the more it departs from a circular form (whose eccentricity is zero). Hidalgo's orbit has an eccentricity of 0.66, which is a very high value, making the orbit as elongated as that of a typical comet and more so than with some comets. Its greatest distance from the sun brings it out to a point beyond Saturn's orbit— much beyond the asteroid zone. Yet some asteroids, like 1177 Gonnessia (whose orbit has the eccentricity 0.0068) have orbits more nearly circular than that of Venus, the most circular of the major planets.

Inclination is another of the important qualities of an orbit; this is the amount by which the plane of the asteroid's orbit is tilted to the plane of the earth's orbit, the latter (plane of the ecliptic) being used as a standard. Inclination of plane to the ecliptic plane is often higher in asteroids than with the major planets. The highest inclination of all is that of Hidalgo, being 42°.5 to the ecliptic plane, while the lowest is that of 1383 Limburgia (0°.009), which is sensibly in the plane of the ecliptic.

While it is true that ordinarily the asteroids stay forever out beyond Mars' orbit, there are some that wander in toward the sun and so come much nearer the earth than the average asteroid. Our table (see Appendix) shows the most interesting data concerning the planets known to approach close to the earth. It will be noticed that they are all very small bodies. On account of their diminutive size and occasional nearness, they rush across the sky at such critical times with prodigious velocity, visibly changing position while under observation, with the result that they are discovered only by "accident" during observation.

Thus it was that Hermes approached so close to the earth in 1937. A little world no larger than a mountain, it was picked up photographically by German astronomers who were doing systematic observations on the other minor planets at the time. It may or may not ever be seen again,

AN ASTEROID IS DISCOVERED

This is an enlargement of the discovery plate of the asteroid 1230 Riceia. The camera was exposed to the surrounding stars and adjusted to follow them in their diurnal motion. The asteroid, only 5 miles in diameter, moved among the stars and hence appeared as a trail while the stars remained as points of light. 1230 Riceia is the short trail indicated by the arrow. The largest star in the picture is Zeta Piscium, almost on the ecliptic. Its magnitude is $5\frac{1}{2}$, so that one can readily see how faint the asteroid is in comparison, and that it requires a long exposure to record such a planet on a plate. Photographed and discovered by Prof. Karl Reinmuth, of Heidelberg, Germany, the asteroid was named for Hugh S. Rice, co-author of this book.

for observations of Hermes were so few that the orbit in space is not well known.

Vesta is the minor planet superb, for it is the brightest and most easily observed. Moreover, the ephemeris is the most extensive of all, and again, knowledge of the orbit has been so perfected that the planet is found exceedingly near its computed place, often the difference between the observed and computed positions being $0^m.0$ in right ascension and $0'.0$ in declination; or, as we say, the planet has "zero-zero" residuals. The ephemeris of Vesta each year is computed for the entire calendar year, including the period of conjunction with the sun—the time of invisibility.

Taking any of the Big Four asteroids, it is possible to begin observing any one of them at the start of an apparition and follow it to the end of visibility. Sometime after conjunction, the asteroid can be picked up near the eastern horizon before sunrise. Then with the progress of the season, it can be found rising earlier and earlier each day until opposition time, when it is at the observer's meridian at midnight. At this time it is retrograding. Its appearance continues like that of any other outer planet in this way, that it rises earlier each evening, until finally it is seen in the western sky after sunset, and gradually becomes lost near the next conjunction as the sun in its eastward apparent motion among the stars overtakes it, inaugurating a new cycle. This same routine happens to all superior planets.

In observing, one starts with an ephemeris of the asteroid. This is a table of exact positions of the object for regular intervals of time, and the positions are given in coördinates of right ascension and declination. Professional ephemerides are published annually by the Cincinnati Observatory: these correspond to the ephemerides of planets as published in the *American Ephemeris and Nautical Almanac* of the U. S. Naval Observatory, the *Nautical Almanac* (London), and others. These positions are also given for the first four minor planets in the yearly *Handbook of the British Astronomical Association.* There are also a very few monthly periodicals—such as *Popular Astronomy*—in which the positions are published for the asteroids easiest to see during the period covered.

Half the entire work of picking up an asteroid (and similarly a comet) lies in plotting its course from the ephemeris positions. The simplest method is to plot the apparent course, or else use a chart already made. A chart can be made which will cover one to several months' course, so that usually no further chart-work need be done for that particular apparition of the object, extending around the time of opposition of the planet to the sun, and occupying several months.

The positions needed could be plotted at once on a star chart, if there were no precession of the equinoxes to cause a constant change of reference points. Any star atlas has fixed coördinates of right ascension and declination. This framework of coördinates is placed in position on the atlas according to the actual positions of the vernal equinox and celestial pole for a specified year. Obviously it cannot be changed to match the equinox of every ephemeris published, without a new edition of the atlas every year. While the change from year to year is very small, it is cumulative and throws an object out by several minutes of right ascension for a number of years of equinox change. The star charts and atlases have their equinoxes, or the relations of the right ascension and declination network to the constellation groups, placed to correspond with equinox positions of standard star catalogs. So you must invariably make a precession-allowance, a process which is shown by example in one of our appendices.

Assume now that you are at the telescope and that you have a chart before you. If observing, you are commonly using the instrument on dates lying between the ones marked on the chart, as the probabilities are against your starting at precisely the day and hour of the marked positions. Obviously the position where the asteroid should be at the moment of observation is somewhere along the apparent path or smooth curve drawn, the exact place being easily estimated according to the date and hour of observing. After having marked the predicted position by interpolating along the path, you are ready to observe.

The telescope ideally would be in a really dark place open to the constellation containing the asteroid. Hold the chart near the telescope (using as dim a light as possible) and tilt it so that the north-south line on the chart is parallel to the hour-circle of the field of view (this is important), and inverted—that is, with the "south" of the chart toward the north celestial pole, *not* the north point of the horizon. Then after a few moments of being in darkness, you can see the star configurations just as they are on the chart. (We assume use of an inverting telescope.)

Locate first the brightest star of the region near the planetoid, and gradually move the field of view to the planet, identifying all the stars by their configurations and relative magnitudes as on the diagram. The asteroid should be found in its proper place, according to the date of observation with respect to the dates marked on the chart. With practice and good sky conditions identifications can often be made in a few minutes. At times they have even been made instantly, especially if one has picked up the asteroid a day or so before and is familiar with the star groups, or if the asteroid's place is close to a bright star. The planet will, then, be an extra star-point distinct from all the other points that are real stars; and moreover by this method you can identify the asteroid with confidence without having to wait a few hours for movement of the object to take place against the starry background.

Except at the stationary points in their apparent paths, just before they are reversing direction, a movement from one day to the next is apparent. When the object passes close to a star (as seen from the earth), movement can be detected in an hour's time, more or less, depending upon circumstances of magnification and other factors.

An asteroid can be followed by means of the above technique for as long a time as the ephemeris and sky conditions allow, often for months at a stretch. Sometimes one performs a neat retrograde loop around opposition time and stays in one general region of the sky for several months. Only the "Big Four" of the asteroids—Ceres, Pallas, Juno, and Vesta—have their ephemerides given for an extensive period each year. With the hundreds of others only about 6 weeks around opposition are given in the ephemeris.

Telescopically asteroids are not spectacular. They cannot be distinguished by appearance from stars of the same magnitude, except that possibly they sparkle less, and some of them do have characteristic colors, like Vesta, which appears distinctly orange or pinkish. However, the daily motion against the stellar background is a positive indication of their character. A telescope-user invariably gets much practice and fun—even a thrill—by following the movements of these tiny worlds, which may be but 100 miles in diameter and 250,000,000 miles away.

Double and Multiple Stars

Two tiny points of light—one a rich orange, the other a deep blue—placed close together in the telescopic field—such is the appearance of Albireo, certainly one of the most spectacular examples of a double star in all the heavens. And the concealed beauties of many similar stellar objects lie unsuspected until discovered in the telescope. Definite enjoyment is afforded by the repeated observation of double stars; for colored doubles are jewels of the sky.

There is a surprizingly large number of doubles within reach of the telescope. In almost any quarter of the sky there are some available for any size of instrument, and they offer various combinations of color, magnitude, and other features. The observer becomes familiar with as many as he desires; and once learned, doubles seem like old friends when reobserved from time to time. At least $\frac{1}{5}$ of all the stars are binary or multiple, if we include the spectroscopic binaries; and $\frac{1}{18}$ of all stars are visual binaries.

What would a planetary system be like were its sun a double or multiple star, instead of a single one such as ours? The question is not unreasonable in view of the high proportion of double and multiple suns; and it applies only to binary stars, for with more than two suns, enormous gravitational complexities would preclude any planetary or solar system like ours.

Imagine our sun replaced by an immense globe of a distinct greenish color; also picture with it in the heavens another immense ball of rich blue, both forming together a double sun. At times both would be visible simultaneously in the sky; at other times one alone would be discernible for a few hours, following which the other one would likewise rise and illuminate the heavens and the landscape, so that there would actually be no real night at all!

It is impossible to know at present of the existence of any planets attending other stars, for they would be far too remote to see in any existing telescope. It is quite conceivable that, where a planet revolved around one component of a binary, its orbit would not be so simple as those in our solar system, and the planet's physical environment due to day and night and seasons would be very complex. Moreover in case a planet passed from one sun to another, these complexities would increase to an unconscionable degree; the irregularity and extremes of light and temperature at various times would be prodigious.

The astronomer at home can have unending pleasure with a program of double-star activity planned to be within the range of his ability and instrument. Beyond this, professional double-star observation includes the more serious features of exact micrometric, photographic, or other measurement in large telescopes, in order to learn over a period of years the precise details of the stellar system involved. Records and "reductions" are made, giving various data that will establish an orbit and help toward forming a true picture of the distant system.

Double star means simply a star that is single to the naked eye but can be separated (resolved) with a telescope into two stars not more than, say, a few seconds of arc apart on the celestial sphere. A professional astronomer classifies as real doubles only those that are to us closer together than can be seen as separate points with the naked eye. In direct visual work, the largest telescopes can separate stars down to an angle of about $0''.02$, and by the use of the stellar interferometer, an instrument for measuring exceedingly small angles, resolution 10 times as great can be effected. A naked-eye double is a pair in which the components are relatively very far apart, sufficiently so that they can just be seen as separate points with the unaided eye. Naked-eye doubles are of no special interest to professional astronomers.

The most important distinction is between optical and physical doubles. In an optical double, both stars are in nearly the same line-of-sight from the earth, but they have no physical connection, one being perhaps trillions of miles behind the other. All other double stars are physical systems, in which two of these great suns belong gravitationally together. To prove a pair of stars composes a physical system, we note that there is orbital motion of the components around a common center of gravity, or else that they both show a common proper motion—are moving together in space. The star Delta Herculis is an optical pair. The triple star Krüger 60 is both optical and physical: the largest two components (A and B) form an optical pair, while one of these (A) together with a faint companion (C) represents a physical system that shows orbital motion. But the study of stellar motion itself is the work of the large observatory.

In binary stars there is definite evidence of this orbital motion. Distinction between the terms physical system and binary is that in the former we may only detect that the components of the pair are drifting together in space and so appear to belong together. There may not have been enough time yet to detect a motion in orbit; but with a binary, motion has been proved. Visual binaries are those seen by the eye, including those needing great magnification in the telescope. Some, however, are so close together from our earthly point of view that they are inseparable in the most powerful telescope; yet the spectograph reveals their compound character by a small periodic shifting of spectral lines, this effect signifying a change in velocity toward or

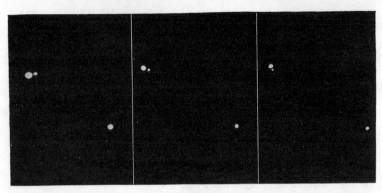

PROOF!

Far out in the depths of interstellar space, two stars move about a common center of gravity. In three pictures, taken in 1908, 1915, and 1920, astronomer E. E. Barnard at Yerkes Observatory catches them on his plates and proves, beyond doubt, the rotation of the binary, Krüger 60.

away from us; and these stars are the spectroscopic binaries. There is no difference between them and visual binaries, in respect to motion.

And then there are also complex systems of more than two suns, known as multiple stars. Many examples prove to belong to more than one of these groups, on account of the circumstance that they may be double in a small telescope but prove to be triple or multiple in a large glass, besides which the spectrograph may reveal one of the components to be also a spectroscopic binary. A good example of multiple star is the quadruple Theta Orionis whose components form the trapezium in the Great Nebula of Orion. The stars range in magnitude from 4.7 to 8 and are called white, lilac, garnet, and reddish in color. For this object, various effects are obtained by using instruments from a field-glass to a 10-inch telescope.

To be a double star, so to speak, seems not to be a unique situation among the population of stars, for about 11 per cent of naked-eye stars are double. Doubles have been cataloged in monumental works by Burnham, Aitken, and others, for future study. Not every pair of stars that appear close together is a double star, however. As a general rule, the fainter the star, the farther it is away, so that two very faint stars are probably very far away from us, and hence they would also be far apart from each other. Each stellar magnitude therefore has a limiting separation measured in seconds of arc. Stars closer together than this limit may be known as double. For example, Aitken suggests a separation of 10″ for ninth magnitude, and any two stars of such magnitude farther apart than this would not be known as a double. There are a few thousand doubles in the northern half of the sky that are above magnitude 9.

The range of visibility of the various examples depends mainly upon aperture of the telescope, sensitivity of the eye, and "seeing" conditions of the atmosphere at the moment. Obviously, another factor is the question of whether the star is above the horizon at all, at the given latitude and at a particular hour of the night.

Whether or not the star can be seen because of range of brightness in the components is dependent upon aperture of the telescope. Along with this goes the resolving power or ability to "split" a star into components, when only one is seen without such optical aid (these factors are explained in the chapter on the telescope). However, the ability to split depends also upon the magnification used and the quality of the objective or mirror. A high magnifying power can often resolve where a lower one cannot, and the higher the optical corrections, the better the results. As to sensitivity of the human eye, here is a place where acuity of vision is singularly of benefit. Also in double-star work the matter of atmosphere plays an important part, a clear atmosphere commonly being very good for this type of observation, unless there be too much turbulence, with dancing images.

One who appreciates the beauty of color has no trouble in becoming enthusiastic over the wide range of color in the various doubles. Moreover, there is often striking contrast, as in Albireo and Epsilon Boötis, the latter affording a superb combination of orange and green. On account of difference in color correction and aperture of lens or mirror, and variation of different eyes and even of atmosphere, the reports of color in doubles have always been notoriously discordant and as a result are recorded variously in double-star lists. In some stars, the hues are very distinct and give no difficulty, whereas in certain others they are particularly elusive.

The observer's training is something of a factor, too, for a real beginner does not often state the colors of even Albireo correctly—which seems incredible to the trained telescope-user. Probably the faint pastel tints showing traces of violet or else blue-green, or perhaps some called ashen, are the most difficult. In any case, the stars should be kept in the middle of the field of view of the telescope to minimize color aberration in the glass.

To get the best effect in double-star observing, we use magnifying power with care. The best rule is to use the lowest power that will resolve the pair nicely. In the case of Albireo, for instance, we need not use over 18× on a 2-inch glass, this star being a wide double. Too large a magnification separates the components unduly, losing the best effect. Yet in the case of Epsilon Boötis, 150 to 250× is needed. However, for *measuring* doubles (as with the filar micrometer) the best rule is to use the highest magnification which the "seeing" will allow. The choice of power is determined by closeness and brightness of the two stars, together with the definition allowed by atmosphere and optics of the instrument.

The expert telescope-user commonly learns a number of spectacular or "show" doubles scattered over the sky, so that he may have some specially fine samples to exhibit to persons coming to the telescope for a view of the heavens. Nor are colored components the sole attraction, for some white doubles are particularly striking, as Zeta Ursae

Majoris (Mizar), and also Castor. Both of these are magnificent sights.

Castor is really a multiple star, but only two components are visible in a small glass. It is one of the best known visual doubles. Each component is known to be a spectroscopic binary, having periods of 9 and 3 days. Then the period of the one binary system around the other binary at a distance of 95 astronomical units is very much longer, perhaps 300 years. At a distance of 73″ there is another star, of magnitude 9, whose drift in space is the same as Castor's and which probably belongs to the system, at a distance of 1000 astronomical units (a unit being the distance sun to earth). Add to this the fact that it also is a spectroscopic eclipsing binary of period 0.8 day, and we have the remarkable situation of Castor consisting of six suns.

One of the objects learned by the telescopist is the star Epsilon Lyrae. It is a complex system, this famous "double double". It consists of two binary systems with a separation between the systems of 207″ of arc and therefore is a naked-eye double. When looking into the glass we find a transformation, for now the two larger components are widely separated and each component is double, the components of each half being close together compared to the distance between the original pair. The brightest of the four stars is also a spectroscopic binary. According to authorities, the periods of the closer pairs are probably several hundred years in each case, and it is said that the period of revolution of the one pair around the other may be something like 1,000,000 years. At least these two larger pairs appear to be drifting together in space, having a common proper motion.

Many examples of particularly beautiful doubles could be given, such as Gamma Andromedae (gold and blue) and Gamma Leporis (pale yellow and garnet). Others are interesting for other reasons. It seems that home telescope-users

[161]

are as a rule particularly interested in becoming familiar with various doubles. It is not enough that such persons be content to observe certain of these objects once or twice; nearly every time the telescope is set up, they turn onto old favorites and make observations time and again. Notable among such stars are Polaris, Albireo, Epsilon Boötis, Castor, Aldebaran, and others, each observer having his own favorites. One reason for repeated observing is the beauty of the double in question. Another reason concerns the instrument used, for with a different glass, the same double may or may not be resolved. It may or may not be of the same color or sparkle; and under differing atmosphere, the same star may or may not look the same as before. Obviously too the human eye is a factor that varies considerably from person to person.

The essentials for double-star work are a list of objects and an atlas by which to locate them. Our list at the end of this chapter includes enough doubles and multiples to afford typical examples, but a full list includes thousands of stars showing range of color, separation, ease of resolving with various apertures, etc. Naturally an atlas should be in the possession of every telescope-user and student of astronomy. One constructed along the lines of Norton's *Star Atlas* is the best for general purposes, and the observer would do well to have one. When the doubles in the elementary lists are exhausted, very many more await the observer in such books as Olcott and Putnam's *Field Book of the Skies*. To find the double, we note the name of the constellation, look at the chart under that constellation, find the star, and then identify it in the sky. Thus we learn something of the constellations too. Take the triple star 14 Aurigae: we look for the star 14 in Auriga, and find it on the chart without difficulty about $3\frac{1}{2}°$ east of Iota, the southwest star in that famous pentagon. Moreover, while we are there it would not do to miss several Messier objects (M 36, M 37, M 38, M 39, the first three being especially fine star clusters).

Each of the books mentioned has many important double stars, as well as nebulae and star clusters.

In developing a system of observing doubles and multiples, there are certain features to watch in each pair examined. Chief among these are the following points, the data of which can be marked or checked in one's observing notebook.

First, note from the list the category of the star, as to whether it is double, triple, quadruple, etc., remembering that they are double in the lower magnifications but perhaps multiple with higher telescopic power.

Apparent brightness: this is known before we look into the telescope, for magnitudes are designated in the lists. All the professionals can measure and record are position on celestial sphere, direction of one component from another (position angle), magnitude, and date of observation.

Relative brightness: a double such as Aldebaran presents a very bright component and a faint companion (besides which, two other fainter companions), whereas with Rho Ophiuchi, a fine pair, components are each of magnitude 6.

Separation, or distance apart of the components, expressed in seconds of arc: the smaller the separation, the greater the aperture of lens or mirror needed. Of course innumerable doubles are beyond the reach of any given aperture, but the observer soon learns the theoretical limits of any instrument; and the separation changes with time.

Closely associated with the separation is the "position angle", or direction of one component from another. Consider a line joining two components; taking the main or brighter component as the standard star, the actual direction of the other component (on the celestial sphere) is expressed in degrees (see diagram). These position angles are given in lists because they offer a guide as to where the companion star—perhaps difficult to see—is to be found, and because in advanced work position angles are recorded from year to year so that eventually binary orbits may be

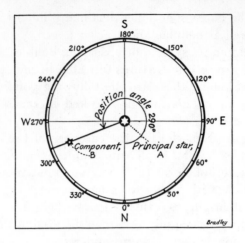

POSITION ANGLE

The above diagram as presented illustrates the position angle of a double star. It appears as seen with an inverting telescope looking southward from the northern hemisphere. Brighter star (*A*) is at center, with line drawn to component (*B*). Position angle is measured from the north point toward the east and around to this line.

computed. In some cases it takes 1000 years and more for such a system to complete a revolution. 40 Eridani is an interesting case, with components of magnitude 4.5 and 9.2 at a distance of 82″. Both of these stars show a large drift in space; however they present little relative motion, being so far apart. The revolution period is about 7000 years, and the orbit about 44,000,000,000 miles in diameter. Also, the faint companion is a visual double star itself with an orbit about as large as that of Neptune and a period of 180 years, so that the system is not a simple one. Some of the orbits (like those of eclipsing binaries) are presented edgewise to us, in which case the stars seem to go back and forth in one line. A visual binary with such an orbit is 42 Comae. Other orbits show us a "plan" view, and the stars move in ellipses. But in most cases the orbits are tilted at various angles to our line-of-sight. The visual binary with shortest period is BD −8° 4352, with period 1.7 years, and the components each are tenth magnitude. Another of short

[164]

period (5.7 years) is Delta Equulei, with components about fifth magnitude each.

Colors are the most variable factor for reasons already mentioned. The significance of color in stars lies not only in their intrinsic beauty, but in the fact that these bodies represent other suns, at various stages of temperature and evolution, with possible planets attending them, just as our sun represents the center of our solar system. The only sun we know is a yellow-white object, but suppose it had a rich blue color and had a companion sun of an orange hue— like some of the doubles we know! Blue light or orange light, or a combination, would necessarily fall onto the planet and the results would be astounding.

Telescopic diameter and magnification needed to split the stars, observers find very interesting. The pole star, Webb says in *Celestial Objects for Common Telescopes*, can be resolved with $1\frac{7}{8}$ inches, yet we have had difficulty in seeing the companion star at all, even with a 5-inch glass. On account of binary-star motion of revolution, often after the lapse of 50 years the components are really much closer to us than when formerly observed, and hence cannot be resolved with similar apertures—or else they have separated and become easy with smaller diameters.

With doubles of the same separation, some are easier to resolve than others. Rigel's eighth-magnitude companion is none too easy, being fairly lost in the bright glare of the primary (magnitude −0.3). This star also has two other components. Another, Delta Cygni, is notoriously difficult of separation. It is close for a small telescope (1″.9), besides which the image of the companion falls on the "diffraction ring" of the primary, and so is obscured. Yet these difficulties offer a challenge to the observer. The constellation Cygnus contains a vast array of interesting telescopic doubles and multiples with a range of color, magnitude, and separation.

Is it an optical double or a physical system? The question cannot be decided by the casual observer but is one of the features of the star determined after long observation by specialists. By far the larger proportion of cases are physical systems. Theory of probability leads to the conclusion that, for a random distribution of stars, in only a small proportion of cases out of many would two of them lie in a straight line as seen by us and be so close together as we find many of them to be.

Miscellaneous remarks or special features include, among other things, notes by great observers of the past. As an example, in the case of Epsilon Pegasi, Webb says that Herschel noticed a "pendulum-like oscillation of a small star in the same vertical with the large one, when the telescope is swung from side to side". This, he thinks, is "due to the longer time required for a fainter light to affect the retina, so that the reversal of motion is first perceived in the brighter objects". We would therefore see if we could detect the same phenomenon and possibly, in the light of modern knowledge, offer a better explanation. Agnes Clerke, famous astronomical historian, says of a certain component (the companion of Regulus) that it is "seemingly steeped in indigo"—a curious remark, and we would try to confirm this.

How the binaries ever originated is a question that is at present cloaked in mystery. The fission theory has for its start a great parent nebula, an enormous mass which rotates. If rotation were slow it would condense into a single star—if rapid into a binary; that is, it would divide by its own forces of gravitation, rotation, or radiation pressure, etc., into two or more parts. Then there is the modified-capture theory, which says that for untold eons a star and a planet with it pass through extensive regions of cosmic material or meteoric matter and dust, and the planet adds to its mass by accretion of this material. Also, there is the separate-nuclei theory, by which condensation of nebulae that have two nuclei might conceivably form separate stars "near" each other. However, Aitken concludes

[166]

that, while our observations indicate clearly the common origin of binaries, no proposed theory of origin and later development of the system as we see it is satisfactory, so that the question is open for further observation and research.

Double-star Observation List

The subjoined list is, we believe, the finest observing list of double and multiple stars. It incorporates a wide range as to position in the heavens, magnitude and separation of components, colors, and ease of observation. The most brilliant doubles are to be found here, as well as many having especially fine colors. The doubles of Pickering's finest objects are included.

In column 3 are given the respective magnitudes of the components. The first value is that of the brighter component (A), the second value is that of component B, etc. In column 4, the position angle refers to the direction on the celestial sphere, of the small component with respect to the large one (see diagram of position angle). Distance in column 5 represents the separation of the components in seconds of arc. Inasmuch as binary stars are perpetually in motion around a common center of gravity, the distance apart, as seen by us, and the position angle vary with the years, so in column 6 appears the year when the given position angle and distance were observed. As to colors of components in column 7, this feature is the least objective, and our color data are only approximate, various observers often disagreeing as to the exact color; moreover in a few cases, color is said actually to change with time.

The observer can get but a vague notion of the interest or beauty of these doubles from our list. For best results no greater magnification should be used than is needed to resolve the stars into components. Many stars are needed in order that there will always be a few available in any definite region of the sky open to observation from a particular locality and on a certain night of the year.

DOUBLE STARS—*North Circumpolar Regions*

Star	Position, 1950 R.A.	Dec.	Magnitude	P.A.	Dist.	Year	Colors	Remarks
	h m	° ′	m	°	″			
α Cassiopeiae............(Alpha)	0 37.6	+56 16	3.0...9.0	281	62.6	'13	Yellow, bluish	Resolved with 1-inch aperture by Burnham
η Cassiopeiae............(Eta)	0 46.1	+57 33	3.7...7.4	279	9.1	'38	Yellow, purple	Very easy, and within the reach of a small glass
α Ursae Minoris (Polaris)....(Alpha)	1 48.8	+89 2	2.0...9.0	217	18.3	'24	B, bluish	Has been seen with 1-inch; commonly more difficult
γ Andromedae............(Gamma)	2 0.8	+42 6	3.0...5.0	63	10.0	'25	Gold, blue	One of the most picturesque for small glasses
ι Cassiopeiae............(Iota)	2 24.9	+67 11	4.2..7.1..8.1	AB 251 AC 112	2.4 7.5	'25 '25	Yellow, blue, blue	Called very fine
η Persei................(Eta)	2 47.0	+55 41	4.0...8.5	301	28.4	'25	Very yellow, very blue	Another companion, AC, 10M.0, 269°, 66″.3
ε Persei................(Epsilon)	3 54.5	+39 52	3.1...8.3	9	9.0	'24	Green, blue-white	B supposedly changes color, blue to red
ω Aurigae...............(Omega)	4 55.8	+37 49	5.0...8.0	355	5.8	'25	Greenish, blue-white	
23 Ursae Majoris.........	9 27.6	+63 17	3.8...9.0	271	22.8	'24	Green-white, ashen	"Pale yellow and violet" and fine contrast
2 Canum Venaticorum......	12 13.6	+40 56	5.7...8.0	260	11.5	'25	Very gold, blue	First double discovered; good for low power
ζ Ursae Majoris (Mizar)......(Zeta)	13 21.9	+55 11	2.1...4.2	150	14.5	'25	Both green-white	A pretty pair
μ Draconis..............(Mu)	17 4.3	+54 32	5.0...5.1	101	2.2	'39	White	
(ν¹, ν²) Draconis........(Nu)	17 31.2	+55 13	4.6...4.6	312	62.0	'24	Both yellow-white	
δ Cygni.................(Delta)	19 43.4	+45 0	3.0...7.9	261	1.9	'39	Greenish, ashen	
ε Draconis..............(Epsilon)	19 48.3	+70 8	4.0...7.6	12	3.3	'26	Yellow, blue	
(o²) Cygni..............(Omicron)	20 12.0	+46 35	3.7..6.5..5.0	AB 174 AC 323	107.1 337.1	'24 '24	A, very yellow; BC, blue	
β Cephei................(Beta)	21 28.0	+70 20	3.3...8.0	250	13.7	'22	Green-white, blue	Cepheid variable with period 0d.1904795
Σ 2840 Cephei...........(Struve)	21 50.3	+55 33	6.0...7.0	197	19.8	'25	Green-white; blue-white	Very fine pair. B possibly purple

DOUBLE STARS—North Circumpolar Regions.—(Continued)

Star	Position, 1950 R.A. Dec.	Magnitude	P.A.	Dist.	Year	Colors	Remarks
	h m ° '	m	°	"			
δ Cephei............(Delta)	22 27.3 +58 10	Var...7.5	192	41.0	'24	B, blue	Type star of Cepheid variable; magnitude range, 3.7...4.6
o Cephei............(Omicron)	23 16.4 +67 50	5.2...7.8	205	3.0	'26	Very yellow; very blue	
σ Cassiopeiae............(Sigma)	23 56.4 +55 29	5.4...7.5	326	3.1	'26	Green; very blue	
Middle Regions							
55 Piscium............	0 37.3 +21 10	5.5...8.2	193	6.6	'20	Very yellow; very blue	
γ Arietis............(Gamma)	1 50.8 +19 3	4.2...4.4	0	8.4	'24	Very white, yellow-white	Binary
α Piscium............(Alpha)	1 59.4 + 2 31	4.0...5.0	306	2.5	'36	Green-white; blue or brown	Difficult in 3-inch; color contrast remarkable
30 Arietis............	2 34.1 +24 26	6.1...7.1	274	38.7	'20	Yellow-white; white or azure	
γ Ceti............(Gamma)	2 40.7 + 3 2	3.0...6.8	293	3.0	'35	Yellowish, ashen	Beautiful
Σ 422 Tauri............(Struve)	3 34.2 + 0 26	6.0...8.2	253	6.5	'24	Golden, blue	
30 (= e) Tauri............	3 45.5 +10 59	4.5...9.6	59	9.2	'23	Bluish-green, orange	Also called emerald and purple
32 (= w) Eridani............	3 51.8 - 3 6	4.0...6.0	347	7.0	'22	Yellow, blue	Called topaz and green; magnificent colors
φ Tauri............(Phi)	4 17.3 +27 14	5.1...8.5	250	52.1	'25	Red, blue	Called rose-red. Has been seen with 1⅜-inch; not easy in 3-inch
α Tauri (Aldebaran)............(Alpha)	4 33.0 +16 25	1.0...11.2	33	121.7	'23	Gold, orange	
β Orionis (Rigel)............(Beta)	5 12.1 - 8 15	1.0...8.0	202	9.4	'25	Yellow-white, orange	
14 Aurigae............	5 12.2 +32 38	5.0...7.2	225	14.5	'22	Greenish, blue-white	

DOUBLE STARS—*Middle Regions.*—*(Continued)*

Star	Position, 1950 R.A.	Dec.	Magnitude	P.A.	Dist.	Year	Colors	Remarks
	h m	° ′	m	°	″			
δ Orionis...............(Delta)	5 29.4	− 0 20	2.0...6.8	0	52.8	'22	Green-white, white or lilac	
λ Orionis................(Lambda)	5 32.4	+ 9 54	4.0...6.0	43	4.2	'34	Yellow, purple	Magnitudes 7.0...8.0...4.7
(θ¹) Orionis..............(Theta)	5 32.8	− 5 25	(See remarks)	AB 32	8.7	'25	White, lilac, garnet, reddish, and	..6.3..11.3. At least 7
				AC 131	13.1	'25		known stars in the system
				AD 96	21.6	'25		
				AE 351	4.3	'25		
σ Orionis...............(Sigma)	5 36.2	− 2 38	4.0...10.3..7.5..6.3	AB 236	11.1	'24	Gray, white, blue, red	A very remarkable multiple star
				AC 85	12.9	'24		
				AD 61	41.6	'24		
ζ Orionis................(Zeta)	5 38.2	− 1 58	2.0...5.7...10.0	AB 158	2.6	'24	Yellow, reddish-olive, and	
				AC 10	57.6	'24		
γ Leporis...............(Gamma)	5 42.4	−22 27	5.0...8.0	351	84.9	'14	Pale yellow, garnet	Easy
11 (= β) Monocerotis........(Beta)	6 26.4	− 7 0	5.0...5.5..6.0	AB 132	7.4	'23	White, gray	One of the most beautiful sights in the sky (Herschel)
				AC 125	10.1	'22		
α Canis Majoris (Sirius)......(Alpha)	6 43.0	−16 39	−1.6...8.4	56	11.1	'26	Blue-white	Fine pair; also called fiery red, green-blue
H 3945 (= 145) Canis Majoris......	7 14.5	−23 13	5.0...7.0	58	27.4	'26	Orange, pale blue	
α Geminorum (Castor)......(Alpha)	7 31.4	+32 0	2.7..3.7..9.5	AB 213	4.6	'26	AB greenish-white	Very luminous pair; one of the finest doubles
				AC 165	73.4	'25		
κ Geminorum..............(Kappa)	7 41.4	+24 31	4.0...8.5	236	6.8	'24	Yellow, ashen	Also called orange and blue; "very delicate and beautiful" (Webb)
ι Cancri.................(Iota)	8 43.7	+28 57	4.4...6.5	307	30.7	'22	Yellowish, blue	
ε Hydrae...............(Epsilon)	8 44.2	+ 6 36	3.8...7.8	247	3.2	'25	Yellow, blue	
α Leonis (Regulus)........(Alpha)	10 5.7	+12 13	1.5...8.0	307	176.5	'24	Blue-white, white	
γ Leonis...............(Gamma)	10 17.2	+20 6	2.6...3.6	119	4.0	'39	Gold, green-red	A very fine object
54 Leonis.................	10 52.9	+25 1	5.0...7.0	108	6.3	'25	Green-white, blue	
τ Leonis.................(Tau)	11 25.4	+ 3 8	5.0...7.0	170	90.	'25	B, of peculiar color	

DOUBLE STARS—*Middle Regions.*—(*Continued*)

Star	Position, 1950 R.A. h m	Dec. ° '	Magnitude m	P.A. °	Dist. "	Year	Colors	Remarks
17 Virginis..........	12 20.0	+ 5 35	6.2...9.0	337	19.6	'25	Green-white, orange	A fine pair and easy
δ Corvi......(Delta)	12 27.3	-16 15	3.0...7.5	212	24.2	'26	Yellow, lilac	
24 Comae Berenicis.......	12 32.6	+18 39	4.7...6.2	271	20.1	'22	Yellow, very blue	
γ Virginis......(Gamma)	12 39.1	- 1 11	3.6...3.7	318	5.7	'39	Both yellow	
α (= 12) Canum Venaticorum (Alpha)	12 53.7	+38 35	3.2...5.7	228	19.7	'25	Yellow-white, lilac	Also known as Cor Caroli
θ Virginis......(Theta)	13 7.4	- 5 16	4.0..9.0..10.0	AB 343 / AC 299	7.2 / 71.5	'21 / '20	White, violet, dusky	Fine triple, but difficult with 3-inch
ε Boötis......(Epsilon)	14 42.8	+27 17	3.0...6.3	334	2.8	'38	Very yellow, green	
54 Hydrae......	14 43.1	-25 14	5.2...7.1	128	8.9	'15	Red, blue	
ξ Boötis......(Xi)	14 49.1	+19 19	4.7...6.6	11	5.1	'39	Yellow, purple-red	
δ Serpentis......(Delta)	15 32.4	+10 42	3.0...4.0	183	3.8	'25	Yellow-white, ashen	In Serpens Caput
Σ 1962 Librae......(Struve)	15 36.0	- 8 38	6.3...6.4	189	11.8	'26	White	
ζ Coronae Borealis......(Zeta)	15 37.5	+36 48	4.1...5.0	304	6.3	'25	Green-white, greenish	A pretty double
β Scorpii......(Beta)	16 2.5	-19 40	2.0...6.0	23	13.7	'25	Yellow, green	
ν Scorpii......(Nu)	16 9.1	-19 21	4.2..6.7.7.0..8.0	AB 2 / AC 336 / CD 50	1.0 / 41.4 / 2.1	'24 / '25 / '24		
α Scorpii (Antares)......(Alpha)	16 26.5	-26 20	1.2...5.2	275	3.0	'35	Red, green	Beautiful
α Herculis......(Alpha)	17 12.4	+14 27	3.0...6.1	110	4.8	'39	Very yellow, intense blue	
δ Herculis......(Delta)	17 13.0	+24 54	3.0...8.1	206	11.3	'26	Red, green	
39 Ophiuchi......	17 15.0	-24 14	6.0...7.0	355	10.8	'25	Green, ashen	Optical pair
ν Serpentis......(Nu)	17 18.0	-12 47	5.0...9.0	31	47.3	'14	Red, blue	In Serpens Cauda
ρ Herculis......(Rho)	17 22.0	+37 11	4.0...5.1	314	4.0	'25	Green-white, greenish	
95 Herculis......	17 59.4	+21 36	4.9...4.9	259	6.2	'36	Green-yellow, red-yellow	Called "apple-green and cherry-red"—also beryl-sardonyx

[171]

DOUBLE STARS—Middle Regions.—(Continued)

Star	Position, 1950 R.A. (h m)	Dec. (° ')	Magnitude (m)	P.A. (°)	Dist. (")	Year	Colors	Remarks
70 Ophiuchi...........(Struve)	18 2.9	+ 2 32	4.1...6.1	116	6.6	'39	Yellow, purple	Very fine
Σ 2306 Scuti............	18 19.4	−15 7	7.2...7.9	220	11.2	'22	Yellow, very blue	
α Lyrae (Vega)...........(Alpha)	18 35.2	+38 44	1.0...10.5	169	56.4	'25	Blue-white, orange	
ε¹, ε² Lyrae............(Epsilon)	18 42.7	+39 37	4.6...4.9	173	207.8		Green-white, blue-white	ε¹, 5.1...6.0, 5°, 2″.9 ('35) green-white, blue-white ε², 5.1...5.4, 112°, 2″.3 ('35) very white
ζ Lyrae................(Zeta)	18 43.0	+37 33	4.2...5.5	150	43.7	'24	Yellow-green, white	Has 3 other faint companions
β Lyrae................(Beta)	18 48.2	+33 18	(See remarks)	AB 149 AC 247 AD 68 AE 318 AF 19	46.6 46.4 64.3 68.6 85.7	'25 '13 1898 '25 '25	AB yellow-white	Mags. 3.0...6.7..13.0...14.3..9.2...9.0; A, multiple and variable, magnitude 3.4...4.1
11 Aquilae............	18 56.8	+13 33	5.7...9.2	275	16.2	'25	Green-white, ashen	
γ Coronae Australis......(Gamma)	19 3.0	−37 8	5.0...5.0	241	2.4	'38		
β Cygni (Albireo).......(Beta)	19 28.7	+27 51	3.0...5.3	55	34.6	'24	Yellow, blue	Absolutely superb! Needs only 18× on 2-inch; likely a binary
57 Aquilae............	19 51.9	− 8 21	5.2...6.2	171	36.1	'25	Very white	Colors variously recorded
θ Sagittae............(Theta)	20 7.7	+20 46	6.0..8.5..7.1	AB 328 AC 221	11.6 79.4	'22 '25	Yellow-white, ashen, yellow	
α¹, α² Capricorni............(Alpha)	20 14.9	−12 40	4 ...9.0	221	45.5	'24		α², α¹, 3.2...4.2, 291°, 375″ (1885); naked-eye double—a magnificent object
	20 15.3	−12 42	3.8...9.5	157	154.9	'09		
β², β¹ Capricorni.........(Beta)	20 18.2	−14 56	2.5...6.0	267	205	1835	Very yellow, blue	
γ Delphini..............(Gamma)	20 44.4	+15 57	4.0...5.0	270	10.6	'24	Golden, blue-green	
Σ (= λ) Equulei...........(Lambda)	20 59.8	+ 6 59	7.1...7.1	220	2.7	'26	Very white	

DOUBLE STARS—*Middle Regions.—(Continued)*

Star	Position, 1950 R.A. Dec.	Magnitude	P.A.	Dist.	Year	Colors	Remarks
	h m ° ′	m	°	′′			
ε Pegasi...............(Epsilon)	21 41.7 + 9 39	2.7...8.7	320	142.6	'13	Yellow, violet	Naked-eye pair
μ Cygni................(Mu)	21 41.9 +28 31	4.7...6.2	52	203.7	'24	White, blue	A, given also as reddish, also topaz
41 Aquarii............	22 11.5 −21 19	5.7...7.7	116	5.0	'26		
ζ Aquarii.............(Zeta)	22 26.2 − 0 17	4.4...4.6	289	2.3	'37	Green-white	Very fine; easy with small aperture
τ¹ Aquarii............(Tau)	22 45.0 −14 19	6.0...9.2	120	25.6	'25	A, very yellow	Uncommon color contrast
94 Aquarii............	23 16.4 −13 44	5.2...7.2	348	13.3	'22	Yellow-white, blue	
		South Circumpolar Regions					
θ² Eridani............(Theta)	2 56.4 −40 30	3.1...4.1	85	8.2	'00		"One of the most beautiful objects in the heavens"
γ² Velorum...........(Gamma)	8 8.0 −47 11	2.7...3	220	42			
α Crucis..............(Alpha)	12 23.8 −62 49	1.6...2.1	118	5		White	Third brightest star in heavens, combined magnitude +0.06; "by far the finest double in the sky" (W. H. Pickering). C, the 11th-magnitude companion (Proxima Centauri) is the nearest star to us, except the sun.
α Centauri............(Alpha)	14 36.2 −60 38	0.3...1.7...11	AB 310 AC ...	4 (2½°)	'36	White, red	

Variable Stars

THERE is one field above all others in which the amateur astronomer has distinguished himself by his help to professionals, and in that field even today there are new horizons waiting to be crossed. The giant telescopes of the world's great observatories are seldom turned on the brighter regular variable stars, for these telescopes have elaborate programs in other fields mapped out for their use. They cannot be spared for routine day-by-day visual observations of this kind, and so the work has fallen to the humble instruments of the back yard and to the devotion of amateurs.

Variable stars, the surprize packages of the universe, are stars that change their brightness, sometimes from hour to hour and in some cases from month to month. Except for one type, science does not yet know exactly why. Unending detailed observations are the only means by which the mystery can be solved, for only when we know how they fluctuate may we hope to know why. When the answer is found it may provide new keys to an understanding of the universe.

Variable stars are everywhere in the sky, and some are even visible to the naked eye. Polaris, landmark of the northern skies, is one, and it undergoes a 10 per cent variation in its light in slightly less than 4 days. Betelgeuse, the red star of Orion, is another. It changes by one-half magnitude, but irregularly, so that no one can predict when next it will fade.

These stars are of different types. Variables are grouped in several well-defined divisions.

Periodic variables:

Eclipsing variables (not intrinsically variable). Algol, for instance
Cepheids
    Cluster type, with approximately ½-day period, such as RR Lyrae
    Classical Cepheid, period about 5.6 days, such as Delta Cephei
Long-period variables, as Omicron Ceti

Non-periodic variables:

Irregular variables, similar to R Coronae
Novae, or temporary stars, typified by Tycho's star of 1572

The easiest type to understand is the periodic eclipsing variable. These are binary stars circling around a common center of gravity, in which one component is brighter than the other. As the fainter of the pair comes before the brighter, the combined light of the two fades. As the brighter emerges, the light increases. The individual stars in these binary systems, of course, do not actually change their brilliance, but the systems seem to vary because we happen to be in their plane of motion and see the components eclipsing each other. From a position in space outside that plane, they would not appear to eclipse each other. Algol in Perseus is a typical example of the eclipsing group and changes from magnitude 2.1 to 3.2 as regularly as clockwork every $2^d20^h48^m$. It is visible to the unaided eye throughout the period. It was from spectroscopic observations of Algol that the first determination of a star's diameter was made.

But the real problem of variables rests in those stars which change their intrinsic brilliance—the Cepheids, the long-period variables, the irregular variables, and the novae. Already, though mystery still surrounds them, science has used some of them as measuring sticks to tell us how far away are the globular clusters and the island universes of outer space.

[175]

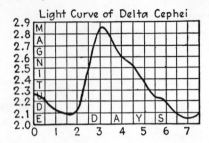

Light Curve of Delta Cephei

The Cepheid classification has two subdivisions, based mainly on the difference in period. Cluster variables, or RR Lyrae stars, are the shorter, and "classical" Cepheids the longer. Cluster variables include no stars visible to the naked eye, speed through space at velocities up to 200 miles per second, have an average period of 0.56 day. Classical Cepheids offer several specimens visible to the unaided eye, such as Polaris and Delta Cephei, from which the classification derived its name. They move at comparatively slow speeds and have an average period of 5.6 days. Despite the fact that there are undeniable similarities between the groups and that the causes of their fluctuations are quite possibly the same, there seems to be sufficient warrant for discussing them as separate types.

There were recently some 620 examples of the cluster-type variables known to astronomers. They are spectacular objects, whose variations seem the result of a pulsation within the stars themselves. Spectral study shows the brilliant lines of hydrogen gas to be prominent in their make-up. A typical range in brightness would be one in which the star at its maximum was $2\frac{1}{2}$ times as bright as when at its minimum.

The period of a variable star is defined as the time in which the object goes from one minimum to another, or from one maximum to another. On an average, these cluster variables run twice through this range, from dim to bright, in slightly more than a day. One unique specimen in Aquarius completes its period in 1 hour 28 minutes.

The classical Cepheids, aside from the fact that their periods are on an average 10 times longer than those of the cluster variables, also have a slightly smaller range in variation. Their average maximum is 2.1 times as bright as the minimum. Like the cluster stars, they are believed to pulsate like a toy balloon that is alternately inflated and deflated. As they go from maximum brightness to minimum, their surface temperature drops from 5300° to 4600°C.

On the other hand, the long-period variables, which have a comparatively small range in surface temperature, 1800° to 2300°C., have a much greater range in light variation. The fluctuations are such that the average star is at maximum 63 times as brilliant as at minimum.

In considering any question of magnitude range within a variable star, it is well to remember that the magnitude scale is based upon ratio of light intensity. Stating the different magnitudes of two stars does *not* state the actual numerical difference in light intensity between them; because if two stars are one magnitude apart, the brighter of the pair is $2\frac{1}{2}$ times as bright as the other. If, however, they are two magnitudes apart, the intensities differ by $2\frac{1}{2} \times 2\frac{1}{2}$, or $6\frac{1}{4}$ times; similarly, if four magnitudes, by about 39 times; if five magnitudes, by 100 times; and, finally, if 20 magnitudes, by 100,000,000 times. This magnitude scale, for various reasons, is better adapted to the uses of astronomy than one measuring the numerical difference in intensities. It compresses, within a few divisions, intensity differences that would otherwise become difficult to express: a twentieth-magnitude star would require nine figures.

Frequently, the long-period variables have an intensity range of 100 times, and there is at least one specimen that is 10,000 times as brilliant at maximum as at minimum. Perhaps the great changes that take place within them require a longer interval of time than do the comparatively small variations of the cluster-type and classical Cepheid stars, for the long-period group requires an average of 280 days to run the gamut of brightness.

These long-period variables are, like the first classification, characterized by an extremely rapid motion through space, and although their temperature is low as compared with the cluster-type and Cepheid stars, there is something distinctly mysterious about even that fact. For the spectroscope reveals in their outer layers blazing clouds of hydrogen gas. Something more than a red-hot star at the comparatively low temperatures attributed to these giants is needed to make hydrogen shine so in that atmosphere. And no one can yet say what it is.

The long-period variables, furthermore, are amongst the largest of known stars. They are indeed super-giants, and the biggest of them have a volume 25,000,000 times that of the sun. Yet they are extremely tenuous, and their average density is about $\frac{1}{1000}$ that of the air we breathe—a density that would be considered a vacuum in our laboratories. They are then, as various scientists have noted, little more than red-hot vacuums.

In color they are red or deep orange, a fact which caused Chandler in 1888 to advance the comment that the redness of variable stars, generally speaking, is proportional to the length of their periods of light variation, so that one might say "the redder the tint, the longer the period".

And then there are the novae. Literally, these objects are termed "new" stars, although this term fits them as badly as the adjective "temporary" which is used frequently in connection with them. Actually, novae are stars which (so far as we know) have always been in existence but which, for some reason, suddenly flare up to unheard-of brilliance. They maintain a tremendous expenditure of energy for a while, after which they fade to their former obscurity.

A typical nova may increase its brightness by 70,000 or 80,000 times, and at the peak of its eruption may be among

the most brilliant of objects. Occasionally there occurs a
super-nova, a star which has all characteristics common to
ordinary novae but which, during the period of its expan-
sion, is in itself nearly as bright as the entire galaxy in
which it appears. Super-novae are extremely rare, only a
few having been discovered, and those in other universes
than ours. Strangely enough only one super-nova—Tycho's
star, of 1572—seems definitely to belong to the Milky Way,
although ordinary novae are as a rule thought to be members of our galaxy because of their brightness and proximity
to the Milky Way.

It is notable that practically all of those visible to the
naked eye are discovered by amateur astronomers who are
familiar with the constellations and detect the changes in
outline wrought by the appearance of a "new" star. Professional astronomers, whose work is directed along a
specialized line of research, do not have time for the general
surveys of the constellations that are constantly made by
amateurs.

And so an amateur who sees what he believes to be a new
star in the heavens may well rush to check it against all
known objects in the hope that he, too, has made an
important discovery. The first thing to do, of course, is to
compare the suspected star with a good chart of the region,
making absolutely certain that the object really isn't a star
that the observer has simply overlooked before. Then
check upon the positions of all the naked-eye planets to be
positive that every one of them can be accounted for, and
also consider the possibility of a comet. After that go to a
telephone or telegraph office and notify the nearest observatory as accurately as possible of the position, magnitude,
and color of the object. Every night of observation is
important in the early stages of a nova; so, having made
absolutely certain that the object is not a normal object in
the skies, waste no time in reporting it.

Invariably, when astronomers check on the sudden appearance of a nova, they discover a faint star in its place on old photographs of the region. And, incidentally, these faint stars are usually of about the same brightness as our sun, which therefore might be considered a potential nova.

At any rate, spectroscopic study of novae shows that there is a terrific outward rush of incandescent gases, an effect not dissimilar to that which would be caused by an explosion within the star. It has been suggested that the outer strata of the object suddenly get beyond control of the star's gravitational attraction, and that perhaps the reason for this may lie in some increase of light-pressure from the center of the star, which is probably unstable.

In general, all well-investigated intrinsically variable stars have proved to be giants or super-giants, stars of large volume and low density. Oddly enough those stars with the lowest density and greatest size seem most disposed toward variability.

The pulsation theory is based on the premise that, in the normal star, gravitation and light-pressure—the one holding matter to the star, the other forcing it away—are equal and maintain a fairly constant balance. If, the exponents of the theory state, the materials of this star were in some manner compressed and then released, they would rush outward at an accelerating velocity until they passed the point at which gravity and light-pressure were equal. Then they would slow down until they stopped and would begin a return trip. Again passing the balance point, they would slow down, stop, and begin to rush outward again, continuing the process rhythmically.

Mathematicians have calculated that for each star there would be a natural period of such vibration, and observations of the Cepheids, for instance, give them a period not inconsistent with that which is calculated for them on the basis of their dimensions and physical construction. Estimates for the long-period variables, based on a very tenuous composition, also seem to agree.

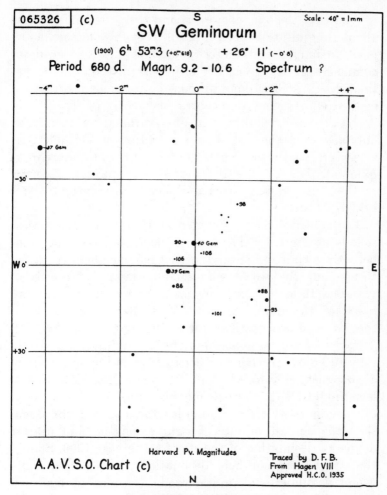

VARIABLE-STAR CHART

A star chart of the type sent observers and members of the American Association of Variable Star Observers for use in recording light fluctuations in variables.

Whatever the true answer is, and there are some doubts about the pulsation theory, it will probably not be known until an immensely greater amount of data has been accumulated. And a great deal of important routine observation in this field is done by non-professionals coördinated in their efforts through a central agency.

Detailed charts for use in observational work may be obtained from the American Association of Variable Star Observers, as well as a further outline of the procedure to be followed. For information address the current recorder of the A.A.V.S.O., Harvard College Observatory, Cambridge, Mass.

The association was founded in 1911 to relieve professionals of a great deal of work that could be done competently by amateurs, and it now has members scattered throughout the world who send in monthly records of variables to which they are assigned by the association. Some of the more experienced of these workers make thousands of observations during the course of a year.

Variables are designated both by the capital-letter system introduced by Argelander prior to 1850 and by a numerical arrangement developed at the Harvard Observatory. The latter indicates the variable by a six-digit number composed of three units which give, in order, the hour of right ascension, the nearest minute of right ascension, and nearest degree of declination of the star for the year 1900. Should the star have a southern declination, the last two digits would be underlined or italicized. A typical designation under this system would be that of R Leonis, given as 094211. The star has a right ascension of approximately 9^h42^m and a declination of $+11°$.

Making actual observations of a variable star is a matter that requires painstaking care, and should not be attempted without remembering two things: that the human eye cannot, without long training, estimate accurately divisions smaller than one-third of a magnitude; and that the method to be used in making estimates depends entirely upon the star in question.

There are, as the table at the end of this chapter will show, several variables that are visible to the naked eye and that are, therefore, excellent material for the attention of the casual amateur. However, in all but a few instances, serious observation of variables requires the use of a telescope. Other equipment needed includes a good chart or atlas and a pencil and notebook. Graph paper, for clearly illustrating the light curves of the stars under study, is also desirable. Detailed recommendations as to equipment, of course, can always be obtained from the American Association of Variable Star Observers. Three different methods are employed in the scientific observation of variable stars—direct visual study, delicate measurements of light changes with the photoelectric cell, and the permanent recording of stars on the photographic plate. For present purposes, only the visual methods are considered.

Considering the variable under observation to be ideally situated, the usual method of estimating its fluctuations can best be described by quoting from *Circular* 1 of the American Association of Variable Star Observers, on instructions to observers:

On the charts, many of the stars are designated with numbers which indicate their magnitudes to tenths. These magnitudes have been carefully determined and are to be considered as a sort of measuring rod in estimating the magnitude of the variable. Thus 84 and 90 indicate two stars whose magnitudes are 8.4 and 9.0, respectively. Select two comparison stars, one a little brighter and the other a little fainter than the variable and estimate how bright the variable is in terms of these two stars. This may seem at first to be very difficult, but as the eye becomes better trained, precision is readily attained. For example, suppose there are three comparison stars in the field with the variable, marked respectively 86, 88, and 92, and that the variable is fainter than the 86 but brighter than the 92. If it seems equal to the 88 star, consider this as the estimate of the brightness of the variable. If it is about half way between 88 and 92, your estimate is 9.0. If nearer the 88 than the

92, call it 8.9, etc. Use at least two comparison stars, and if possible, more. If the interval is very large, say 0.5 or greater, use extreme care in estimating how the interval between the brighter comparison star and the variable compares with that between the variable and the fainter comparison star. Record exactly what you see, regardless of seeming discrepancies in your observations. If the variable is not seen, that is, is invisible because of extreme faintness, clouds, or moonlight, note the faintest star visible; if that star should be an 115, record your observation of the variable as <11.5, meaning that the variable is invisible and must have been at least below magnitude 11.5.

To picture adequately the problems of a variable-star observer, let us study the process of making observations on a specific star, R Leonis. To begin with, we must remember that an astronomical telescope inverts objects, and so we must turn the charts with which we are working upside down—unless they have been prepared to show the stars as they appear in an inverted field. In addition, if the telescope in use be not equipped with setting circles, it will be necessary to plot the position of the variable on a map and then pick up the field by guiding from a bright star in the vicinity.

For this work it is useful to determine the diameter of the field of view of the telescope. It can be done easily by focusing the instrument on a star which is as close to the celestial equator as possible, and timing the passage of that star from one side of the telescope field to the other. This time interval in minutes, divided by 4, is equal to the diameter of the telescope field in degrees of arc, which is exactly what is required. Additional hints that may help the beginner in this work may be found in the chapter on Use of the Telescope.

Now, for the task of actually locating R Leonis, let us suppose we are using a telescope the diameter of field of which we have found to be 1°, and that we have focused the instrument so that Omicron Leonis is centered in the field.

By examining a chart of the naked-eye stars near R Leonis we can determine that the variable is about $1\frac{1}{2}°$ east and 1½° north of Omicron. So the first movement is to adjust the telescope east just 1½ diameters of the field, bringing the point that is 1½° east of Omicron into the center of view. From this point, we move 1½° north and we should be able to recognize the field of stars from the chart and thus identify the variable R Leonis. We would see two bright stars on a line running southeast-northwest, with a small equilateral triangle to the south. The variable is one of the members of the tiny triangle, and by proper orientation of the chart we should have no trouble in identifying it. All variable fields are not so easily found, of course, but by patient work they may be located if within range of the telescope in use. Always it should be remembered that if the telescope field be inverted, so are north and south, and east and west reversed in the field.

Once having tracked down the variable, our next task is to estimate its magnitude. Let us suppose in this case that we use the other two stars in the triangle for comparison. They are of magnitudes 9.0 and 9.6 as the atlas tells us, and if we estimated that R Leonis were just between them in brilliance, then we would record it as of magnitude 9.3 at that date and time. This method is only a slight departure from the procedure outlined before, but it serves to show how circumstances may alter or modify that standard of procedure. No definite rule can be advanced for this work, because all working conditions vary, but this method will fit most cases with slight adaptations.

The fluctuations of a variable may be simply illustrated by the construction of a graph. The time, usually in days, is scaled horizontally, and the magnitude, preferably in tenths, can be scaled vertically. The accompanying graph of Delta Cephei will serve as an illustration of such a record.

List of Variables for Observation

The following are some of the important variable stars observable with small telescopes. The list has been approved

by Campbell, former secretary of the A.A.V.S.O. For the
stars with asterisks, there are charts with comparison
stars indicated thereon, which can be obtained from the
A.A.V.S.O. chart curator. The last four stars are for south-
circumpolar observation.

Star	R.A. and Dec. 1950				Magnitude range	Period, etc.
	h	m	°	′	m	
Gamma (γ) Cassiopeiae..	0	54	+60	27	1.6– 2.6	Peculiar
*Omicron (o) Ceti (Mira).	2	17	– 3	12	1.7– 9.5	331^d, irregular
*R Trianguli..............	2	34	+34	2	5.3–12.0	266^d
Beta (β) Persei........	3	5	+40	46	2.3– 3.5	2^{d}20^{h}48^m
Lambda (λ) Tauri......	3	58	+12	21	3.8– 4.1	3^{d}22^{h}52^m
Epsilon (ε) Aurigae......	4	58	+43	45	3.0– 4.5	9883^d
Zeta (ζ) Aurigae........	4	59	+41	0	4.9– 5.6	972^d
Alpha (α) Orionis......	5	52	+ 7	24	0.7– 1.5	Irregular
*U Orionis..............	5	53	+20	10	5.4–12.2	373^d
Eta (η) Geminorum.....	6	12	+22	31	3.2– 4.2	231^d
Zeta (ζ) Geminorum....	7	1	+20	39	3.7– 4.5	10^d 3^{h}41^m
R Canis Majoris........	7	17	–16	18	5.9– 6.7	1^d 3^{h}15^m
*R Leonis..............	9	45	+11	40	5.0–10.8	310^d
*R Hydrae.............	13	27	–23	1	3.5–10.1	406^d
Delta (δ) Librae........	14	58	– 8	19	4.8– 6.2	2^d.3
*R Coronae Borealis......	15	47	+28	19	5.9–15.0	Peculiar
u Herculis..............	17	15	+33	9	4.8– 5.3	2^d.05
W Sagittarii...........	18	2	–29	35	4.3– 5.1	7^d.59
*R Scuti...............	18	45	– 5	46	4.9– 9.0	145^d
Beta (β) Lyrae........	18	48	+33	18	3.5– 4.1	12^d.91
*Chi (χ) Cygni.........	19	49	+32	47	4.2–13.7	409^d
Eta (η) Aquilae........	19	50	+ 0	53	3.7– 4.5	7^d.18
S (= 10) Sagittae.......	19	54	+16	30	5.4– 6.1	8^d.4
T Vulpeculae...........	20	49	+28	4	5.5– 6.5	4^{d}10^{h}27^m
Mu (μ) Cephei.........	21	42	+58	33	4.0– 5.5	430^d
Delta (δ) Cephei........	22	27	+58	10	3.6– 4.3	5^d 8^{h}47^m
*R Aquarii..............	23	41	–15	34	5.8–11.0	387^d, has peculiarities
*R Cassiopeiae..........	23	56	+51	7	4.8–13.6	426^d
R Doradus.............	4	36	–62	11	4.5– 7.0	335^d
L^2 Puppis.............	7	12	–44	33	3.1– 6.3	141^d
R Carinae.............	9	31	–62	34	4.0–10.0	305^d
Kappa (κ) Pavonis.......	18	52	–67	18	4.0– 5.0	9^d.10

Star Clusters and Nebulae

D O YOU know that you are living in a triple nebula?
Sounds sensational, but that is only one of the facts
discovered by astronomers with great telescopes. And
although such facts about the universe are determined as a
result of exhaustive investigation with large instruments, it
is possible to stay in one's own yard with small telescopes
and examine and appreciate many of the objects that make
up the unfathomable depths of space around us. Two types
of objects are of interest in this way, the star clusters and
the nebulae.

Close inspection of the stellar universe discloses not only
a prodigious number of single and multiple stars, but
thousands of aggregations of these bodies in far-distant
space. They are the star clusters. Such great collections of
suns are not enlarged double-star systems but a distinct
kind of unit of structure in the universe. Not only are they
of interest in themselves, but they have the peculiar advantage of helping to measure the extent of the universe.

Star clusters fall into two types: the open cluster, such as
the Pleiades, which are probably the best known example,
and the globular cluster, like Messier 13, the Great Star
Cluster in Hercules.

Of the open type, also called galactic clusters, several
examples are visible to the unaided eye. Besides the
Pleiades, in Taurus, another group—the Hyades—is easily
located because of the reddish first-magnitude star Aldebaran. Another for the naked eye is the Coma Berenices

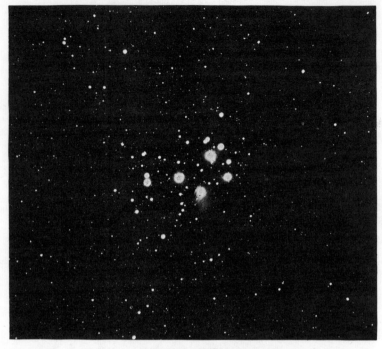

"SEVEN SISTERS"

A professional picture of an amateur subject—the star cluster of the Pleiades. Only a slight haziness is shown around the stars in this photograph, but longer exposures reveal considerable nebulosity surrounding the stars. (*Lick Observatory*.)

group. In Perseus is a beautiful double cluster that is likewise observable without optical aid, on a good night. Not quite as easy as this is the Praesepe cluster within the quadrilateral of Cancer.

Naked-eye views of these objects mean nothing, however, compared to the views afforded by even a low-powered telescope. Indeed to get the best effect, one of the best means of seeing the objects is to magnify them only about 15 to 20 times and have as wide a field of view as possible. In this manner many of these groups offer an almost indescribable sight. In a good glass with very low power either one of the Perseus clusters appears like a scattering of gold dust. In 18× binoculars the Pleiades just nicely fill the field and look like a brilliant array of diamonds on a black background.

The open clusters really belong to the Milky Way, the stellar system in which we are placed. These galactic clusters appear to be most numerous in the apparent direction of the star clouds in Scorpius and Sagittarius. The Hyades and the Pleiades and also the Coma and Praesepe groups are the nearest to the solar system. The Hyades are closest at a distance of 130 light-years, although very few clusters are within a radius of 1000 light-years. Only indirect measurements can establish this great distance. The bright star Aldebaran seemingly in the midst of the Hyades does not really belong to it but is simply in the same line-of-sight from us. About 300 to 400 open clusters are known; some contain a few stars, others a few hundred, and all have widely scattered members, rather than a condensed mass of suns. The average diameter of such clusters is about 20 light-years.

Many such groups show that they are moving together or going through space *en masse*. One of these moving clusters includes 5 of the stars of the Big Dipper, as well as Sirius, Deneb, and some fainter stars scattered over the sky. Although the sun is located in this group, it does not belong to it. Another moving cluster includes the stars of the Southern Cross as well as Alpha Centauri and various other bright stars in the south celestial region.

The globular clusters lend themselves better to higher telescopic power, for they cover a much smaller area, appearing like a star in size until magnified, although the nearest ones are over half the moon's diameter in extent. They are, in the telescope, a dense aggregation of untold numbers of stars, seemingly so compact toward the center that it is difficult if not impossible to distinguish individual stars. At first glance they appear to be spherical, but upon closer examination, somewhat oblate.

Globular clusters are not as numerous as the open or galactic type; only about 100 are known. A few are more "open", like the open-cluster type. Others have many thousands of stars in a seemingly dense mass, and the average has perhaps 20,000 stars as bright as the sun. Distribution of globular clusters is different from the open type, for the globulars are not found in the Milky Way regions. Evidence points to their being outside this system in space, although Shapley holds that they are essential features of the Milky Way even if they are outside its stars and star clouds. Most of the globular clusters are located in a large section of the sky, with Sagittarius as the center.

The nearest and brightest of these singular objects are Omega Centauri and 47 Tucanae, which are about 22,000 light-years away. The former is considered the finest star cluster in the heavens, and the latter is almost as fine a spectacle. Both of them however are for observers in southern latitudes, 47 Tucanae being located near the Smaller Magellanic Cloud, a southern object.

Another globular which is comparatively near is the Hercules Cluster (M 13), which is 34,000 light-years away. It is the finest globular star cluster for observers of the northern hemisphere. The real diameter is about 100 light-years, and many thousands of stars can be counted on photographs made of this cluster. Moreover, these points of light do not include the more frequently occurring low-luminosity stars, so Moulton concludes that there must be *several millions of stars* in M 13! At our immense distance the stars seem closely packed, yet they are not actually so, for on the average each is about 1 light-year from the next one. The individual stars of this stupendous group are too far away for us to detect any movement, but they undoubtedly are moving in orbits of their own and at speeds of a few miles per second.

The beginner in astronomy cannot have the least idea of the superb and entrancing view obtained in a good telescope

AN ISLAND UNIVERSE

The beautiful spiral nebula, M 101, in the constellation Ursa Major. Its striking spiral appearance seems to give evidence of motion, which, however, we could never see in a lifetime. (*Mt. Wilson Observatory.*)

when the Hercules cluster is in the field. A 3-inch glass under the best conditions begins to show something; a 6-inch does much better, and for a *really* magnificent view, a 12-inch telescope is desirable. Words are inadequate to describe the object, particularly when seen against a black sky, with a good glass, a good ocular, and other favorable conditions. Small wonder that owners of telescopes have the habit of turning their instruments onto it at almost every opportunity. To see a few such remarkable assem-

[191]

blages of suns—so far away—is helpful in forming something of a picture of our universe. Only a very few are
visible without a telescope, and real research is done by
long-exposure photography.

The nebulae belong to an entirely different class of celestial objects. There are two large divisions of nebulae: the
galactic nebulae and the extra-galactic nebulae. The class
of galactic nebulae includes two types: the diffuse nebula
such as the Great Nebula in Orion, the Trifid Nebula, the
Filamentary Nebula in Cygnus—and the other type—the
planetary nebula, like the Owl Nebula.

The galactic nebulae are found in the Milky Way. The
diffuse type are irregular in shape and immense in size. They
may present an appearance of great shapeless clouds or
may be only hazy patches, in any case showing as extended
areas and thus being fainter than stars. Some of them are
comparatively luminous, and others have no source of
illumination, appearing only as dark masses.

A neighboring star seems to be the source of light for the
more luminous of the diffuse nebulae, and there is a definite
association of stars with these nebulae. In the Pleiades, for
example, the unaided eye discerns simply stars, but a long-
exposure photograph reveals the group immersed in a great
extent of nebulosity. The Orion Nebula is also connected
with the group of stars known as the Trapezium, and there
are other examples. Some proportion of the light coming to
us from these nebulae is really starlight reflected by the
nebula, but more of it is radiation received from the hot
stars and transformed by the nebula and radiated again to
us; that is, the stars stimulate the nebula to send off rays
of their own. Their spectra reveal much hydrogen and
helium, so that these gases and dust are supposedly the
materials of which they are composed.

A number of the diffuse group are *dark nebulae.* For many
years these great dark irregular areas in the heavens were
thought to be "holes" in the sky in which there were no

DARK NEBULA

This is the spectacular Dark Bay or Horse-head nebula in Orion, and the silhouette is caused by clouds of cosmic dust which blot out the light of stars in the
background. (*Photograph by Duncan, exposure* 3^h, *Mt. Wilson Observatory.*)

stars, but we know that the dark regions are silhouettes of
unilluminated nebulae that hide the stars beyond. The
famous Horse-head or Dark Bay Nebula in Orion is the
most spectacular example. Dark nebulae are not absolutely
dark, for occasionally they are brighter than the general
stellar background. Classed among such objects are extensive rifts in the Milky Way like that from Cygnus to the
south circumpolar regions. Striking examples near the star
Antares have been photographed by Barnard. Such masses,
it is held, would be luminous if near enough to ultra-violet
and blue stars.

[193]

LAGOON NEBULA

One of the best known of the diffuse nebulae, the magnificent Messier 8, which is located in the constellation Scorpius. The picture shows stars, clouds, bays, rifts, the great lagoon, and a profusion of delicate detail. (*Lick Observatory.*)

It has been thought that this obscuring matter of the dark nebulae may be composed of meteors, but it seems more probable that it is dust a few hundredths or thousandths of an inch in diameter. Inasmuch as the edges of the masses are often sharp, as in the Horse-head nebula, it is concluded that likely the clouds of this material are held together by gravitation.

Besides the dark lanes in the Milky Way there are two other especially black areas called coal-sacks. The Coal-sack in Cygnus is a dark hole southeast of Deneb. Another is north of Antares and east of the star cluster M 80. A third is near Delta Cephei, and the most notable one is the coal-sack near the Southern Cross. The last is an irregular, very dark region in the Milky Way, east of Alpha Crucis.

The planetary nebulae are so called because of their

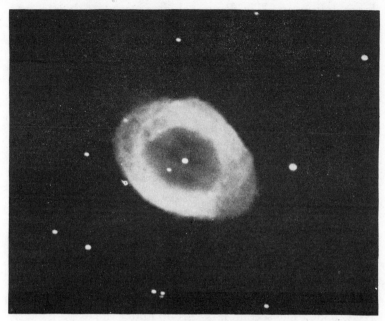

A STELLAR "SMOKE-RING"

The well-known Ring Nebula in Lyra, Messier 57. In a telescope it appears just
like a smoke-ring. In a large instrument the complex structural details are visible,
as well as the 15th-magnitude star in the middle. (*Mt. Wilson Observatory.*)

fancied resemblance to a planet. They are envelopes of
nebular material surrounding stars; that is, in most cases
there seems to be a star in the center of each. About 130
planetaries are known, and they range in size from almost
star-like points to objects as large as NGC 7293 Aquarii,
about $\frac{1}{4}°$ in diameter. None is bright enough for naked-eye
visibility. The distance of planetaries from the solar system
is large: the nearest (NGC 7293) is 1000 light-years off, and
most of them are much farther. Diameters average a trillion
miles, several times the extent of the solar system.

Probably the best planetary nebula to see is M 57, the
Ring Nebula in Lyra. Its diameter is over 1', and it is composed of a nearly perfect elliptical ring with a fifteenth-
magnitude star in the center that is invisible except in a

[1 9 5]

large telescope. The Ring nebula is easy to locate in a 3-inch telescope by means of the stars Beta and Gamma Lyrae between which it lies. Appearing in such a telescope as a faint misty round patch, it reveals itself in a 6-inch glass in its true annular shape and looks just like a "smoke-ring".

The Crab Nebula, M 1 in Taurus, is another planetary (?) for the telescope; this appears to be expanding as if from an explosion. In Ursa Major is the Owl Nebula, over 3' of arc in diameter and looking rather spherical and somewhat owl-like. Another planetary is the Dumbbell Nebula in Vulpecula. In Andromeda is still another, H.IV 18, an imperfect smoke-ring with a relatively large star in the middle.

The extra-galactic nebulae include regular nebulae, which may be either elliptical (as NGC 4486 and NGC 3115) or spiral nebulae. The latter are either normal spirals, as M 31 and M 101, or barred spirals, like NGC 7479 and NGC 5850. The second large group under the extra-galactic nebulae are the irregular nebulae, with the Magellanic Clouds as an example. See classification, Appendix IX.

Entirely dissimilar to the galactic nebulae are the extra-galactic nebulae. The latter are most numerous near the galactic poles and appear to be absent from the Milky Way regions, and it is believed the reason lies in their being hidden (if there at all) by dark nebulae in the Milky Way. Inasmuch as extra-galactic nebulae are outside our own system, they are known as exterior systems or external galaxies. Such galaxies occur not only alone in space, but even in clusters, the most notable being the Coma-Virgo group with about 100 nebulae at a distance of 10,000,000 light-years!

Most of the exterior systems are of the "regular" type, and in these there exist many forms, beginning with spherical masses like NGC 4486 and ending with spiral nebulae that have open arms. There appears to be a regular sequence of forms of these nebulae. In general they are much more difficult to see visually than many other celestial objects, so that we must resort to photographs in order to see the finest details and structure of these far-away units of the universe. Innumerable extra-galactic nebulae can be reached by photography, yet relatively few are bright enough for satisfactory scrutiny. It seems that the number of nebulae increases as the brightness goes down, and on astro-photo plates, many thousands are recorded as small images scarcely larger than stars.

Elliptical nebulae may assume various degrees of flattening from nearly spherical shapes like NGC 3379 to flattened or oblate kinds, as Messier 32, then to spindle forms (actually ellipsoidal) like NGC 3115. Elliptical nebulae are concentrated and probably contain elemental star or cosmic material, but do not manifest resolution into stars. They fade away in luminosity from those with bright nuclei to those with boundaries ill-defined.

The spiral nebulae—"island universes"—are famous objects that have interested astronomers since about 1845 when the Earl of Rosse scanned the heavens with his great 6-foot reflector in Ireland. They fall into two classes, the normal spirals and barred spirals. Of the former the best representative is M 31, the Great Nebula in Andromeda. They have a nucleus with a large region of nebulosity surrounding it, often with knots of nebular material, and they seem to be in various stages of evolution. At first the nebulous material appears not to be found resolved into stars, but in the later stages resolution reaches even the nucleus. The shapes imply rotation, but we cannot observe that directly.

The Great Nebula in Andromeda is the only spiral seen clearly with the unaided eye. With low telescopic power it shows as a very misty ellipse whose diameters extend 15′ to 30′ of arc in the sky. In reality the great system is an enormous universe in itself, inclined about 15° to our line

ANDROMEDA NEBULA

Delicate shadings of light and dark mark the characteristic spirals of the Great Nebula in Andromeda, typical of the island universes, as it appears in this marvelously detailed picture of the central regions. (*Mt. Wilson Observatory.*)

of vision. Only the central condensation can be seen with very low power. It is the nearest of these island universes, of the order of 800,000 light-years from us. Actually, not over five galaxies are within 1,000,000 light-years of the solar system. Messier 31 is an enormous system: the denser parts are perhaps 40,000 light-years across, and this is but half the real length, for it takes hours of exposure on the photo plate to pile up an image. Enough mass is represented in M 31 to make 10,000,000,000 suns like ours! This nebula is supposedly comparable in essential ways to our own Milky Way system.

[198]

Even the enormous Andromeda nebula is but a single example. It is held that within a sphere of radius 10,000,000 light-years, there are over 1000 galaxies with dimensions and properties that we can determine. At present the greatest telescopes reach out into space to the inconceivable distance of 1,000,000,000 light-years and within this sphere there are untold *millions of galaxies* of stars.

A few of the spirals (like NGC 4565 Comae) are seen exactly edgewise to us. They often have a dark rift running across the long dimension, which is probably absorbing-matter of the nature of the dark nebulae; and sometimes the black streaks are sharply enough defined to appear to cut the nebula in two.

The barred spirals also show evolutionary stages, the last stage presenting an s-shaped spiral with thin arms having its material resolved into stars. In all specimens of this type there is a broad bar extending across the nuclei.

The last class of nebulae, the irregular extra-galactic type, are represented best by the nearest and brightest of all those in our stellar system—the Magellanic Clouds. They are too near the south celestial pole to be seen by northern observers but are clearly visible to the unaided eye from the proper latitude in the southern hemisphere.

The Greater Magellanic Cloud is in the constellation Dorado, and is 75,000 light-years away. It is an enormous object, of diameter 18,000 light-years including the outlying portions. In it are 500,000 giant stars or over, and probably many times more smaller stars. The Smaller Cloud is in Tucana, at a distance of 84,000 light-years, and its over-all diameter is about 12,000 light-years.

The Clouds are typical irregular nebulae and are not duplicates of the Milky Way—not showing the spiral organization that is supposedly so characteristic of the Milky Way and of the external galaxies. But they can be highly resolved into stars, do resemble the star clouds in the Milky Way, and contain various types of stars, clusters, nebulous clouds, etc. In the large cloud is 30 Doradus or NGC 2070, a diffuse nebula and the largest known object of its kind, the diameter being 260 light-years.

It is noticed that stars are not the only thing on the celestial vault that can be organized in double or multiple systems, for double and triple nebulae are by no means lacking. The Whirlpool Nebula (M 51) is double; M 31 with companions (M 32 and NGC 205) is triple, while the Milky Way—our own great stellar system—with the two Magellanic Clouds as companions, forms a triple nebula.

In observing star clusters and nebulae with the telescope, large aperture is the first essential, that we may gather the greatest possible amount of light, and magnification comes next. With a 6-inch or larger glass many objects are definitely within range and with such a diameter, glorious views are obtained.

We give below a list of many of the very best star clusters and nebulae adapted to a small telescope. Others can be found in Webb, *Celestial Objects for Common Telescopes*, and Olcott and Putnam, *Field Book of the Skies*. Our Appendix IX gives the complete list of Messier objects.

Selected List of Nebulae and Star Clusters

The following is an observing list of most of the very best nebulae and clusters in the heavens, for telescopic observation. A wide range is selected, from those of naked-eye visibility to some needing a medium-sized instrument. Naturally the naked-eye objects will be seen to far greater advantage by using a telescope.

In designating the object's number, M stands for Messier: thus Messier 1 is number 1 in his famous catalog. NGC refers to Dreyer's *New General Catalogue*, which designation is the one oftenest used by professional astronomers. H refers to Sir William Herschel's catalog, the numbers following the H being his original numbers.

The most outstanding examples of the various types of

nebulae and clusters are given, and some of them will be recognized as objects photographed with the world's largest telescopes. The list incorporates nearly every one of the list of the 60 finest objects of the sky, as offered by the well-known observer, William H. Pickering. Poignant remarks are included from certain pioneer observers of the past, including Webb, Smyth, etc., in order to point out leading telescopic features of the nebulae and clusters.

NORTH CIRCUMPOLAR REGIONS (See chart, page 17)

M 31, NGC 224. The Great Nebula in Andromeda. This grand spiral is visible to the naked eye as a hazy "star" and is the brightest spiral in the sky. A most interesting object: with low telescopic power, a large bright elliptical nebulous mass; more detail and spiral structure are seen with larger instruments, and parts become resolved into stars with the greatest telescopes. In same field, in low power, is a small, bright satellite nebula (M 32), and near-by H.V 18, a large faint nebula.

H.VI 30, NGC 7789. Star cluster in Cassiopeia, a large cloud of small stars "on a ground of star dust" (Smyth)—"a glorious assemblage . . . with spangly rays of stars . . . a vast region of inexpressible splendor . . . ". Several other clusters and star fields in this constellation.

H.VI 33, NGC 869; H.VI 34, NGC 884. Chi-h in Perseus. Double star cluster, visible to naked eye. Either one is a splendid group, and, under good observing conditions, the pair is one of the most brilliant and spectacular objects of its kind. Near-by is M 34, a cluster just visible to the naked eye and a fine sight for low magnifications.

M 81, NGC 3031; M 82, NGC 3034. Bode's Nebulae, in Ursa Major, ½° apart. M 81 is bright with fine elliptical form, having distinct nuclear area. Mt. Wilson photos picture it with extraordinary beauty, outer whirls showing strong spiral movement. M 82 is long, narrow, and fainter, but an exceptional object, crossed by dark bands.

M 97, NGC 3587. The Owl Nebula in Ursa Major. A large, round planetary nebula, called remarkable by Webb, and looking somewhat owl-like. Also in Ursa Major is M 101, a large and faint nebula.

M 51, NGC 5194. The famous Whirlpool Nebula in Canes Venatici, and a spiral pictured in many books. It is a magnificent object, the finest of its class, and seen nearly in plan view from the earth. Has central condensation, distinct spiral arms, and at one end another condensation, the two nuclei making the nebula appear double. But the spiral structure is not revealed visually except in the largest telescopes. This amazing outer universe has been likened to our stellar system, the Milky Way. Another spiral, M 94, is also in this constellation; it is bright but not large.

M 92, NGC 6341. A fine globular star cluster in Hercules, with luminous center.

CENTRAL REGIONS (See charts, pages 206 to 209)

H.V 1, NGC 253. Spiral nebula in Sculptor. Very large; the next brightest of the spirals after M 31.

M 33, NGC 598. Spiral nebula in Triangulum. Very large but not clearly defined, and needing low telescopic power with large enough aperture. Called a very curious object by Webb. Full of detail in spiral structure, with nebulous condensations. Beautiful in large-telescope photos.

H.VII 32, NGC 752. Star cluster in Andromeda; unusually large, with larger stars scattered about. A rich region.

H.IV 26, NGC 1535. Planetary nebula in Eridanus. Very fine; bright and grayish. Lassell says a most extraordinary object. A faint star in the center.

M 1, NGC 1952. The Crab Nebula in Taurus. A fine object, large, irregular and pearly white. In this constellation is another nebula, NGC 1435, a faint haziness involving some of the Pleiades. This nebulosity is so weak that it cannot always be seen in telescopes, but is revealed in photos. Also in Taurus are the Hyades and the Pleiades, well-known open clusters (see text).

M 42, NGC 1976. Great Nebula in Orion. A vast gaseous nebula and one of the most wonderful objects in the heavens. Called by Pickering undoubtedly the finest in the heavens. Visible to the naked eye and easily observed. Here is found the fascinating colored multiple star, Theta-one Orionis, known as the trapezium. The nebula is greenish and of irregular form. Much detail with branches, rifts, and bays; and the entire nebula with its stars repays long observation. In Orion are also M 78 and other objects including NGC 1981, one of Pickering's finest objects.

M 79, NGC 1904. Globular star cluster in Lepus. Fairly bright, milk-white, and a "fine object, blazing toward the center", and resolvable into stars.

M 37, NGC 2099. Star cluster in Auriga. Smyth says, "A magnificent object, the whole field being strewed as it were with sparkling gold-dust . . . it resolves into infinitely minute points of lucid light . . . ".

M 38, NGC 1912. Star cluster in Auriga. Has an unusual shape, forming an "oblique cross with a pair of large stars in each arm" and one at the center. The whole region is attractive in binoculars, with other clusters inside the pentagon of Auriga, including M 36, a fine one with a double star.

M 35, NGC 2168. Star cluster in Gemini, seen with the naked eye under favorable conditions. Lassell says it is "a marvelously striking object. No one can see it for the first time without an exclamation". Faint stars form curves and festoons, with a reddish star in the center. Superior to the Perseus clusters.

H.IV 45, NGC 2392. Planetary nebula in Gemini. Called curious and remarkable; a star of magnitude 8 or 9 enveloped in a bright nebulosity.

H.VII 2, NGC 2244. Star cluster in Monoceros, visible to the naked eye. Very pretty, with stars of various magnitudes, including a yellow star, 12 Monocerotis. In Monoceros is also M 50, a bright cluster, superb, with a red star.

M 41, NGC 2287. Scattered star cluster in Canis Major, but a fine group, seen with the unaided eye, the stars dividing into groups and curves with a reddish star near the middle. Called superior to the Perseus clusters.

M 44, NGC 2632. Praesepe, the Beehive cluster in Cancer. This open cluster contains hundreds of small stars. In a very clear sky it is seen with the naked eye as a hazy object. Near-by is M 67, another open cluster, with stars of ninth and fainter magnitudes, partly encircled by brighter stars.

H.IV 27, NGC 3242. Ring Nebula of Hydra. A planetary, very bright but small. Called remarkable. Secchi described a circular nebulosity, with two clusters, and arches forming a ring. Needs high magnification.

M 95, NGC 3351; and M 96, NGC 3368. Two large round nebulae in Leo, M 95 being bright.

M 99, NGC 4254. Triply branched spiral nebula in Coma. Large, bright, and called very remarkable. In Coma and Virgo are a profusion of bright nebulae, etc., as M 60, M 61, M 84, M 86, M 87, M 88, M 98, and many Herschel numbers, as H.I 31 and H.I 43.

M 49, NGC 4472. Nebula in Virgo. Large, bright, round, and pearly, situated between two bright telescopic stars.

M 68, NGC 4590. Globular star cluster in Hydra, south of Corvus. Well resolved into stars, with medium telescope.

H.V 24, NGC 4565. Spiral nebula in Coma, seen on edge. A long, peculiar object, with central condensation, the whole nebula appearing cut in two by a great dark band of obscuring matter along its edge. Like many nebulae, needs a 9-inch telescope to be seen to advantage.

M 64, NGC 4826. Nebula in Coma. Called magnificent, large, bright, and conspicuous. Smyth says, "blazing to a nucleus"; the form is spiral.

M 53, NGC 5024. Globular star cluster in Coma. A mass of minute stars and "star dust"; but resolvable with medium instruments. Shows "curved appendages of stars" running out from it.

M 83, NGC 5236. Triply branched spiral nebula in Hydra. Called by J. Herschel very bright, very large. Nuclear condensation near center, and the entire nebula of s-shape backward.

M 3, NGC 5272. Globular star cluster in Canes. A beautiful, bright assemblage of stars; a "noble object" (Smyth); it "blazes splendidly" toward the center, with many outliers. Resolved with about 8-inch reflector. The cluster itself is large, being hundreds of light-years in diameter. Photos reveal 30,000 stars, and these are only the brighter ones. Also in Canes is M 94, a "comet-like" nebula.

M 5, NGC 5904. Globular star cluster in Serpens Caput. Rated by Pickering as only slightly inferior to M 13. Smyth says, "This superb object is a noble mass, refreshing to the senses after searching for faint objects . . . ". Has a bright, central blaze and outliers in many directions.

M 80, NGC 6093. Globular star cluster in Scorpius. A compressed mass of stellar points reminding early observers of a comet. William Herschel called it "the richest and most condensed mass of stars which the firmament can offer to the contemplation of astronomers". Other Scorpius objects include M 4, a cluster of small stars; M 6, an irregular cluster; and M 7, a bright cluster— one of Pickering's finest.

M 13, NGC 6205. Great Star Cluster in Hercules. Globular. Generally considered the finest star cluster in the northern heavens. Visible to the naked eye. An amazing sight; the outer stars are resolved in a small telescope, and with a larger glass the entrancing beauty of the great globe of stars is revealed.

M 12, NGC 6218. Globular star cluster in Ophiuchus. A rich, fine, bright cluster, with central condensation, and stars resolvable. Also in Ophiuchus: M 10, another rich globular, easily resolvable; M 19, a globular; M 9, a globular with "a myriad of minute stars"; M 14, a large globular of minute stars; and M 62, a globular cluster in the southwest corner of Ophiuchus.

M 20, NGC 6514. The Trifid Nebula in Sagittarius. Diffuse type, very large and bright, and divided into irregular sections by dark lanes. Called a remarkable and curious nebula. With double and multiple stars.

M 8, NGC 6523. The great Lagoon Nebula in Sagittarius. This diffuse galactic nebula is visible to the naked eye. A large, bright, and very singular body, nearly cut in two by a central dark lane. Various bright and nebulous stars appear involved in the nebula. A magnificent object in long-exposure photos.

M 24, NGC 6603. Open star cluster in Sagittarius. A beautiful stellar field, and a rich part of the Milky Way.

M 17, NGC 6618. The Horseshoe or Omega Nebula in Sagittarius. A very fine object, of arched form, with an interesting group of stars. A rich Milky Way region.

M 22, NGC 6656. Globular star cluster in Sagittarius. Called the finest cluster after M 13, visible from northern latitudes. Bright and very fine, composed of tenth-magnitude and fainter stars, so compact that the object is visible to the naked eye. Sagittarius has other nebulae and clusters: M 21, a coarse cluster of telescopic stars; M 25, another irregular, coarse cluster; H.IV 51, a pale-blue planetary nebula; M 70, a globular; M 18, a glorious star cluster; M 28, a globular much condensed; M 75, a globular with bright nucleus, and the most "open" of the large globulars.

M 11, NGC 6705. Star cluster in Scutum. A fine galactic cluster, semiglobular, in a star cloud visible to the unaided eye in a dark sky. An eighth-magnitude star near center, the other stars being fainter. In Scutum are also: M 26, a coarse cluster; H.I 47, a beautiful globular star cluster.

M 57, NGC 6720. Famous Ring Nebula in Lyra. Planetary type and a striking object in any telescope of aperture 4 inches or more. Appears just like a smoke-ring; this ring is probably a translucent gaseous shell. In large apertures, a fifteenth-magnitude star in center.

M 27, NGC 6853. Dumbbell Nebula in Vulpecula. Planetary type, very large and bright; picked up with very low power as two hazy patches of light. Assumes a dumbbell appearance in larger apertures, and a complete disc can be photographed. Thirteenth-magnitude star near center.

H.V 15, NGC 6960. The Filamentary Nebula. Also H.V 14, NGC 6992. The Network Nebula. Together known as the Veil Nebulae in Cygnus. Often pictured from Mt. Wilson photos with the 100-inch telescope. Both "remarkable objects" appearing in photos as lacework against the sky. 6960 is pretty bright and large, while 6992 is faint. They belong to the diffuse type and are best seen in a large glass. It is thought both are really one great nebula. M 39, a loose open cluster, and the faint North America Nebula are also in Cygnus.

H.IV 1, NGC 7009. The Saturn Nebula in Aquarius. A planetary and one of the finest specimens—also bright for a planetary; Dreyer calls it magnificent. The color is pale blue.

M 15, NGC 7078. Globular star cluster in Pegasus. A "noble cluster"; a fine, large, bright globe of stars.

M 30, NGC 7099. Globular star cluster in Capricornus. Pale white and fairly bright; elliptical, with a "central blaze"; forms a nice contrast with a star beside it. Resolvable into stars, with medium apertures.

M 2, NGC 7089. Globular star cluster in Aquarius. Its magnificent stellar components resolvable in 9-inch or larger instrument and affording a superb view. Also in Aquarius, M 72, a fine globular star cluster.

SOUTH CIRCUMPOLAR REGIONS (See chart, page 57)

47 Tucanae, NGC 104. Globular star cluster. A most magnificent cluster (J. Herschel), a stupendous object (Webb), by far the finest of all globular clusters (Pickering). A round ball of countless stars of magnitude 12 to 14. One of the nearest globulars.

NGC 2070. The Great Looped Nebula surrounding the star 30 Doradus in the Greater Magellanic Cloud. A diffuse nebula, the central part very fine. The largest irregular nebula known. Visible to the naked eye.

NGC 2516. Star cluster in Carina. Large and brilliant; visible to the naked eye. A reddish star within.

NGC 3114. Star cluster in Carina, comparable to one part of the Perseus double cluster. Very large, the loose type, and visible to the naked eye.

NGC 3372. The Keyhole Nebula, surrounding Eta Carinae. Diffuse type, and branching. One of the largest and brightest of the naked-eye nebulae. Good in a small telescope; needs a large field of view.

NGC 3532. Irregular star cluster in Carina. Very brilliant and large, and held by Pickering as by far the finest irregular cluster in the sky. Needs a wide field of view.

NGC 3918. Planetary nebula in Centaurus. "Beautiful rich blue" (Webb).

NGC 4755. Star cluster in Crux. Striking and beautiful, with several colored stars.

Omega Centauri, NGC 5139. Globular star cluster. Usually known as the finest globular of all. J. Herschel called it "the richest and largest object of its kind in the heavens . . . the stars are literally innumerable". Held to be the nearest of the globular clusters to us, as well as the brightest known.

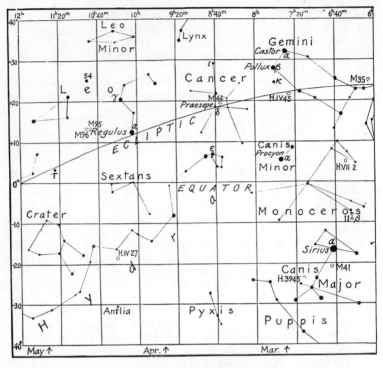

EQUATORIAL CONSTELLATIONS

The four charts herewith constitute the equatorial band of constellations, extending entirely around the sky in a cylindrical fashion as far as 40° of declination on either side of the celestial equator. North is at the top of the chart, south at the bottom, east at the left, and west at the right side.

These charts, together with the north and the south circumpolar charts, show all the constellations. Not all the individual stars, however, are drawn, but only enough of the brighter ones to enable the observer to identify the star groups, by means of the geometrical patterns.

At any one moment, not all the groups are visible, for the section of the constellations near the sun are invisible, being in the daytime sky. To locate the sec-

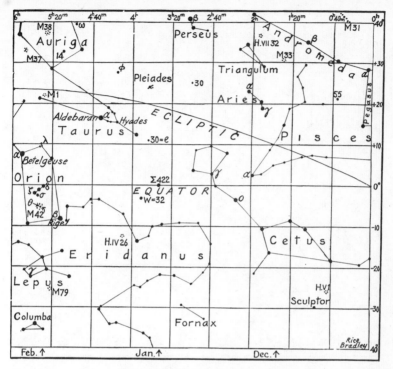

EQUATORIAL CONSTELLATIONS (Continued)

tion of the heavens visible on a certain evening, we refer to the month name at the bottom of the chart. The arrow indicates the position of the celestial meridian at 9 p.m. local time on the first of the respective month. An hour later, those star groups an hour of right ascension east of the 9 p.m. group will have moved to the meridian. Thus there is a ceaseless procession of stars rising in the east and setting in the west.

At the top of the charts the right ascension is marked in hours and minutes, while on the sides, the declination in degrees is indicated. The tops of the maps connect up with the north circumpolar charts at the same right ascension, and

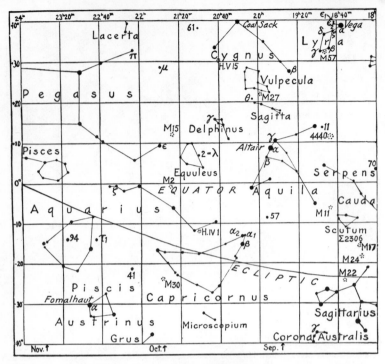

EQUATORIAL CONSTELLATIONS (Continued)

the bottoms connect with the corresponding regions of the south circumpolar regions.

To orient oneself properly by means of these charts, we note first that the first two charts are to be used together, for they extend from right ascension 0ʰ to R.A. 12ʰ. Similarly, the next two charts form an unbroken map, extending from R.A. 12ʰ to R.A. 24ʰ; also the two series naturally connect at R.A. 12ʰ.

Next, by holding a chart vertically with the proper meridian in view, it is found that the chart corresponds to the heavens near the meridian. But when we consider parts of the celestial sphere near the rising or the setting point, it will be found that the hour-circles on the sky (represented by the vertical lines on the

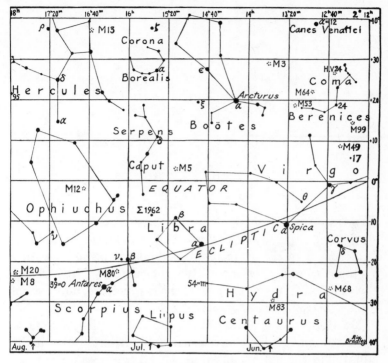

EQUATORIAL CONSTELLATIONS (Concluded)

chart) intersect the horizon at an angle, except when the observer is at the geographic equator or the earth's poles. Consequently the chart must be oriented or tilted so that the hour-circles always point in the north-and-south direction on the celestial sphere. For a rising object in the northern hemisphere, therefore, the top of the chart is tilted to the left, and for a setting object to the right. At the earth's equator, one would tilt the chart 90° from its present position on the page.

Besides the constellation groups there will be found the star clusters and nebulae described in the foregoing lists of these objects.

15

Rainbows, Auroras, and Other Wonders

RAINBOWS, sun-dogs, moon halos, auroras, and northern lights appear in the sky from time to time. All of these really occur in the atmosphere and could not be seen from a planet that had no air. Often considered with these are the zodiacal light and the gegenschein which are, however, of a truly astronomical nature.

Most spectacular of all these are the northern lights or aurora borealis which have their counterpart south of the equator in the aurora australis. Of all types, you are most likely to see that featuring broad, low arcs above and parallel to the northern horizon. From this base, moving rays that seem like searchlights flutter through the heavens. A rarer but more beautiful appearance that may displace the arc is that of a gigantic curtain which seems definitely to have three dimensions. But the rarest and most beautiful of all is the auroral corona, in which multicolored streamers radiate from a crown of light at a point almost overhead.

Most auroras are yellowish white with shades of green; some are red and pink, and an occasional few are blue. At other times the effect may be totally different with all the colors of the rainbow thrown together in a weird hodge-podge of shimmering curtains and heaving arcs. Often on a night when the aurora is visible it appears first as a faint glow on the horizon, but as the observer watches he finds

[210]

THE NORTHERN AURORA

A remarkable appearance of the aurora borealis, or northern lights, in which flickering colored vertical streamers cross long eerie arcs over the northern horizon. (*Drawing by Trouvelot, Charles Scribner's Sons.*)

this breaking into an arc and occasionally into successive arcs that rise to the zenith. Usually, however, when the arc has appeared and is easily defined, a ray perpendicular to the horizon appears. It is joined by still other rays that finally shimmer like a fan, sometimes for many hours. Commonly these are the pale yellow type that shades into green, but sometimes they acquire brilliant color. Auroras of this type can be seen at any season of the year and sometimes reappear for several nights in succession.

The average frequency of auroral displays is about 13 to 15 a year for any one locality in the middle northern latitudes. Observers in various parts of the world have reported personal observations of 100 auroras in 15 years, while other reports have increased the number actually visible from such a place to twice that number.

Although it is impossible to predict the real times of appearance of the aurora or connect them in any way with the fluctuations of the seasons, there is a definite relationship with the spots upon the sun. So definite is this correlation that, if a large black spot is seen approaching the solar meridian, one can be fairly certain that an auroral display will follow very closely, for seldom does such a spot pass without an aurora appearing within 2 or 3 days after its solar-meridian transit. If this same spot should survive one rotation of the sun it may bring a second display in its wake. And furthermore, the relationship is demonstrated still more clearly by the fact that when sun-spots are plentiful, displays of the aurora are also frequent. In fact, the northern lights seem to wax and wane in frequency with the rise and fall of the sun-spot cycle. If you observe a fine aurora, then look next day at the sun, and you will doubtless see some noticeable spots.

The close correlation of spots and auroras has led to a reinvestigation of their relationship. It seems now quite certain that the aurora is actually caused by radiation from the sun-spots. A stream of electrons hurled out from the solar cyclone reaches the atmosphere of the earth. There, striking the rarefied gases in the upper atmosphere, it causes them to glow and to vibrate. The effect is one similar to that produced in neon advertizing signs where a rarefied gas is animated by an electric charge so that it glows.

The auroras are an electromagnetic effect, and supposedly streams of electrons from the sun are drawn along lines of force toward the earth's magnetic poles, resulting in the apparent concentration of auroral displays in the northern skies. The north magnetic pole, however, is a long way from the geographic pole—at latitude 74°N. and longitude 97°W., in extreme northern Canada. The aurora is visible in latitudes quite distant from the poles and best seen in a band that runs from the middle latitudes to the arctic circle. Occasionally outbursts are seen as far south as Bermuda

AURORA AUSTRALIS

Spectacular, shimmering curtains of the southern aurora hanging in the antarctic heavens. They are typical of the weird effect of the curtain form of aurora. Types like the above are seen to change shape while under observation. (*Drawing from the National Antarctic Expedition of the Royal Society of Great Britain*, 1902.)

and also in the polar regions, but they occur most frequently near latitude 60° both north and south in the western hemisphere. Very definitely an atmospheric effect, the aurora occurs within the air and is observed between 40 and 600 miles above the surface of the earth, averaging about 60 miles. These measurements have been an important factor in establishing the upper limits of the atmosphere.

Related to the auroral disturbances and no doubt directly influenced by the sun-spots are disturbances in the compass, interruption of radio and telegraph, and closely associated phenomena. At times of great auroral displays, there are tremendous disturbances in the earth's magnetic field, known as magnetic storms. Magnetic compasses vary several degrees an hour. At times, too, radio reception, especially short-wave, is affected and sometimes completely cut off. Long-distance telephone cables are also disturbed because of this electromagnetic excitation.

A wealth of folk-lore has grown up in the various countries where the aurora is best seen, and consistently included in this have been the stories of sound at time of the aurora. It is likened to the swish of a silk dress, or the wind whistling in a ship's rigging. At present the problem is perplexing, because equally reliable witnesses have given conflicting reports as to any audible phenomenon. Probably the best suggestion is that the supposed effect emanates from a "local brush discharge" of electricity from bushes or snow in the vicinity, similar to the electric discharge from the mast of a ship.

Rainbows are almost as well known as the sun and the moon and are frequently seen in the wake of a rainstorm. They come when the sun peeps through rain clouds, and can be seen, too, as the sun strikes the spray from a lawn sprinkler or wisps of a fog. Such a display may be seen in the west after a morning shower or in the east after a downpour in the late afternoon. Since rainbows in the popular mind are most commonly associated with summer afternoon storms, they are usually looked for in the east. A rainbow is a group of circular or nearly circular arcs of color that appears as a huge arch in the heavens. No two persons, though they may be standing side by side, ever see the same rainbow, for the bow is an arc of a circle whose center is on the line stretching from the sun to the eye of the observer.

The ordinary rainbow is an arch of various colors with red on the outside merging into orange, yellow, green, blue, indigo, and violet. Usually the radius of the arc is equal to about one-fourth of the visible sky, or 42° to the red. Once in a while there are two rainbows—the secondary with a greater radius than the first and the order of the colors reversed. Usually the secondary bow is fainter and disappears more quickly than the primary. Observers note that

RARE RAINBOWS

Two unusual photographs of rainbows. The upper picture, made at Aberdeen, Scotland, by G. A. Clarke, shows the primary and secondary bows, with four supernumerary bows inside the primary. (*Photographs from U.S. Weather Bureau.*)

the space between the inner and outer bows is apparently darker than is the sky entirely within the arc of the rainbow or the area entirely outside its sphere of influence. In addition careful watchers observe that the arcs themselves vary in width and that the colors even in the same bow are of variable purity.

Rainbows result from the refraction and reflection of sunlight by raindrops in the atmosphere. Each drop is a prism in miniature breaking the light into various colors. The primary bow is due to light that enters the upper part of the drops and leaves after one internal reflection, so this bow is always brighter than the secondary bow which undergoes more reflections.

Most rainbows are caused by sunlight and are seen in the day, but occasionally the observer is rewarded by a glimpse of a moonbow. So rare are these that sometimes one can hardly believe his eyes.

There are sometimes halos around the sun and moon; they usually have a radius of 22° but sometimes 46°. They are commonly soft white circlets in the sky, caused by reflection of sunlight or moonlight from ice crystals high up in the atmosphere.

The moon halos are similar to the sun halos which are similarly produced in the daytime sky. There are many variations, however, and although the moon halos seldom have much color, the solar phenomena are sometimes vivid circles of color with red on the inside and bluish white on the outside. When other circlets form on the circumference of the primary circle, a comparatively rare occurrence, they are known as mock suns or sun-dogs. The colorless halos are caused by *reflection from* the surface of ice crystals high in the atmosphere, and the colored ones are produced by prismatic *refraction through* the same crystals.

Travelers to the north and south are often puzzled by the length of twilight in these different locations. Explorers in equatorial regions report that night follows day very swiftly, while visitors to the arctic regions observe that the period of twilight is prolonged through several months. Astronomically twilight is defined as ending at any point upon the earth's surface when the sun is 18° below the horizon. The time it takes to get there varies with the latitude and time of year. In the middle latitudes twilight usually lasts, and dawn too for that matter, $1\frac{1}{2}$ to $2\frac{1}{2}$ hours; in higher latitudes even longer. The vital factors controlling this variation are latitude and declination of the sun. At the equator, the variation of twilight from one time of the year to another is not over 6 minutes; at latitude 44°N., the twilight or dawn may be 49 minutes longer on June 21 than in October or March.

The existence of dust particles in the air is responsible for the twilight and dawn effect. These reflect light from the sun after it has set (and before it rises), filling the sky with sunlight even when the sun is invisible. These same dust particles, denser at the horizon where more air lies between the observer and the stellar object, absorb much of the blue end of the spectrum and therefore turn objects low in the sky to a reddish hue.

Again we consider the dust content of the atmosphere for a partial explanation of a phenomenon so commonly observed that it is considered no phenomenon at all. The blue color of the sky is atmospheric; that is, the color is due to the selective scattering of sunlight by dust particles in the air. The particles are large enough to reflect the blue end of the spectrum, but too small to reflect the longer red light-waves at the other end of the spectrum. Dust particles are responsible for a large part of the blue color that we see in the sky but, it should be pointed out, the molecules of air composing the atmosphere could produce a bluish tint in the sky unaided by any other agency, so a planet, if it were airless—like the moon—would have a black daytime sky.

Scintillation (twinkling) of the stars—and even of terrestrial objects, occasionally, when they are viewed through a telescope—is also a phenomenon of the atmosphere. There are really three effects—"dancing" of the object, or change of position, changes of brightness, and a variation of color. When the atmosphere is clear and the temperature cold, the scintillation is particularly noticeable. The cause lies in the fact that temperature, water-vapor, and density of the different layers of the atmosphere are constantly changing. As the object's light passes through the air, it is refracted, or bent, irregularly—with the resultant effect of scintillation.

Another important atmospheric phenomenon is the "lifting" effect of refraction which actually keeps an object in view after it has theoretically set, or allows it to be seen before its actual time of rising. The amount of refraction at most is about $\frac{1}{2}°$, so that when the sun or moon appears to be resting on the horizon it actually is just below it. As a result, the apparent rising time of celestial objects is advanced and the setting time retarded.

The zodiacal light carries us beyond the atmosphere and into the regions of space on either side of the sun. Scientists hesitated a long time before definitely ascribing a place outside the earth to this lighting effect, for its appearance is that of a long half-ellipse glowing dimly in the region of the ecliptic shortly after the sun has set in the evening and shortly before it rises in the morning. It would be difficult to tell merely by observation whether it were in the atmosphere or not. It is now believed, however, that it is *possibly* the reflection of sunlight from countless millions of tiny meteoric particles extending out in the neighborhood of the sun along the plane of the ecliptic. It is best seen in the tropics and least visible in the higher latitudes. Even here, however, the spectacle can be observed from places having a high altitude.

This very fact indicates that the zodiacal light has a very

MYSTERY LIGHT

Still an enigma after long years of study, this is a superb example of a typical apparition of the zodiacal light stretching upward in a narrow cone from the horizon toward the zenith. Only rarely seen because of difficulties of observation, the effect is nevertheless a regularly occurring phenomenon. (*Observed and drawn by the astronomer-artist, Trouvelot, February 20, 1876, Charles Scribner's Sons.*)

considerable surface brightness and certain regions in the extension may be actually brighter than the Milky Way. Careful observation in the twilight is necessary before the observer can actually distinguish the zodiacal light above the glow at the horizon. Yet it lingers after the night has well begun.

The base of the cone of light may extend along the horizon for a distance of 20° to 30°, sometimes even 45° at each side, and the light may stretch half-way toward the zenith. Under specially favorable conditions, when the sky is free from all artificial lighting, smoke and haze, the *zodiacal band* may be discerned running along the entire ecliptic some 5° to 10° wide, sometimes even 20°. The zodiacal light, for northern observers, is best seen in the western sky in late winter and early spring—in the eastern sky in October to December. In the southern hemisphere, of course, the conditions are reversed.

Along the zodiacal band at a point directly opposite the sun there will be found a region where the band is both brighter and wider than at any other point. Here it may reach a visual width of 10° or some 20 times the diameter of the moon. This brighter section is known as the *gegenschein*, or counterglow, and it may be discerned at times when the band itself is not visible.

Always the gegenschein is opposite the sun, and it moves through the sky as the sun does, but 12 hours (180°) behind. At midnight it should be found directly on the meridian in the south and is best seen between 10 p.m. and 2 a.m. The diffuse spot has an average brightness about equal to a sixth-magnitude star, so it is just within the reach of naked-eye observation, but the combined light of the area is equal to the brilliance of Sirius, the brightest star. Because of its extreme faintness, it is best seen with averted vision. The observer, having in mind the place in the zodiac where the gegenschein should be, should look directly toward that spot and then turn his eyes slowly to the side. And slowly

MIDNIGHT SUN

In the summer in the northern hemisphere, the earth's north pole is tilted toward the sun giving the midnight-sun effect. The photograph above was made exactly at midnight, civil time, in Lapland, north of the arctic circle, near the Stora Lule River. (*Photograph by Clyde Fisher.*)

returning his eyes he may be able to discern this large spot of haze.

One of the leading opinions is that the gegenschein is a condensation of the zodiacal band and is caused by sunlight reflected from similar meteoric particles. Since these particles are on the exact opposite side of the sky from the sun, they individually resemble a full moon, turning all of their lighted part toward the earth, and reflecting a greater amount of sunlight—thus producing the concentrated glow at that particular side of the band.

16

Units of the Universe

ON ANY clear evening, from a good vantage point, there are certain things that an observer may see with his own two eyes. Overhead, there is the dark, inverted dome of the heavens, studded with what seems to be a countless number of stars. Here and there are certain objects brighter than the rest, which do not twinkle as the others do and which seem to wander at will. These are the planets. and they are much nearer to the earth than any of the stars. Then there is the moon, a pale disc of light, which also moves about among the stars and which is much bigger to our eyes than any of them. The moon, in turn, is much nearer to us than any of the planets.

Already, before darkness fell, the observer had seen the sun, lighting up all the heavens, blotting out the light of the stars. Now, as the night becomes deeper, he may see in the sky a filmy band of light running among the stars as if it were a faintly luminous cloud. That is the Milky Way. Occasionally, the blackness of the sky is illuminated for an instant by the streak of a "falling star"—a meteor dashing to extinction.

Were our observer equipped with a small telescope, he might turn it on the heavens and find even more. He might see that some of the stars are really twins, that here and there in the firmament are hazy patches of light that do not seem to be stars. These are the nebulae. And too, there are other hazy patches, different from these nebulae, called star clusters. The telescope then might pick up another and still different object, a fuzzy-looking "star" with a tail. That is a comet.

All together, these things are part of the visible universe, that part of the earth's environment available for inspection to anyone interested enough to look. They are part of the universe, indeed. But what relation do they have to each other, and how, if we do not know, are we to solve the various mysteries they present? How can we say what and where they are?

Not long after the invention of the telescope and the adoption of the Copernican theory of astronomy, men knew that the earth, together with its sister planets, moved about the sun. They were aware, then, of the solar system and of the fact that there were myriad stars beyond. But of the relative distances of those stars they were none too sure, and of their nature they were in doubt. It remained for the development of new scientific aids before man's infringement upon the frontiers of knowledge could begin.

And one of the most important of those aids has been a prism—a triangular piece of glass which breaks up sunlight into a series of colors as does the beveled edge of a window-pane or a diamond ring. It does the same thing as a summer thunderstorm—produces a rainbow. That rainbow is called the spectrum, and that prism, with accessories added, the spectroscope.

In the beginning the spectroscope presented more problems than it solved. For when the sun's spectrum is thrown onto a large screen in a darkened room and studied in detail it appears to be crossed with sharp dark lines which separate the otherwise smooth band of colors. The nature of those lines of black remained a mystery for years, and when the answer was found it was found not by looking at the sun but by studying chemicals in the laboratory.

The key to the problem was supplied by Gustav Robert Kirchhoff, a German physicist, who had been observing

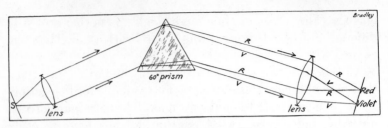

WHAT A PRISM DOES

White light, passing through a prism, is separated into its component parts—the colors of the rainbow—violet, indigo, blue, green, yellow, orange, and red. The diagram shows an arrangement that produces a "pure" spectrum.

incandescent elements in gaseous form with the aid of a spectroscope. Each element, he found, presented a spectrum of one or more bright lines in certain definite relative positions. No two elements had the same lines. If, for instance, he examined the light from incandescent sodium vapor, he obtained two sharp yellow lines—lines of wave-lengths that could not be obtained with any other element and therefore served to identify sodium.

Further, he discovered that if he observed an incandescent solid or liquid—a glowing bar of iron, for instance—which emitted a continuous spectrum, and then brought cool sodium vapor between the light-source and the spectroscope, something very startling occurred. Where the sodium vapor before had emitted bright yellow lines in certain positions, it now removed them from the continuous spectrum and left, in their stead, sharp black lines in the same positions. In other words, he found that when white light passes through a gaseous element, that element tends to extract from the light those bands of color which it itself would emit when incandescent.

This, then, explained the dark lines in the solar spectrum. Light, speeding out from the surface of the sun, passed through the cooler solar atmosphere; and as it did so the gaseous elements in that atmosphere extracted from the light the color bands they themselves would have given forth. Proceeding from these facts, astronomers had only to catalog in the laboratory the spectral lines characteristic of the elements found on the earth and then look for those lines in the spectrum of the sun. Doing so, they found that the elements observed on the sun also exist on the earth.

On the face of this and other evidence, it is generally assumed that the earth and its sister planets were once part of the outer layers of the sun. Further research points to another fact, namely that the elements which are the building-stones of matter on the earth are scattered far and wide throughout the universe. Nowhere has there been found definitely an element that does not exist upon the earth.

While scientists were still enthusiastically developing the chemistry of the stars with their all-powerful spectroscope, they stumbled upon another problem. For a long time it had been known that the stars do move in space, for in examining the ancient maps of the heavens it was found that many stars had changed position the tiniest bit since those maps were prepared. By patiently noting the positions of these stars each year, astronomers were able to learn to just how much their annual motion amounted.

Which was all very well—but what about those stars which were moving directly toward or away from the earth? How to detect those motions? And how about the motions of those stars which were approaching or receding diagonally, whose motions were neither along our line-of-sight nor at right angles to it?

The spectroscope held the answer. In observing the spectra of some stars, it was found that the spectral lines were displaced toward the red, and in other cases, toward the violet. There is a similar effect when a fire-engine races down the street. The bystander notices that its siren screams in a higher than normal pitch as the car approaches, and then suddenly falls off to a pitch lower than normal as the car passes the observer. The same thing is characteristic of a locomotive whistle or of the roar of an airplane engine as it passes overhead.

This apparent change in pitch, known as the Doppler effect, is quite evident to the bystander, although to the men on the fire-engine the pitch remains the same. The pitch of any sound depends upon the frequency with which the sound-waves reach the ear, and when the source of the sound approaches the observer, the waves are piled up so that more reach the ear per second than are actually given out at the source. Conversely, when the source is receding, the sound waves are spaced more widely apart so that fewer reach the ear per second.

A similar explanation applies to light-waves. When the source approaches, the waves strike the spectroscope more frequently and the spectrum shifts toward the short-wave violet; when the source is receding the waves are "stretched" and strike the instrument less frequently, resulting in a shift toward the long-wave red. This was the message the spectroscope had picked up in the depths of space. It was telling astronomers which stars were approaching the earth and which were receding, and it was enabling them to measure the speed of those motions. Knowing the apparent speed of a star at right angles to the line-of-sight and its apparent speed along the line-of-sight, together with its distance, the scientist can compute the resultant motion—giving us the star's actual direction and speed in space.

The same effect provided still another mystery, then unlocked another secret of the stars. All the stars are nothing more than suns located at unimaginable distances from the earth, and their spectra are roughly similar to that of our own sun. To be sure, some elements are lacking in certain stars and predominate in others, but that was more or less to be expected. It was not until they came on several instances where a star produced a double spectrum that astronomers began to wonder.

A typical example would be that of a star—apparently single in the largest of telescopes—which nevertheless produced this phenomenon. The solution lies in the fact that such stars are really close binaries, two stars so close that they are inseparable by any other means than the spectroscope.

With other methods, too, have astronomers advanced. By the mathematics of the surveyor, the earth has been measured, together with its distance from the moon and the sun, the other planets, and the nearer stars. This method of measuring the distance of an unapproachable object depends upon the relationship between the angles and sides of a triangle. If one side of the triangle be known—the base-line—together with the angles made at both ends by the other two sides, then the astronomer can compute the distance from the center of the base-line to an object at the apex of the triangle, where the other two sides meet.

As the distance of objects increased, however, the methods of the surveyor, good enough for the surface of the earth, good enough even for the vast stretches of space within the solar system, became increasingly clumsy. It became more and more difficult and finally impossible to find a base-line that was long enough. In reaching out to the stars the other two sides of the triangle became so long that the longest base-line available to man—the diameter of the earth's orbit—was negligible by comparison. How then to measure distances to the star clusters and the distant spiral nebulae?

The Cepheid variable stars, which change their brightness as regularly as clockwork, show a definite relationship between the length of time required for their variations in light and their absolute magnitude. The apparent brightness of a star is the resultant between actual brightness and distance. A small, dim star may be near to us and seem brilliant while a blazing giant may be so far away that it is almost invisible. If we can reduce the brightness of any star o its real or absolute magnitude—the brilliance it would present at a standard distance of 32.6 light-years—we can estimate its distance.

It was possible to measure the distances of some of the nearer Cepheid variables and determine just what their absolute magnitude was. Further, it developed that every Cepheid variable with the same period possessed the same absolute magnitude. And that was all astronomers needed. Peering off at the spiral nebulae, lost in space at unthinkable distances from the earth, they found that Cepheid variables existed in those nebulae. They timed the period of those variables and thus knew the absolute magnitude—the intrinsic brightness—of the objects. Then, knowing their real brilliance and the brilliance at which they appear to us, it was a comparatively easy matter to estimate just how far away they are, and how distant, too, are the spiral nebulae containing the Cepheids. In addition, once the distance of the nebulae and of the star clusters was known, it wasn't hard to calculate their size.

And so have scientists applied a tape measure to the galaxy and to the space through the universe. So have they studied and classified other galaxies outside our own. The sizes and distances with which they dealt were so great that the old units of length were inadequate to express them. A new one was devised, the light-year, based on the distance which a light-wave, speeding at about 186,000 miles per second, would travel in a year. Equivalent to some 6,000,-000,000,000 miles, it too proved clumsy as the necessity arose to speak in hundreds of thousands of light-years, and millions of light-years. But it is still in use.

At any rate, with the methods and instruments now at our command, it is possible to paint a fairly accurate picture of the universe as it really exists. To start with, of course, we have the solar system, our home unit. At its center is a star of average, or perhaps a little smaller than average, size. It is speeding through space at a tremendous velocity,

THE MILKY WAY

Here is the "universe" to which the solar system belongs. In this unusual mosaic of the Milky Way are shown some of the star clouds and "dark nebulae" visible when we turn our eyes along the plane of our own galaxy. (*Mt. Wilson Observatory.*)

roughly 12 miles a second, carrying with it nine major planets, including the earth, their satellites, thousands of asteroids, a thousand comets, and millions of meteors. It is so separated from the rest of the universe, from even the closest neighboring stars, that its "loneliness" is beyond all comprehension.

The system seems completely isolated. The nearest star, a member of the local star cloud to which the sun also belongs, is about 4 light-years away. Around the solar system on all sides stretches endless and practically empty space— space that is far more devoid of any matter than the most perfect vacuum obtainable in our laboratories, that has virtually no temperature at all, that is pervaded throughout by absolute zero, 459°.4 below zero Fahrenheit. Black and soundless, this space engulfs the solar system.

It surrounds everything in the Milky Way galaxy, in fact, and stretches beyond, setting it off from the other galaxies just as completely as the sun is set off from the other stars. In this Milky Way universe, our own galactic system, there are billions of stars, some like the sun, some thousands of times larger, some smaller. Some are gathered

[229]

ON EDGE!

Of the thousands of nebulae visible to us, some of them, such as this one known as H.V 24 in Coma Berenices, are seen edgewise to us. In this one the nucleus is flattened, and around the periphery of the nebula there is seen a darkened ring, probably composed of cosmic dust. (*Mt. Wilson Observatory.*)

together by the thousands in globular clusters, some travel together in large groups comprising other clusters, some have one or two companions in a closely knit system, and some travel singly along their endless paths.

Among them are a few ring nebulae, hollow spheres of gaseous material; diffuse nebulae, looking almost like fluffs of cotton set against the blackness of space; and the dark nebulae.

Both bright and dark nebulae are believed to be clouds of cosmic dust, composed of extremely tiny particles. Such material is probably scattered very sparsely throughout otherwise empty space. Some of the particles, congregating as a result of various influences, form vast clouds. Probably clouds that blot out great sky regions contain only two or three times as much solid matter as the sun. In their dark form they hide vast sections of the heavens, resulting in what seem to be black holes among the stars. Lighted as the diffuse nebulae, they are illuminated by reflection or excitation from near-by stars.

Even clouds of cosmic dust have their own motion, and so do all the other units of the universe. The sun has its motion, while each of the planets speeds along its own path, their satellites circle around them, and comets, meteors, and asteroids wheel about—all in the retinue of the sun. All the stars are speeding toward some unknown destination, and so are the star clusters, and the ring nebulae. All are rushing in various directions through empty space. But in addition, the entire galactic system as a whole is turning at an immense speed about a central axis located in the direction of the constellation Sagittarius. It requires something on the order of 200,000,000 years for the system to rotate once upon that axis.

This motion the galactic system has in common with the other universes—the spiral nebulae—that have been observed. Similar in many respects to the Milky Way system, these universes are situated at great distances from us, and there are millions of them. The nearest, as well as the largest of these "island universes" is the great spiral nebula in Andromeda, which is about 800,000 light-years away.

The spiral nebulae contain stars, star clusters, variable stars, novae, and great clouds of the same type of cosmic dust as occur in our own system. They, too, seem to rotate about a central axis, although the short time during which they have been under observation precludes our seeing any changes.

There is one outstanding difference, however, between these outer nebulae and our galactic system. All the spirals show an intense concentration of light and star material near the central portion. But in observing the central area of the Milky Way system, we find no such noticeable concentration of stars—unless possibly it is in the star clouds of Sagittarius or hidden by dark nebulae. Further, this difference between the centers of the spiral nebulae and that of our galactic system applies to the concentration of stars throughout the systems. In the spiral nebulae the illumination of star-cloud surfaces is far more intense than any illumination we can assign to the star clouds in our galactic system—at least greater than any we estimate for the clouds in the neighborhood of the sun.

Despite this difference, though, and certain others that are known to exist, the Milky Way can definitely be classed as just another—except that it is apparently the largest—of the spiral nebulae that lie about in space. So much is it one of them that, together with neighboring universes, it comprises what astronomers know as a *local super-galaxy*. The individual members include the Milky Way system, with its billions of stars; the Magellanic Clouds, which are really close companions of the Milky Way; the irregular galaxy NGC 6822; the triple spiral nebula M 33; the great spiral in Andromeda, together with its companion universes M 32 and NGC 205; the nebula IC 1613; and probably others that are obscured by dark cosmic dust clouds in the Milky Way.

There are other such super-galaxies in space, the Coma-Virgo group for instance, which contain many more units than this. Each of the separate galaxies comprises a universe unto itself; with their companions, they become members of a super-universe, bonded together by their location in space. By what ties they are united, of what possibly larger unit they may in turn be members, we have yet to learn. This, for the moment, outlines the boundaries of our knowledge, but men have studied the stars for a very short time, and perhaps some day we may know what lies beyond.

Solar Time

O F ALL the various sorts of time that are in use for different purposes, there are only three main kinds, and any kind of time in practical use may be found under these types:

$$\text{Time} \begin{cases} \text{sidereal} \\ \text{apparent solar} \\ \text{mean solar} \begin{cases} \text{local} \\ \text{standard} \end{cases} \end{cases}$$

Sidereal time is used only for technical purposes, and some features of it are dealt with in Appendix IV. All other kinds of time can be grouped together as *solar time*, because they depend in some way upon the transit of the sun. Such a classification would be only two-fold, but we shall divide the solar time into two categories, for the types differ considerably in use. When speaking of any kind of solar time one usually identifies it by naming the specific type.

Apparent Solar Time

Before there were any clocks, anyone had to tell time by the sun, and the most natural method of regulating time was very likely by means of the sun itself. Indeed, it would seem logical to use the sun because our civil life is based upon the periods of daylight and darkness. If we set up a sun-dial and arrange it properly, it will measure *apparent solar time.* This is the least artificial of all kinds of time; it makes no concessions to time-zones, saving of daylight, or even uniformity. It is still the best method of timekeeping in use by some primitive peoples.

To obtain and use apparent solar time it is necessary to have some kind of measure, and so an angle is used. Indeed, all kinds of time are based on some kind of hour-angle, which means the angular amount by which a given body in the heavens has passed by an observer's meridian. So we speak of the *transit* of a star, the sun, a planet, the moon, when that object is on the observer's meridian, its *hour-angle* then being zero. When the object is on the part of the observer's meridian that contains his zenith, the object is at *upper transit;* and when it is on the part of his meridian that contains his nadir, it is at *lower transit.* When the object has gone by the meridian by an angle of 15°, or 1 hour of time, its hour-angle is 1^h; when it has gone by the meridian by 90°, or 6^h, the hour-angle is said to be 6^h, and so on, to 24^h, or 0^h, again.

Apparent solar time is the hour-angle of the sun plus 12 hours. When the sun is at *lower* transit, its hour-angle is 12^h, for the sun has gone by the upper meridian by 12^h. So if we add 12^h to this we get 24^h, which is equivalent to 0^h. The zero hour then is the beginning of the apparent day, when the sun is at lower transit; and an apparent solar day at any observer's station is the interval of time between two successive lower transits of the sun over the observer's meridian. One uses the lower transit so as to have the moment of change of day occur somewhere near the time of lesser human activity. If we did not say "plus 12 hours" in defining apparent time in the first sentence of this paragraph, we should have the day beginning at noon.

In the apparent solar day we have 24 hours, beginning with zero hour, or midnight by apparent time. Each hour is divided into 60 minutes, and each minute into 60 seconds. Sidereal time is divided similarly; but the minutes and seconds of solar time are each a little longer than the corresponding units of sidereal time.

The question is whether or not the sun is a good timekeeper: if it were, there would be no need of certain other kinds of time. Actually, the sun is not a good timekeeper, the eastward motion along its apparent path for the year being somewhat irregular. Apparent solar days are therefore of unequal duration. Manifestly, if the days vary in length, one with another, it would be impossible for a watch or clock to be regulated according to apparent time; even if it could be, we should still have no precision in our timekeeping. Something else is obviously needed. As an example of the irregularity of apparent time, we note that about December 23 an apparent day is 51^s longer, say from one apparent noon to another, than an apparent day around September 16, as measured by the invariable standard of sidereal time.

There are two reasons for this non-uniformity of the apparent solar days. In the first place, the sun's apparent yearly motion along the ecliptic is not uniform, the sun now seeming to go faster and now more slowly than its average speed. If the earth's orbit were perfectly circular, the earth's movement around the great central luminary would be uniform and we could look out at the sun and trace its uniform motion along the ecliptic in a year. Such a condition does not obtain: the orbit is not circular but eccentric, the earth being some 3,000,000 miles nearer the sun at the perihelion time (Jan. 3, for example, in 1957) than at aphelion time (July 2 for 1957). And when the earth is relatively nearer the sun, it goes faster in its orbit, because of the operation of the law of gravitation, whereas at the opposite times it moves more slowly. When the earth goes faster, the sun is seemingly moving faster too in its annual motion; and as the earth moves more slowly, so the sun likewise seems to go more slowly. Hence the number of minutes of arc covered by the sun per day—

in the eastward motion—is constantly varying but averages nearly 1° per day.

The other reason for lack of uniformity of the apparent solar day has to do with the inclination of the ecliptic to the equator. (Both causes, we notice, are natural phenomena due to the original plan of the solar system.) The sun's apparent course is along the ecliptic rather than along the celestial equator. The point at issue is that time-measurement involves measure of hour-angle, and hour-angle involves measurement *from the meridian, at right angles to the celestial equator*. That is to say, hour-angle is an angle measured from the celestial pole and is not concerned with the ecliptic, whose pole is the "ecliptic pole".

Suppose reason *one* did not hold, but that, instead, the sun moved uniformly along the ecliptic. Even so, at the time of the vernal equinox the sun's movement of 1° on the ecliptic would not be projected as 1° along the equator; for the line of projection must be perpendicular to the equator, and the two great circles are at an angle. Yet it is the apparent eastward movement of the sun as measured along the *equator* that determines an apparent day. But at the time of the summer or the winter solstice the sun is at a place where the equator and the ecliptic are for the moment parallel, so that 1° of solar motion along the ecliptic means 1° along the equator also.

Mean Solar Time

The second category of solar time includes the different types of *mean* time. Inasmuch as the sun itself is inadequate as a timekeeper, it is convenient to invent a fictitious body known as the *mean sun*, which is assumed to have a perfectly uniform motion eastward along the celestial equator (not the ecliptic). Starting together with the true sun at a certain moment, this mean sun is supposed to complete a revolution in just the same time that the true sun takes for a yearly trip along the ecliptic.

Mean solar time is the hour-angle of the mean sun plus 12 hours; and a mean solar day for any observer is the interval of time between two successive lower transits of the mean sun over his meridian. Mean solar days are divided into hours, minutes, and seconds, just as apparent time is. The units of the second, minute, and hour are a trifle longer than those of sidereal time. Moreover, all the days of mean time are of precisely the same length, because of the uniform movement of the mean sun along the equator.

Mean time is the basis of time used in civil life. Both apparent and mean time have their zero hour at midnight when the sun or the mean sun, respectively, is at lower transit. This has not always been so, however, for prior to January 1, 1925, *in astronomy* the apparent day began when the sun was at upper transit, and the mean solar day began with the mean sun at upper transit, though even then the day as used in civil life began at midnight. But, beginning with 1925, the apparent day and the mean solar day both start at midnight, and thus the astronomers' day is made to correspond with the day of civil usage. The matter is important to remember in referring to data in old almanacs.

Civil time is the specific use of mean time that begins the day at midnight. Civil time is the same as mean solar time as the latter has been used beginning with 1925. The term *astronomical time* was the term applied to the astronomer's mean solar day beginning at noon, but this is no longer used, since the astronomer's day coincides with the civil day. The civil day begins 12 hours earlier than the old astronomical day of the same date; for example:

Mar. 18, 1924, 21^h by ast. time = Mar. 19, 9 a.m., civil time,
Mar. 19, 1924, 9^h by ast. time = Mar. 19, 9 p.m., civil time.

In our discussion so far, all the kinds of time are local, that is, the time for an observer at a given meridian is the true time at that meridian only, from the north pole to the

[237]

south pole. 'At any other meridian to the east of the given one, the time is always greater, or later, on the clock-face than on the given meridian, and at any meridian to the west the time is less, or earlier. Thus we see that time, so to speak, goes perpetually around the earth from east to west. Furthermore, the rate is 15° of longitude an hour, or 1° of longitude for every 4 minutes of time—whether it be sidereal or solar.

It becomes necessary to distinguish between local mean time and kinds that are not local. The mean solar time of a particular point on the earth's surface and also of *all points along that meridian* is known specifically as the *local mean time* of that meridian. An important point is that this refers to a kind of time that is *not* used by clocks in civil life. The term *local mean time* (L.M.T.) is practically synonymous with the term *local civil time* (L.C.T.). We say "practically synonymous" because, while L.M.T. is the same kind of time precisely as L.C.T., the term local mean time is more likely to be connected with the former use of the day as beginning at noon instead of at midnight. For this reason the designation *local civil time* is preferred by astronomers and other scientists. Each different longitude —varying even by the smallest amount—has a different local civil time, at any one instant. Or, to be more exact, the time varies by 1^m for each $\frac{1}{4}°$ of longitude.

For navigational and geographic purposes there has to be a zero meridian for the world; and since 1884 Greenwich, England, has been the world's meridian of 0° longitude. Not only is this meridian the basis of longitude designations for the world, but it is the basis of time-measurement, too. Navigators' chronometers are set to this time-standard, and professional astronomers usually base their almanacs and ephemerides on it, also. The local civil time of the Greenwich meridian is known as *Greenwich civil time* (G.C.T.), and its beginning, or zero hour, is at civil midnight. Before 1925, when the day for astronomers began at noon by civil reckoning, such time was called *Greenwich mean time* (G.M.T.), but the latter term has been practically abandoned now in favor of *Greenwich civil time,* in order to distinguish between the days beginning at noon and at midnight. In astronomy another term, *universal time* (U.T.), has been advised by the International Astronomical Union. It is absolutely synonymous with Greenwich civil time and emphasizes the world-wide feature of this time. U.T. is now used by a majority of astronomers, although navigators use G.C.T. We then have the following relation:

$$U.T. = G.C.T. = G.M.T. + 12^h.$$

Time and longitude are intimately related, for the rotation of the earth on its axis, with respect to some particular object in the heavens, is what determines the day's measurement. And whatever object is chosen—defining a certain kind of time—the earth must turn through 360° in a day, or 15° an hour, making time appear to move westward around the globe at this rate. This leads to the fact that the difference of the local times of two observers using the same kind of time equals the difference of their longitudes, expressed in time. If the time, for example, at Greenwich is 11^h30^m G.C.T., then, at station A, longitude 90° ($= 6^h$) W., the time at that moment is 5^h30^m, 90th-meridian local civil time. At the same moment at longitude 165° ($= 11^h$) E., the time is 22^h30^m by 165th-meridian-east local civil time. As a formula we have

$G.C.T.\ (U.T.) - L.C.T.$ at A = longitude of A,
$$G.C.T.\ (U.T.) = L.C.T.\ \text{at } A + \text{long. of } A.$$

Following the formula, for the first example we have

$$11^h30^m - 5^h30^m = 6^h0^m = 90°.$$

Or in the second equation,

$$11^h30^m = 5^h30^m + 6^h0^m.$$

In the second example,

$$11^h30^m - 22^h30^m = -11^h0^m \text{ or } -165°,$$

which is 165° longitude east. Or in the second equation,

$$11^h30^m = 22^h30^m + (-11^h0^m).$$

Equation of Time

The lack of uniformity of apparent time causes a constantly varying difference between the apparent and the mean time of a station. This difference is known as the *equation of time*. More technically, it is the difference in hour-angle between the apparent and the mean sun. It is not really an equation but rather an interval of time. Sometimes the apparent sun is ahead of the mean sun, and sometimes it is behind, the amount varying from zero to more than 16^m. By "ahead of" we mean here that the true sun is farther westward than the mean sun in their daily motion and so transits the meridian sooner.

The causes for the equation of time are those given for the variation of apparent solar days (page 235).

The equation of time may be taken in either of two senses according to how it is to be used. If several books are referred to in this connection, the matter will become confused until it is realized that some authorities use the term in one form, while others use the other form, and commonly but one is mentioned by any author. The two forms are the equation of time, mean minus apparent, and the equation of time, apparent minus mean. The former may be designated E_{m-a}, and the latter E_{a-m}. At any moment the value of one is the same numerically as that of the other, but the signs are opposite. It is believed that the reader will profit most by concentrating on E_{m-a}.

The *equation of time, mean minus apparent,* is the correction to be applied to apparent time, in order to obtain mean solar time. At any given instant it may be negative or positive. When the mean sun is ahead of the true sun in

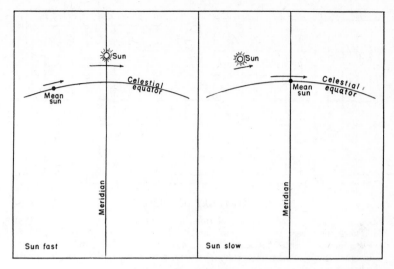

SUN FAST AND SUN SLOW

Usually the actual sun is out of step with the more regular *mean sun*. When the sun is ahead of the mean sun and transits the meridian first, the "sun fast" condition prevails, and the difference of time of arrival of the two suns is the equation of time at the moment. When the mean sun is ahead of the real sun, we have the "sun slow" phenomenon. The mean sun, an imaginary but useful body, travels along the celestial equator, while the sun itself is on the equator only momentarily, twice a year, at equinox times.

their diurnal motions, then mean noon precedes apparent noon, the mean sun coming to the meridian sooner than the real sun. Here the situation is known as *sun slow* in the commercial almanacs. The clock running on local mean time shows a later time than a sun-dial at the same station would. The equation is + in this case. When the mean sun is behind the true sun, mean noon follows apparent noon, the true sun coming to the meridian sooner than the mean sun. Then we have the *sun fast* condition, and the local mean clock shows an earlier time than a sun-dial. Here the equation is −.

The equation-of-time values for any particular day of the year vary slightly from year to year, but the general pattern is the same, as shown here in the standard graph

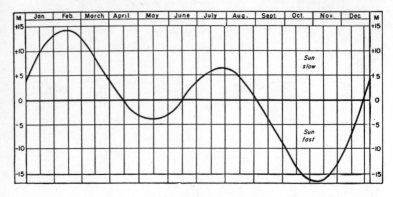

EQUATION OF TIME

Standard graph of the equation of time, mean minus apparent. While plotted for a particular year, it will do approximately for any year. The curved line shows the number of minutes the sun is fast or slow over the mean sun, at any time. The equation of time becomes zero, four times a year, where the curve intersects the line of zero minute.

of the equation of time, mean minus apparent. There is a maximum of sun slow around mid-February and a smaller one near the end of July; for the sun fast there is a maximum in early November and a submaximum in mid-May. Four times a year the equation is zero—about April 15, June 14, September 1, and December 25. The exact values are given for each day of the year in all important almanacs, but in some places one finds the mean-minus-apparent form and in other places the opposite. The *American Ephemeris and Nautical Almanac* tabulates E_{a-m} for 0^h U.T., and (up to 1950) E_{m-a} for noon at Washington. In 1949 the maximum for sun slow is on February 11, the value of E_{m-a} being $+14^m21^s.9$ to the nearest tenth second, whereas on November 3 the maximum for sun fast is $-16^m23^s.7$.

The equation of time, mean minus apparent, is used in various computations whereby the apparent time is reduced to mean time. An important instance is in the case of a sun-dial reading. For example, a sun-dial on September

30 reads 2:45 p.m.; this is apparent time. Suppose the E_{m-a} at the moment is -10^m0^s. Add algebraically: 2^h45^m p.m. $+ (-10^m0^s) = 2^h35^m$ p.m., local civil time. This indicates that the mean time is less than the apparent, or that the sun is "fast" over the mean sun. We may further reduce the local civil time to standard time by the following rule:

To change the local civil time to standard time, decrease the L.C.T. by 4^m for every degree the station is east of the standard meridian, or increase the L.C.T. by 4^m for every degree the station is west of the standard meridian.

Another important use of the equation of time used in this form is in determining the equivalent mean time for the apparent time of noon, in finding the latitude of a station by meridian altitude of the sun. Here one needs to know the approximate transit time so as to know when to begin observing. At transit, the apparent time must be 12^h0^m; so we "place the sun on the meridian", and we have $12^h0^m + E_{m-a} = L.C.T.$ of transit. Then reduce the $L.C.T.$ to standard time or else have the clock set to the local civil time; the latter is simple to do, for at a particular station the difference between $L.C.T.$ and standard time is always the same.

For certain purposes one uses the equation of time in the opposite sense, or E_{a-m}. The *equation of time, apparent minus mean*, is the correction to be applied to mean time, in order to obtain apparent time. Not only is the value on a given day and hour the same as the equation in the other form, except for change of sign, but the situation of sun fast and sun slow remains the same, whichever way the equation is taken. With E_{a-m}, when the apparent sun is ahead of the mean sun (see cut), we have the sun-fast condition, and E_{a-m} is $+$. But when the apparent sun is behind the mean sun, in the sun-slow condition, then E_{a-m} is $-$.

One of the chief uses of the equation of time, apparent

minus mean, is in navigation. You will find the *American Nautical Almanac* tabulates the quantity for every even hour of G.C.T. for each day of the year as an aid in computations in nautical astronomy. As commonly happens in working with ephemeris data, however, we are apt to need the quantity for some time other than that tabulated. Interpolation is needed. Suppose we wish to derive the Greenwich apparent time for $6^h20^m30^s$ p.m., G.C.T., September 22, 1949, given the E_{a-m} at 0^h G.C.T. as $+7^m3^s.1$, and increasing by $21^s.0$ per day. By interpolation we derive $+7^m18^s.9$ for the equation for 6 p.m. as follows: We have $6^h20^m30^s$ p.m. $= 18^h20^m30^s$. Now $18^h = \frac{3}{4}^d$, and so $\frac{3}{4}(21^s.0) = 15^s.8$; add to $7^m3^s.1$, obtaining $7^m18^s.9$, the value of E_{a-m} for the time in question. Now we add $18^h20^m30^s + 7^m18^s.9 = 18^h27^m48^s.9$, Greenwich apparent time for the moment. The sun is therefore "fast" over the mean sun.

Standard Time

It is interesting to consider the actual distance on the earth in miles that causes a variation of a given local time. We have seen that 15° of longitude are covered by 1^h of time; but the question is how many miles are represented. 1° of longitude at the equator corresponds to 69.232 statute miles. But all the meridians converge at the poles, so that the geographic extent east and west covered by a given arc of longitude becomes less and less as one leaves the equator and goes toward either pole. The approximate formula governing this is

$$1° \text{ of longitude} = 69.232 \text{ miles} \times \cos \text{ latitude.}$$

At latitude 40°, 1° of longitude covers 53.06 miles. So two clocks running on local civil time and situated 53.06 miles apart in an east-west direction will differ in their local times by 4^m. A difference of 1^m of time corresponds to $13\frac{1}{4}$ miles, at this latitude.

Local civil time would be the most scientific time to use, were it not that it is necessary to travel around considerably or to consider simultaneous events such as radio reception at different places at the same absolute moment. When any extent of land is considered, one begins to encounter the phenomenon of difference in local time. Over the extent of a few hours' journey a traveler would have to be changing his watch continually as he progressed, if local time were in use. As the traveler went east, for example, in latitude 40°, he would set his watch ahead by 1^m for each $13\frac{1}{4}$ miles; or as he went west, he would set the watch back by 1^m for every $13\frac{1}{4}$ miles.

In the United States it became apparent before 1870 that there was a distinct need for a uniform time over a considerable area of country. There was endless confusion with the railroad situation because of the use of various local times in operation in different sections. Indeed, in some cities, four or five different local times were in use simultaneously, for railroads brought different local times into one terminal. As the result of an international congress held at Washington in 1884, the earth was divided into zones. Each zone covered 15° of longitude, and a uniform time for the whole of each zone was set up, the time being the local mean time of its central meridian. The time used in contiguous zones differed by exactly 1 hour.

The United States had already adopted the scheme of standard time in 1883, in the form used now. This was largely brought about by the untiring efforts of Dr. Charles F. Dowd, principal of the Ladies Seminary at Saratoga Springs, N.Y. For many years he did research on the problem, arranged schedules and times, wrote papers, discussed the matter with the leading railroad officials, and toured the country. C. M. Depew called Dowd "Yale's most famous graduate". *Harper's Weekly* speaks of the "confounding confusion of 1869" thus: "[A traveler's] watch was to him a delusion; clocks in stations, staring each other in the face, defiant of harmony both with one another and with surrounding local time, and all wildly at variance with his watch, were wholly baffling to all intelligence."

The United States is divided into four standard-time zones, centered along certain standard-time meridians. The zones are made to fit in with the system of world zones, inasmuch as the easternmost one was chosen as a whole number of hours west from the zero zone of Greenwich. The United States uses only the last four zones in the following table:

Name of zone	Abbreviation	Central meridian	Time earlier than Greenwich
Atlantic standard time............	A.S.T.	60°W.	4^h
Eastern standard time............	E.S.T.	75°W.	5^h
Central standard time............	C.S.T.	90°W.	6^h
Mountain standard time..........	M.S.T.	105°W.	7^h
Pacific standard time............	P.S.T.	120°W.	8^h

Besides the four zones used in the United States, Canada has two extra time-zones, those of (1) Atlantic standard time, used by New Brunswick, Nova Scotia, and Quebec (east of longitude 68°W.), and (2) 135th-meridian time, or Yukon standard time, 9^h earlier than Greenwich. Newfoundland and the coast of Labrador are under Newfoundland standard time, 3^h30^m earlier than Greenwich. Alaska, being in high northern latitudes, covers considerable distance in longitude and finds four zones necessary—those centered on the meridians of 120°, 135°, 150°, and 165°W. The 150th-meridian time is known as Alaskan standard time (covering most of Alaska), but the name is somewhat ambiguous, for all four zones are in use in Alaska. Mexico, except for part of the west coast and part of Lower Cal., is all in the time-zone governed by the 90th meridian west. This is peculiar since geographically the country is essentially located within the longitudes normally controlled by the 105th meridian of our Mountain standard time.

Standard time is the time used in our everyday civil life. We do not use local mean or local civil time. Of course, just along a standard meridian, the standard time is the same as the local civil time. Everywhere within a standard-time zone, the clocks using standard time read the same hour, minute, and second—assuming they are correct. Between one zone and the next, there is an abrupt jump of $1^h0^m0^s$, the clocks to the west of a given zone reading an earlier time, and those at the east of a given zone a later time.

At sea and over the whole globe in general—at least with navigators—the term *zone time* is in use; but zone time is only another expression for standard time. The world's 24 zones are numbered in succession. Centered on the Greenwich meridian is the *zero zone* (zone 0), and to the west are zones marked successively $+1$, $+2$, $+3$, etc., zone $+5$ being the E.S.T. zone. To the east of zone 0 are zones -1, -2, -3, etc. At longitude 180° is zone 12, which is peculiar: the half of it west of the meridian is marked -12, while the half on the east of the meridian is marked $+12$. The "zone description"—the number of a zone together with its sign—when added algebraically to the civil time, indicates the corresponding G.C.T. For example, 20^h15^m of zone $+7$ ($= $ M.S.T.) gives $20^h15^m + 7^h = 27^h15^m$; deducting 24^h we get 3^h15^m, the G.C.T. of the following day for the corresponding time. For a place east of Greenwich let us take 2^h5^m in zone -8 (120th meridian east): $2^h5^m + (-8)$ $= -5^h55^m$, or 5^h55^m to be counted back from 0^h into the day before, giving 18^h5^m. Or in such cases we may first add 24^h thus: $24^h + 2^h5^m + (-8) = 26^h5^m - 8^h = 18^h5^m$ of the day before, for the corresponding G.C.T.

Theoretically the standard-time zones should be bounded by straight lines, $7\frac{1}{2}°$ from the central meridians. While this ideal is reached on the oceans, it is commonly not nearly so uniform as that on land, the boundaries there being notably irregular. In the United States the boundaries of the time-zones are set by the Interstate Commerce Commission and are revised from time to time. This irregularity is effected purposely for the convenience mainly of the railroads. An extreme case is noted at El Paso, Tex., where the city is located geographically west of the central meridian of the M.S.T. belt, but is put under Central standard time.

Advanced Time

Daylight-saving time (D.S.T.), summer time, and even war time are different expressions for the use of advanced time. This is not a different kind of time but simply a different clock-setting. Advanced time in a given zone is the use, in this zone, of the standard time of one zone to the east of a given zone. This important point—that advanced time is really standard time—is not often realized except by astronomers and other scientists. For example, clocks running on Eastern daylight-saving time are actually keeping normal Atlantic standard time. Thus 3 a.m. E.S.T. would correspond to 4 a.m. E.D.S.T., because 4 a.m. is the A.S.T. equivalent of 3^h E.S.T. When in England the clocks are set to "double summer time", they are of course using the normal time of two zones to the east, or Eastern European time—very disconcerting to a scientist.

In the United States, daylight-saving time was first introduced during the First World War in order to finish the day's activities with as little artificial light as possible. For earlier rising of persons means earlier retiring and hence a saving of light and fuel. Along with this is the advantage of additional daylight in the hours after the evening meal. The advantages apply mostly to the summer months alone and only to the middle latitudes. There is little advantage in using advanced time in low latitudes, for the period of daylight in equatorial regions is nearly the same over the entire year; and there is little if any advantage in high latitudes, for there the period of daylight and twilight is longer than one can use and still obtain sufficient sleep.

Advanced time is unscientific and unwelcome to scientists. Not that scientists object to beginning the day's schedule earlier according to the sun, but that the same result can be achieved by letting the clocks run on normal standard time and instituting an earlier summer schedule for the day's activities when desired. The reason for the use of D.S.T. is the belief that for the majority of persons it is easier to attain the earlier schedule by setting the clocks ahead and letting people keep to their old habits as to hours. The fundamental objection is that it robs us of the true situation of time as related to the natural phenomena of the day, such as daylight and darkness, the rising and setting of the sun, and other natural effects.

The sudden change of clock-setting from normal standard time to advanced time causes the morning hours around rising time to be darker than before, *for the same clock-time*, and the late afternoon or early evening hours to be lighter. Similarly, the sudden shift from advanced time to normal standard time causes the morning hours to be lighter and the late afternoon hours to be darker than before the change.

Besides the general objection, there are innumerable other disconcerting features. It is, for instance, difficult to have young children go to sleep when it is too light and too hot. "War time" used in winter caused one to arise in darkness and use more artificial light than otherwise in the morning. Advanced time is disliked more by rural communities than by the industrial and urban populations. With widely varying activities of people in different places, it is very easy to see that the inhabitants of different communities will not agree on the matter.

Under no circumstances should advanced time be used in any activities undertaken for or notes or records made for astronomical or other scientific observations. Moreover, what-

ever time-system or -zone is used should be clearly indicated. Some opponents of advanced time, when they have
to use this time in civil life, enjoy keeping one clock set to
normal standard time; by frequent reference to this timepiece, the true stituation is more easily kept in mind.

The expression *zero hour* (0^h) is the correct one to use
for the midnight hour and is always used in good scientific
work; besides it is logical and consistent. There is no end of
confusion in regard to the designations "a.m." and "p.m."
in connection with the midnight and the noon hours. A vast
majority of persons use the term in the wrong way. Zero
hour is the beginning of the day; while one can speak of the
hour or moment of "midnight", it is wholly ambiguous to
say, as an example, "Monday midnight", midnight being a
dividing-point and not belonging to any particular day.
One can, however, say correctly "midnight, Monday-
Tuesday", or "midnight, June 5–6", etc. The correct
expression is "0^h, Tuesday", "0^h, June 6", etc. For the noon
hour one says, properly, "Tuesday, 12 noon", etc. If one is
forced to use the designations a.m. and p.m., the midnight
hour is 12 p.m. and the noon hour is 12 a.m.; but the use of
these terms is to be discouraged because, $\frac{9}{10}$ of the time,
persons have them confused.

The Date-line

The date-line is an interesting place. It is sometimes, however, rather a puzzling line. Nevertheless, it is a very necessary boundary-line to have. It is known also as the International Date Line; it is not international but was set up by
agreement between commercial steamship lines.

The effect of solar time, we noted, was that time, so to
speak—or at least the measurement of it—travels around
the earth perpetually westward. If at a certain instant, as
an example, at Ouagadougou, French West Africa, the
standard time is 0^h, six hours later the standard time will be
0^h at Topolobampo, Mexico, six zones farther west. Four

hours later yet it will be 0^h at Héréhérétué, Tuamotu Archipelago, zone +10. Four hours later still it will be 0^h at Dungog, N.S.W., Australia, zone −10. Thus the longitude of places where the time is zero hour increases westward in effect around the globe. Of course, we could take any other hour besides 0^h and proceed similarly.

Zero hour, however, is the moment of beginning of the day, so that a new day is forever on its journey around the earth. To the west of the longitude where the time is 0^h, one has the remains of the "old day", whereas on the eastern side one is bound to have the "new day". No difficulties are introduced so far; but let us consider the situation at the instant when the local time is 0^h of June 1 at Topolobampo (longitude 109°W.). At all places to the east of this station for a considerable distance, the day will be June 1. At all places to the west for a considerable distance, the day will be May 31. At once the question arises as to where in the world the line of division between May 31 and June 1 is. It is not on the opposite side of the earth, say at Diu, India (longitude 71°E.). There, the local time is noon by mean time. At the moment, on either side of Diu, one would not find it noon of May 31 on one side and June 1 on the other; there has to be a more practicable scheme.

The most workable system is used, by which the place of changing the date is located along or near the meridian of 180°. This traverses the Pacific Ocean and cuts across but few series of islands. This is the date-line and is actually coincident over much of its length with longitude 180°, yet in places departs from that meridian to allow no change of date in the midst of a settlement. It was also fixed so that colonies affiliated with America might use the American date, while other colonies more closely connected with Asiatic countries might keep the Asiatic date.

Following the date-line north from the equator we find it lies along the 180° meridian about as far as the Aleutian Islands, where it turns northwest and goes to 170°E., to keep all these islands with the same date, and then turns northeast to the middle of Bering Strait, going northwest again. South of the equator, the date-line soon begins to run southeast and then from a point south of the Samoa Islands runs along the meridian of $172\frac{1}{2}°$W., to a point southeast of the Chatham Islands, and finally goes back to 180°. By this means the Fiji, the Tonga, and the Chatham island groups are all kept on the Asiatic date.

At places east of the date-line the calendar day is 1 day earlier than at points to the west of the line. At a point immediately west of the date-line, let us suppose it to be July 1, 18^h (6 p.m.), local civil time. Consider stations in a westward direction. At this moment it is 12^h at longitude 90°E., 6^h at longitude 0°, and 0^h at longitude 90°W.—all of the same date, July 1. Farther westward yet from longitude 90°W., we find it is not yet midnight (0^h), so that, between 90°W. and 180°, the date must be June 30. At longitude 165°W., it is 19^h (7 p.m.), and at a point just east of the date-line it is 18^h of June 30.

It is interesting to note that any new given date occurs *first on the earth* at the 180th meridian, at which moment it is noon along the meridian of Greenwich. This is the only moment when all the globe has the same date; at other times there are two dates in progress. These statements need modification, for, in the first place, even at the moment described, *all* the globe does not have the same date: there is a region west of Bering Strait that is west of the date-line but east of 180°, and another region around Attu Island in the Aleutian Islands that is east of the date-line but west of 180°, so that peculiar time-conditions exist here, and parts of 3 days may occur on the earth at the same time. Second, any new given date occurs first at the date-line yet not at the 180th meridian but in the first-mentioned of the two areas above.

As one crosses the date-line going eastward, his watch remains the same but the date changes abruptly to 1 day

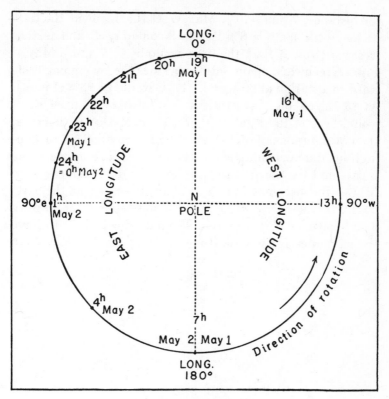

LONG.
0°

20h 19h
May 1

21h

22h

23h
May 1

24h
= 0h May 2

EAST LONGITUDE

90°e 1h
May 2

N
POLE

WEST LONGITUDE

16h
May 1

13h 90°w.

Direction of rotation

4h
May 2

7h

May 2 May 1

LONG.
180°

DATE-LINE PROBLEM

earlier, causing the traveler to repeat a calendar day. As one crosses the date-line going westward, the date changes abruptly to 1 day later, causing him to omit a day by the calendar. Theoretically, in traveling across the boundary, one would have the day change at the moment of crossing. The actual practice at sea, however, varies from this, for it appears to be the custom to change the date at night as though passing over the line at midnight. Moreover, it is the usual rule neither to omit nor to repeat a Sunday or a holiday.

Let us take one more example to clarify the matter. Take any day and hour at the prime meridian of Greenwich—

for instance, 7 p.m. (19^h), May 1. At this moment the time at longitude 90° ($= 6^h$) W. is 13^h on May 1, and farther westward yet, at 180°, the time would be 7^h (7 a.m.), May 1. From Greenwich, again, let us consider the time going eastward to a station at 60° ($= 4^h$) E.; it would be 23^h (11 p.m.). At 75°E., 24^h on May 1, which is 0^h of May 2; at 90°E., it would be 1^h, May 2; at 180°, 7^h (7 a.m.), May 2. There is, then, a discrepancy of 1 day in the two methods of reckoning, but our reckoning is correct in each. The moment the westbound traveler crosses the line, the date changes from May 1 and becomes May 2 for him; the moment the eastbound traveler crosses the line, the date changes from May 2 and becomes May 1 to him. The date-line is there to solve the circumnavigation-and-time problem (see figure, p. 253).

18

The Art of Navigation

Y ou can "thank your lucky stars" for much of the food you eat, for many of the clothes you wear, and for scores of articles you use—in fact, for everything that comes to you from across the seas. You can thank the stars literally, for only through their guidance were the ships that carried these goods able to wend their way across trackless oceans and come unerringly to port.

Ever since the early days of man, those same stars have been sign-posts in the sky to those who could read them; sign-posts that carried men safely to new worlds; sign-posts that, today, mark the great sea and air lanes of commerce between the continents.

True, the modern art of navigation is a comparatively recent development. For thousands of years men explored the unknown without it. Columbus sailed with only a compass to guide him, and others ventured forth with even less. But all of them, beyond a doubt, possessed some elementary knowledge of the heavens and depended to a degree upon sun, moon, and stars to aid them in finding their direction.

Even the primitive peoples did so. The Polynesians, for example, were superb sailors, and the ease and accuracy with which they guided their craft among the islands were due largely to their observations of the heavens.

The Polynesian picture of the universe was a simple one. The Polynesians considered themselves to be inside a huge shell—the star-studded heavens—which revolved around them. By watching the heavens, wise men learned that the stars on the inner surface of this shell rose over the eastern horizon, crossed the skies, and vanished in the west; that they remained always in the same relation to one another; and that month after month the same stars passed directly over the same islands.

They observed other things, too—that the stars rose earlier each night and that after a full year they could be seen again in the same positions in the sky. But the important fact—and it was an item of such overwhelming value that it won high position for those who knew the secret—was that the same stars always passed over the same islands.

Thus, if you studied the heavens well, you need only set sail toward a star that you knew to be directly above the island that was your destination and you would be guided to it. Furthermore, you could even judge how near to your destination you were getting, because as you approached it that star would come nearer and nearer to your own zenith. The principle would be the same if you were to see a light atop a tall building. By walking toward that light, you would approach the building; and as you approached, the light would seem to climb higher and higher in the skies.

In actual practice, of course, it was not quite as simple as that. The Polynesian navigator, to earn his laurels, had to be familiar with *all* the stars which passed over the islands to which he sailed, so that, as one moved on and ceased to mark his destination, he could select another to take its place. And, since he followed this heavenly guidance without instruments, it was only approximate. He had to be able to read the signs of the seas as well, so that he could tell by the birds and fishes, by clouds, by odors, and by countless other small indications, when he was nearing a landfall.

But the system worked well enough to support a flourishing traffic between the islands and win great fame for the masters who guided the ships. Today, when an incomparably finer system of navigation exists, so that ships and planes are aimed at their geographic targets with pin-point accuracy, the navigator still falls heir to some of the awe with which the ancients beheld him.

And this despite the fact that the actual practice of modern navigation has been stripped of practically all its trigonometric and astronomical mystery and reduced to the point where, with proper instruction and considerable care, almost any intelligent person can find his way by the stars. More than one sailor has learned the tricks of his trade from the books in the New York Public Library—and one Robinson circumnavigated the globe in a small sailing vessel armed only with the knowledge gained in such a fashion.

Today, thanks to the U. S. Naval Observatory, the Hydrographic Office, and other government agencies, there exist a few brief volumes that, taken together, solve all the perplexing riddles of navigation, leaving the sailor little more to do than make observations and look up the answers in the published tables. The task is much easier than that which confronted the Polynesian master; for all the trigonometric and astronomical computations have been worked out in advance, and simple arithmetic can take care of the remainder.

Navigation is not, of course, so ridiculously easy that you can learn the art by reading one brief chapter in a book devoted to numerous other aspects of astronomy, nor would any sensible student venture forth on the high seas without giving himself extensive practice in making observations with the sextant and performing the other routine tasks involved.

These operations, simple though they may be in theory and in practice, call for a high degree of accuracy and, consequently, for a well-developed skill. The slightest error may be greatly magnified, with the result that the navigator might miss his destination as a reward for carlessness. In using the sextant, an instrument with which the angular distances of sun, moon, and stars are determined, practice is essential. You can discharge a rifle by squeezing the trigger, but few people can consistently hit the bull's-eye without constant practice.

However, the principles involved in following the pathway of the stars can be grasped without undue difficulty, and, once they are understood, the reason for each step in navigation and the importance of painfully careful observations become clear.

One of the things to be recalled at the start is that the modern mariner no longer thinks of directions in such terms as "north-northeast" or "south by southwest". He measures directions in degrees clockwise around the horizon from the north point, north being both 0° and 360°; east being, on the modern compass, 90°; south, 180°; and west, 270°.

Thus it is possible for him to indicate direction accurately and simply—when a bearing is given as 35°, there is no question as to how far north of northeast it is. He merely marks 35° around the horizon from the north point and proceeds in that direction, assuming, of course, that he possesses a reliable compass with which to make the measurements.

There are, naturally, other and simpler methods of navigation than that which depends upon observations of the stars and other heavenly bodies. But they are inadequate for trans-oceanic travel and serve as supplements to celestial navigation rather than as substitutes. Under limited circumstances, they may stand on their own.

Piloting, for example, is nothing more than finding one's way by reference to known landmarks—the boatman uses it in familiar waters, the airplane pilot while flying in short hops over well-mapped country. Once out of sight of land, however, it is of small use to the mariner, and high in the substratosphere the aviator, too, finds it of little aid.

Dead-reckoning is more important, and, when for various reasons it is impossible to refer to the heavenly bodies, both sailor and flier fall back on it for extended periods. Moreover, the flier can supplement dead-reckoning with radio signals—he can "ride the beam" and know, with fair certainty, where he is. The advantages and disadvantages of dead-reckoning, however, are implicit in the method itself, for it is extremely simple.

If you were to travel, afoot, from your home to a town or other location that was 10 miles due north, the chances are you would use the dead-reckoning method of navigation to judge your progress. You would know your own rate of walking—let's say it is 4 miles per hour—and you would also know that so long as you walked due north you would have 10 miles to travel. Thus, after an hour and a half, you would figure that you had gone 6 miles and were slightly more than halfway to your destination.

But you would actually judge your progress as "about six miles", because you'd realize that your walking speed was not constant, nor did you stay constantly on a straight line to your destination.

The example points out both the strength and the weakness of dead-reckoning—it is simple and self-contained but subject to factors beyond exact calculation or control. The mariner, for example, employs the same principle; he judges his location by the speed he travels, the length of time he has been under way, and the direction he has traveled. Of these factors, time is constant; the others are not. Ocean currents may alter both the ship's actual speed of progress and its true direction. And the aviator, similarly, is subject to the motion of the air-mass through which he flies, a motion which is bound to affect his ground speed and actual direction of flight and for which he must constantly endeavor to make correction.

And so dead-reckoning, although it serves to indicate roughly the location of boat or aircraft, does not do so accurately. Moreover, its inaccuracy grows over a long period of time—and something else is obviously needed if a ship is to sail from New York and put in at London on schedule.

That something is celestial navigation—almost as simple in basic concept as dead-reckoning, not nearly so simple in application, but incomparably superior in results.

To understand the principles underlying navigation by the stars, imagine yourself sailing a small boat along a coastline. You sight an island that is clearly marked on your charts, and you determine, carefully, its bearing from you. Then you mark that bearing, that line of direction from the island to you, on your chart. Having done so, you know that your boat is located somewhere along that line. But you don't know at exactly what point (diagram a).

Suppose that you see another island and repeat the process. You will then have two lines marked on your chart, and, what is more, they will cross one another. Since your boat is located somewhere on each of these lines, it must be at that intersection.

To take another example, suppose that there is only one island in view and you obtain its bearing. If you also have on board a range-finder, you will be able to determine how far away the island is, and on your chart you can mark the line indicating the bearing and measure off, according to the scale accompanying the chart, your distance from the island. Once again, you know where you are (diagram b).

There is still a third method by which you could determine your location after sighting the islands. Assuming that you had no compass or other device with which to measure your bearing but did have a range-finder, you could sight the first island and obtain its distance from you. Then you could draw, on the chart, an arc of a circle in which all points were at the specified distance from the

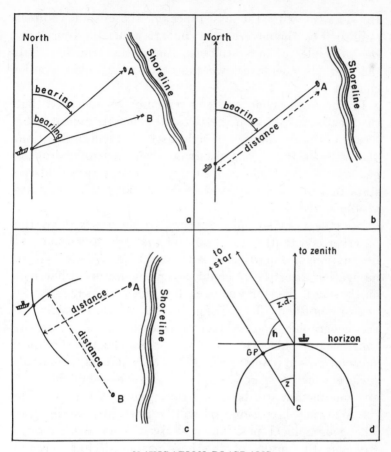

NAVIGATION DIAGRAMS

island. You would know that you were located somewhere along that arc, but you wouldn't know exactly where. However, if you performed the same operation on the second island, you would find that your two arcs crossed, and once again the intersection would give you a "fix"—would mark the location of your craft (diagram *c*).

The latter method is similar to the one that is largely relied upon in navigation, but since the mariner is on the high seas and has no islands in sight he must use the stars.

[261]

He does so with the assistance of those slim volumes published by the government; but, to understand just how the principles of our coastwise islands are transferred to the stars in the skies, we must grasp one more simple concept.

In our earlier chapters, you remember, we learned that the location of stars on the celestial sphere is indicated by means of the coördinates of right ascension and declination. This is excellent, as long as our interests are confined to the heavens, for by these coördinates we can always find the stars in which we are interested, provided that they are visible at the time.

But the celestial sphere seems to revolve around the observer constantly, and knowing the right ascension and declination of a particular star would be of little help in navigation, because we could never be sure just what spot on the earth the star was over at a given moment.

So we must, in effect, bring the star "down to earth", to the geographic point directly beneath the star—or the substellar or subastral point (or it may be the sublunar, subsolar, or subplanetary point). This point on the earth's surface which is exactly under a given heavenly body at any one instant will be called the geographical position in the following discussion and will be referred to as the GP. The geographical position is derived from the *Nautical Almanac* by means of the headings of declination and Greenwich hour-angle. The latter (GHA) becomes the geographic longitude of the GP, or the subpoint, and the declination becomes its latitude.

Because of this, the GP can be used by the navigator in determining his own latitude and longitude—just as though it were one of those coastwise islands we were considering a few moments ago. The position of the GP is constantly changing as the star seems to swing across the heavens in its diurnal motion, but the *Nautical Almanac* annually lists the coördinates of GHA and declination of all the principal stars useful in navigation and the sun, moon, and planets, for any day throughout the year and shows how to derive the positions for a particular hour.

By reference to navigation diagram *d*, note that the zenith distance is equal to the angle *z*, formed at the earth's center by a line to the zenith and a line to the star. Moreover, it is seen that the angle *z* represents the angular distance from the ship to the star's GP. Thus, by subtracting the altitude of the star over the horizon from 90°, we obtain the zenith distance and also the angular measurement of the distance from the ship to the GP.

The importance of this latter fact is immediately obvious when we realize that one minute of arc on the earth's surface equals one nautical mile; for if the reading of altitude is subtracted from 90° and changed to minutes of arc, the answer is the distance from ship to GP in nautical miles.

For instance, if the observed altitude of the star were 50°, we should have $90° - 50° = 40°$. Then $40 \times 60' = 2400'$, or 2400 miles from the GP.

This, however, is pure theory. The navigator's problem is made more difficult by the fact that he is dealing with great distances. The natural distortion of maps, which represent a rounded surface on flat paper, makes it impractical for him simply to draw his circles and let it go at that —and consequently, in actual practice, he has to resort to "lines of position", which, for his purposes, are essentially the same as arcs of a large circle.

There are several methods by which he might obtain his position through astronomical observations. He might "shoot the sun" when it passes the meridian—that is, he might measure the sun's altitude with a sextant when that body is exactly at transit and, by means of a simple calculation, obtain the latitude. Or he might make observations on Polaris, if that star were visible. For longitude, he might make altitude readings on stars, planets, and other celestial objects when they were near the prime vertical. By such means, the latitude and longitude could be calculated separately.

These procedures, however, have been largely left for high-precision work with the better instruments at observatories. The modern way at sea is to use "Sumner lines" or "lines of position", with which the navigator can establish his position (known as a "fix") in both latitude and longitude. The present method, originally used by Capt. Thomas H. Sumner, was improved by Marc Saint-Hilaire.

To develop this method, the navigator refers to the position of his vessel as derived by the dead-reckoning procedure. This is sufficiently close to the actual location of the ship—especially if the procedure has not been relied upon too long—so that it furnishes a suitable starting-point for the navigator.

The problem of the navigator at sea, then, is similar in principle to the problem we faced when we were in a small boat measuring distances and directions from islands, except that the navigator, since he is using the GP of a star as his island, must go through a more complicated procedure.

Having selected the star, he "shoots" it with his sextant; that is, he uses an extremely accurate angle-measuring device to determine the altitude of the star above the horizon. This is the most difficult part of the process of celestial navigation.

As he does so, he makes a note of the exact time of the observation, in terms of Greenwich civil time (G.C.T). All data in the *Nautical Almanac* are recorded in G.C.T, and ships' chronometers, set to this time-standard, are constantly checked by radio so that corrections for loss or gain by the timepiece can be made.

With the correct G.C.T of observation, it is an easy matter for the navigator to refer to the *Nautical Almanac* to learn the position of the star's GP at the instant the observation was made, and once he has this knowledge he is in somewhat the same situation as we when we first sighted our island along the coast. He has seen his "island", he knows where it is located, but he has yet to measure his distance from it.

To understand how this is done, we look for help to the diagram d, in which the ship, the star, the GP, the horizon, and the zenith are represented. We also have the angle h, which represents the altitude of the star and is obtained from the sextant reading; and the zenith distance, which represents the angular measure of the star from the zenith. The value of the zenith distance may be obtained by subtracting the star's altitude from 90°; naturally one could not measure the zenith distance directly.

He chooses on his charts a point within, say, 40 miles of his dead-reckoning position (and which meets certain qualifications) and designates that spot as assumed point AP. With this position on his plotting sheet as a center, he selects a star and, using a protractor, marks off the number of degrees in its computed azimuth at AP, as obtained from the tables.

That azimuth gives him the bearing from AP to the star's GP. To enter it on his chart, he draws a line from AP at the proper azimuth-angle. If he had chosen Sirius as his observation star, the navigator would designate this line as "to Sirius".

Having noted the observed altitude of the star, together with the exact instant of observation, he next turns to his navigation tables and finds there the computed altitude for Sirius at that time for the assumed point AP. He then subtracts one from the other to determine the difference between them.

If the observed altitude were greater than the computed altitude, he would know that his ship's position was nearer to the GP than the assumed position AP. If the observed altitude were less, then the true position would be further from the GP than the assumed position.

Supposing it were greater, the navigator would lay off

along the Sirius line, from the AP *toward* the star, the number of minutes (= nautical miles) of this difference and at the point indicated would draw a line (the Sumner line) at right angles to the Sirius—or azimuth—line. If the observed altitude were less than the computed altitude, he would lay off, as the intercept, the number of minutes from the AP *away from* the star and draw the Sumner line as before.

The Sirius line has the same value as the radius of a circle based on the GP of the star, and the new line drawn at right angles to it—the "line of position"—is for all practical purposes equal to an arc of a great circle.

Hence, the navigator has in effect drawn one arc of a circle marking his distance from the GP, just as we did with our islands offshore. All that is now required is to repeat the procedure on a second star, and the intersection of the two position lines will show the location of the ship— just as the intersection of our two circles showed our posi- tion when we were dealing with the coastwise islands.

In actual practice, the operation boils down simply to observing the altitude of the star and comparing it with the computed altitude (from the tables) to obtain the distance in minutes of arc (or miles) of the ship from the assumed point AP. The Sumner line is then drawn, after which the process is repeated. Ideally, the second observation for altitude—on a different heavenly body—is made on an object about 90° in azimuth from the first star, planet, etc. In this manner a more accurate fix is obtained than other- wise; for if two lines of position cross at right angles, an error in one will make a lesser error in the result.

We remarked earlier that the government, in publishing certain volumes of tabular material, has enabled the mariner to do his work without recourse to knowledge of trigonometry or other mathematics than simple addi- tion and subtraction and the most obvious sort of geometry. But, in avoiding these added computations, we must make

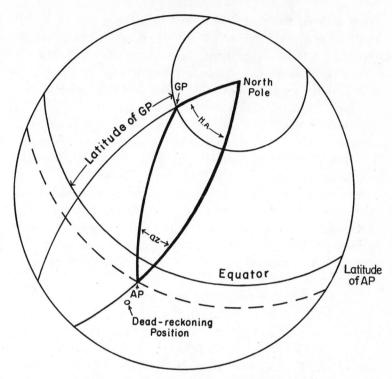

POSITION BY SPHERICAL TRIGONOMETRY

certain concessions to the published tables, and that is why there are qualifications governing our selection of assumed point AP in the foregoing process of determining position lines.

It would be possible to compute the distance and bearing from the star's GP to AP by use of the "astronomical triangle", which is illustrated in the accompanying diagram. The distance from north pole to equator is 90°; thus, as the cut shows, the distance of the GP from the north pole is 90° minus the latitude of the GP. Also, the distance of AP from the north pole is 90° plus the latitude of AP (because in this case latitude represents distance south of the equator).

The hour-angle, indicated as the angle H.A. in the dia-

gram, is equal to the difference between the longitude of AP
and that of the GP. Since we know two sides of the triangle
and the angle between them, we could compute the length
of the third side—the distance from the AP to the GP—
and also the bearing between them, az (azimuth) in the
diagram, by employing spherical trigonometry.

But that work has already been done for us, and the
answers to the problem are in the books of tables for many
different positions of the GP and AP. The tables, though,
cannot cover every conceivable point on the earth's surface.

And we, if we wish to avoid the employment of spherical
trigonometry, want to select a position for AP that will
enable us to find the answer in the tables. Since the tables
list every full degree from the equator to 80°, we select the
nearest full degree of latitude to the dead-reckoning position and place AP upon it.

The difference in longitude between the GP and AP is
also set forth in the table in whole degrees, and so we select
such a longitude for AP as will give a whole degree for the
hour-angle, for simplicity in taking values out of the table.
One of the tables—known as H.O. 211—is so made that
actual dead-reckoning positions may be used.

The entire operation, related in detail and with the
reasons for each step described in progression, may seem
complicated. Actually, though, it boils down to these steps:

1. Select an assumed position for the ship, based on dead-
reckoning or determined by other means.

2. Select a star or other celestial object and observe its
altitude; note the time.

3. From published data, obtain the azimuth (bearing) of
the star (= bearing of the star's GP) and the computed
altitude for the star at the assumed position.

4. Compare the observed and computed altitudes and
mark off in a certain direction along the bearing line through
the assumed position the difference in minutes of arc

(nautical miles). At that point, draw a line of position for the ship, at right angles to the bearing.

5. Repeat on a second star, and find the ship's position at the intersection of the two Sumner lines.

And that is the story of navigation by the stars—in theory, and according to one of the several variations of method. Navigation by the sun is similar in principle, but less accurate. Actually a special case of navigation by the stars, it is complicated by the fact that there is only one sun in the sky. Consequently, the navigator, in order to obtain two GP's, must shoot the sun once, wait until it has moved across the heavens, and shoot it again.

However, since his first line of position would be too far from the sun to be of any use, he must advance it constantly across his chart while waiting to make his second observation. This, naturally, introduces a source of inaccuracy, and the large diameter of the sun also makes it difficult to obtain an accurate sextant reading.

Navigation for aircraft is also based on the same theory as navigation at sea, but it must take into consideration many problems that are peculiar to flight, such as the rapid speed of the plane and its altitude above the earth's surface. The air navigator employs a special type of sextant and the *Air Almanac*, a simplified form of the *Nautical Almanac*, but he still relies upon the same principles as the mariner— still brings the stars down to earth and uses them as islands on which to judge his distance.

In practice, the operations described require less time than it takes to tell, but learning how to perform them calls for considerably more. For our exposition, we have assumed the taking of corrected and accurate sextant readings. Merely to operate such an instrument accurately calls for constant practice and improvement of technique, for the slightest error in reading angles with this instrument is reflected in a ship's position that is miles from its true location. Greenwich civil time, also, must be highly accurate, and the chronometer constantly corrected.

We have, of course, deliberately avoided some of the technical terms and concepts that might be introduced into this discussion but that, we feel, would prolong it and complicate it far beyond the requirements of the moment. It is not our intention, in this volume, to duplicate the fine works on navigation that have already been published, nor to enable our reader to set out over the sea; rather, we have tried to acquaint him with the basic methods and the theory involved, so that he may have some understanding of the art of navigation.

For the reader whose interest has been whetted and who may have a practical purpose in familiarizing himself with the use of the sextant and of the tables in the *Nautical Almanac*, we suggest the following: Bradley, A. D., *Mathematics of Air and Marine Navigation*, American Book Company, New York, 1942; Dutton, B., *Navigation and Nautical Astronomy*, U. S. Naval Institute, Annapolis, 1948; Lyon, Thoburn C., *Practical Air Navigation*, Government Printing Office, Washington, D.C., 1940; Bowditch, *American Practical Navigator*, Government Printing Office, Washington D.C.; Mefferd, Gerry, *The Cruising Manual*, McGraw-Hill Book Company, Inc., New York, 1941.

19

Photography of the Heavens

Some of the most beautiful pictures ever made are of celestial objects. Modern photographs of the Horsehead Nebula and the Lagoon Nebula, comets, meteors—all elicit feelings of wonder. The very spectacular photos commonly are made with great telescopes at large observatories, with elaborate and expensive equipment, equatorial mountings driven by clockwork, and "guided" by most experienced astro-photo workers. Such pictures are made primarily for research and used incidentally for book illustrations. Parts of long-exposure negatives made in the observatory show details that no human eye can ever see in even the greatest of existing telescopes, typically the delicate spiral structure of nebulae.

Astro-photography is a special adaptation of ordinary photography. There are two main functions. The first is to record structural details in heavenly objects. For this purpose great light-gathering power of lens or mirror of telescope is essential, together with long exposures where the light "piles up" an image by the cumulative effect of time and photo-chemical action. The second purpose is to derive exact positions of comets, planets, asteroids, and other moving objects of this type, and even of stars. These are essential to astronomy, for with this data celestial mechanicians can compute orbits. For this purpose photography is ordinarily used.

The Fixed Camera

The reader can make some photographs even with inexpensive equipment, and such pictures will be pleasing as well as enjoyable to make. Of the three types of celestial photography the first method uses a fixed camera with no mounting; and with this trails, conjunctions, and other simple phenomena are recorded. Stellar trails give an exceedingly neat demonstration of the diurnal movement of objects on the celestial sphere as produced directly by the earth's rotation. Trails are, in fact, more interesting than one might think, because it is more difficult to get a good negative of trails than one might suppose.

As the earth turns on its axis, it carries the observer and his camera with it, while the stars actually stand still forming lines of light on the plate. The camera is pointed toward the desired region of the sky, is very firmly propped; and is not by any means jarred during the long exposure. The trails will be arcs on the negative covering 15° for each sidereal hour of exposure.

While it is true the camera may be pointed to equatorial stars, or any region, the most interesting phase of star-trail photography is the circumpolar region where the celestial pole is in the center of the picture. The arcs are concentric with the real, invisible celestial pole in the center of the arcs. If a camera having ground-glass be used, focus on Polaris with a magnifier. In any case centering and focusing should be done carefully. Under certain atmospheric conditions, dew forms on the lens and must be wiped off at intervals. Extremely cautious use of a flashlight at an acute angle helps with this.

The camera shutter should be opened to the widest aperture at which sufficiently good definition is obtained. A fast plate or film is used, to record the greatest number of stars, and development can be carried for contrast. It is a mistake to believe that longer exposures in this type

VENUS AND THE MOON

As Venus and the moon sink toward the western horizon, an amateur astronomer opens his camera. The earth turns, the planet and the satellite trail on the plate, and this interesting view results. (*Photograph by Robert Fleischer.*)

of work will bring out many more stars than shorter ones. The object is theoretically moving during exposure so that it does not have time to accumulate intensity. Moreover, with single points of light, it is the size of lens aperture that governs the faintness of star seen. For circumpolar trails, the most desirable exposure is about 2 to 4 hours.

The trails become nearly straight lines when the camera is directed onto the equatorial sky areas. Here we center on a bright region, such as Orion, and expose, say, $\frac{1}{2}$ hour. The star group reproduces its natural configuration, only showing "movement".

The developed circumpolar negative shows that Polaris is not at the north celestial pole, but that this star itself moves in a little arc around the pole. Indeed a good negative

[273]

IT'S ALL OVER!

Venus, emerging from behind dark limb of moon after occultation. An exposure of 1 second was made every 5 minutes. Photograph was made without using any type of mounting or telescope. Carl Zeiss Apo-Tessar at f 9. Camera placed directly on roof of building. (*By Hugh S. Rice.*)

made with a sufficiently long-focus lens shows many stars between the north star and the pole.

There is one other case where a fixed camera with no equatorial mount, and with no telescope in connection with it, can be effective in astro-photo work. Planet conjunctions and occultations can be recorded in the case of the bright planets if a fast enough lens be used (always with a fast plate), or if particularly good technical work be done; for a slow lens can achieve results (see illustration of Venus at occultation). If the lens is sufficiently good in quality, combined with precise focusing and perfect "register" and also a fast, fine-grain plate, a good enlargement can be made. Add to this, that the focus of the lens should be as long as possible, for the original size of the image is so small that a considerable enlargement of the negative is necessary. If the exposure is too short, too faint an image results, and if too long, the diurnal motion causes a trail instead of a point. The brighter planets can be photographed in 1 second with the fastest plates and 1-inch aperture.

It becomes obvious that the best photo work with the heavens is done with cameras having a ground-glass with which to focus. Pictures can, however, be made with roll-film cameras and instruments that by focusing scale can be set on "infinity"; although nothing can excel plates for such work, and the holders should be carefully checked for register. Certain types of pictures can be made with a miniature camera, but in general, a $3\frac{1}{4} \times 4\frac{1}{4}$ plate or 4×5, with a lens not shorter than 8 inches (and preferably longer), is best to secure as large an image as possible.

With the Telescope

There are two general kinds of telescope mountings—the altazimuth and the equatorial. The former is a simple affair, but time exposures cannot be made with it, and need not be attempted. Yet exposures of about $\frac{1}{2}$ second on the moon or sun may be attempted, and it is only on account of the short exposure that an altazimuth can be used at all.

At the ocular (eyepiece) end of a telescope of 3 inches or more, we mount a small camera rigidly so that its axis is precisely in line with the telescope and looking through it. A board extending along the telescope tube supports the camera, or metal strips may be arranged instead. The entire camera need not be used, but rather we may institute a light plate-holder back (as described by King or Waters).

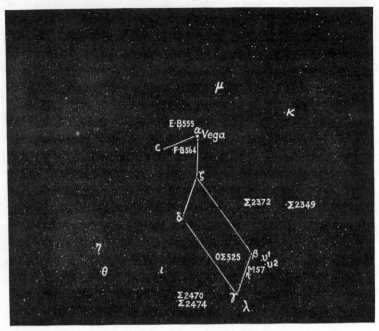

THE CONSTELLATION LYRA—

Photographed with a small Graflex mounted on an excellent 12-inch equatorial refractor. The camera was carefully guided both by hand and by electric drive to follow the stars in their diurnal movement. Exposure 20 minutes, f 5, Zeiss Tessar lens. Features of interest within the star group are indicated.

There are several methods of handling the optics, and it is interesting to try them all.

The first, simplest, and in general the best method is to remove the ocular and the camera lens, so using the objective or mirror of the telescope as the only optical element and effectually making a camera lens out of the telescope lens or mirror. The image is now thrown directly onto the ground-glass and focused with magnifier. Distance between lens and ground-glass is the focal length of the telescope. Of the three methods we describe, this one gives the smallest images and the sharpest, because the optical system is the simplest.

In the second method of celestial photography with telescope but preferably with an equatorial, we put an ocular on the telescope and by racking out somewhat, project the image onto the ground-glass of the camera; this is the method of showing sun-spots on a screen (see Sun chapter), only a photographic emulsion takes the place of the screen. The image is considerably larger by this method, the size depending for one thing upon the eyepiece used. Consequently, greater care and technique are required for good results. Larger images need more exposure: as the size of the same image is doubled, the area is increased by four, and four times as much exposure time is required.

A third method entails the use of the telescope entire, and the camera also, but using the regular camera lens. There should be about an inch between the ocular and the camera lens. This method likewise gives large images and is more adapted to the equatorial mounting than the altazimuth. Considerable care will have to be exercised to obtain sharp images and hold them in the center when exposing. The focus of the camera is at infinity.

One of the easiest and most interesting objects with which to begin our photography of the heavens is the moon. Short exposures of the moon can be made without guiding, but if they are much over $\frac{1}{2}$ second, movement due to earth rotation blurs the picture. Lunar maria, mountain-walled plains, mountain ranges, and various selenographic details all can be faithfully reproduced. Panchromatic emulsions must be used here and for practically all negative-making in astro-photo work. There is enough light that medium-speed plates can be used for the moon in most of the work. A brand should be used that gives very fine grain and good resolving power of image. Exposures over $\frac{1}{2}$ second are made with the equatorial mount, by using the driving mechanism, or else guiding by hand.

With small telescopes the diameter of the moon's image on the plate is as follows: focal length of telescope 45 inches, moon diameter 0.4 inch; focus 60 inches, 0.54 inch; focus 78 inches, 0.7 inch. A lot of experimenting will result in some good negatives which should stand enlargement of a few diameters. We should, then, aim for definition, color value, correct exposure, and development. Lack of red-sensitivity in the plates leads to the "seas" being represented too dark. Also overdevelopment leads to harshness of contrast with accompanying darkness of the maria. The lighting on the moon to us is uneven on all but the full phase so that the values in high light and terminator are difficult to reproduce in one print. Sometimes the negative can be printed by shading parts of it while printing, but the photograph should not be tampered with so much that unfaithful tones are recorded.

Aside from reproducing the lunar topography, there is the question of the varying size of the moon, which can be shown as it goes nearer to or farther away from us during the lunar month. Then there is the libration phenomenon that can be recorded by the objects visible or not at the limb. Mare Smythii, for example, may or may not be seen at any given time, as explained in the lunar chapter.

At full-moon times, our satellite is far brighter than at other phases, so the crescent phases need very much more exposure. Experiment, recording data. Of course at full-moon we can get a complete record of the maria in one picture. Also at this time the rays stand out most prominently. But in general, the full moon does not offer the multitude of topographic detail that the quarter and gibbous phases do. Very interesting are the narrow crescent phases including the earthshine phenomenon, but turbulence in the atmosphere when the moon is low over the horizon tends to blur the image.

Lunar eclipses are suited to photography, so that a plate can be made with multiple images, showing the moon every 5 minutes. Various phenomena differ from eclipse to eclipse, and no one can forecast some of the differences. Not infrequently surprizes more than reward the observer for his efforts at astro-photo work.

Photos of the sun are made in the same way by shorter exposures and a cutting down of the objective or mirror by a diaphragm in the form of a ring placed over the lens or mirror. Also, slow plates can be used.

When photographing through the telescope, we may guide by means of the finder, using a high magnification and cross-hairs at right angles so that a star or other object in the field may be held precisely at the intersection. The guiding will likely prove the most tedious and difficult part of the work, but it helps to produce fine negatives.

With the Astro-camera

A third general type of celestial photography is that of the astro-camera mounted on an equatorial telescope. This gives constellations, star fields, small-scale comet views, etc. With the equatorial mount we can follow the stars in diurnal motion and thus give long exposures. It is imperative for photographing to have the mounting accurately adjusted and free of vibration, with smoothly working mechanical parts. The image once centered stays there as long as we either guide or else set in motion the driving clock, which does the "following" automatically. The driving clock alone is sufficient for short exposures, but for long ones, one must counteract irregularities in the mechanism by guiding by hand with the slow-motion screws.

In making an astro-camera at home, we simply mount the camera on the telescope tube and parallel to it, and guide visually through the telescope under high magnification. A graflex-type or other plate (or cut-film) camera is very good for this work, although any plate camera will do, the important feature being the lens. Also it needs an equatorial mounting, but in these days of extensive amateur telescope-making, such mountings are not difficult to procure from telescope-makers.

ORION

The constellation of Orion, as photographed with an astro-camera on an equatorial mounting. On the original, hundreds of faint stars can be seen, and about the same result can be achieved by amateurs. (*Harvard College Observatory*.)

As to the lens, the wider the actual diameter (rather than its "f-value" or ratio of diameter to focal length), the more the efficiency in photographing faint stars. The ultra-rapid lens for most work is not the best, because the focal length is short, giving small images. Sometimes a good lens of the older "portrait" type is found which is very satisfactory. The central definition is good and the aperture is large. If it covers a wide enough field of view sharply, it may be suitable. The anastigmat is a better type. The very best lenses of the kinds used in general photography are the specially highly corrected lenses known as *apochromats*, although they are expensive, especially in wide actual apertures. Special lenses for astronomical work are better yet. They too are apochromats. One of the finest is the Carl Zeiss astro-fünflinser; another the Ross-Fecker lens; but as these are expensive, the best we can do is to use an anastigmat of good quality.

Fainter stellar objects than the eye can see can be photographed in a few minutes with proper guiding. Naturally there should be cross-hairs made of fine wire in the telescope ocular used for the guiding. Comets offer a very interesting field. In addition to their diurnal motion in the sky they show also a "proper motion" or drift with respect to the stars, so that the comet head should be held with precision on the cross-hairs during every moment of the exposure. Experience shows what exposures are needed for various plates and different degrees of brightness.

Both refractors and reflectors have their advantages. For refractors we have a larger field of view covered sharply in the photograph, but the reflectors possess the advantage of greater illumination (f-value to photographers) and a better color correction.

There is not a large volume of modern special literature on astro-photographic topics. H. H. Waters, *Astronomical Photography for Amateurs*, London, 1921, is still quite good. The best advanced work at present is E. S. King, *Manual of Celestial Photography.* In King's book an excellent photographic method is given for adjusting and setting an equatorial telescope to make its polar axis exactly parallel to the earth's axis. The work is authoritative, and many excellent references on the subject are given. In our Appendix V, some hints on specific photo topics are given.

Advanced workers should obtain from the Eastman Kodak Company, Rochester, N. Y., the latest edition of *Photographic Plates for Scientific and Technical Use.*

20

Use of the Telescope

THE first really good view of a heavenly body in a telescope is illuminating and often entrancing. A new universe is unfolded, opening the door to celestial vistas that lift us above the mundane and the commonplace in which we dwell. Until you try it, you are simply missing one of the finest inspirations in science.

The Milky Way—to the naked eye but a broad band of light—is in the telescope resolved into myriads of sparkling stars, some colored, some forming curious configurations, and is resplendent with double and multiple stars, with glorious star clusters, hazy nebulae that are outer universes in themselves. Then there are various planets, each with its unique set of physical conditions different from the earth's, the many moons, innumerable asteroids, the periodic comets. The telescope is the only means by which we can even begin to grasp the significance of the vast universe of which the earth is but a small fragment.

Even a field-glass is somewhat better than the naked eye; a pair of prism binoculars is better yet; while to get the most out of astronomy, a telescope is an essential instrument. A field-glass is really a low-powered simple binocular with straight, short telescope tubes, and magnification 3 to 6 diameters. Prism binoculars are more expensive and much finer. One needs a magnification of 10 to 20 diameters to begin to do astronomical work, which involves either high-power binoculars or a 2-inch glass. A 3- to 4-inch telescope is necessary for getting much of a start in sky observations.

Two chief functions of a telescope are to gather more light than the unaided eye and to magnify the view. For the latter we always consider linear magnification and not areal. To test roughly the magnification of a telescope, focus it on a distant sign and with one eye examine the sign and with the other look along the outside of the tube; if now the letters of the sign in the glass are, say, 20 times the length of the letters seen with the eye alone, we say the instrument has a magnification of 20 diameters.

Telescopes are of two general types, the refractor and the reflector. The former is a glorified spy-glass except that it produces an upside-down image, which is no disadvantage in astronomy, and minimizes loss of light from absorption by lenses. In a refractor the large lens or objective collects the light and forms an image in the air near the eye end of the instrument. The image is then magnified by an ocular (eyepiece), and by our selection of an eyepiece of the proper focal length, different magnifications become available according to the purpose and the observing conditions.

With a reflector there is no objective, the light from a distant object being collected and brought to a focus by a concave mirror. By reflection from a prism or a small plane mirror, the light rays are sent to the side of the tube, where they are magnified and examined with the ocular. There are modifications from this simple type, but all utilize much the same principle.

When the question of the type of telescope comes up, it is well to remember that refracting telescopes are superior to reflectors in certain respects. They are much less liable to damage from handling or neglect, and they offer a wider field of view and better definition. Further, they are always more nearly ready for instant use than reflectors. Reflectors are much cheaper, taken aperture for aperture, but it is necessary to resilver reflector mirrors every few weeks or months, depending on local atmospheric conditions—a very troublesome process at best—unless one has the mirror *aluminized* at a laboratory specializing in this process. So while the initial cost is greater for a refractor, it obviates this perpetual annoyance of reconditioning the mirror, or if not that at least the frequent centering of prism, mirror, etc.

To summarize the chief advantages of a reflector, we would list cheaper price for the same aperture, at least if home made; larger aperture for the same size of instrument (for the aperture ratio is greater); and color-correct qualities, always useful in noting colors of double stars and sometimes for lunar topography and planet detail. The second factor gives us the advantage of better photography of faint detail, as in nebulae, although not as large a field is covered as in refractors.

Ordinarily, it is the refractor type that is on sale at the market. Reflectors are usually home-made instruments, but the art of telescope-making is now so well developed that excellent instruments can be purchased. In selecting a telescope, it is preferable to get a smaller aperture with good lens and mounting rather than a larger telescope with an unsteady mount or poor lens. Perhaps one-half of the entire value of the telescope is in the mounting. A long tube has a tendency to vibrate, but a good rigid mounting will minimize vibration. Invariably, excessive vibration of the tube makes the stellar image "dance" and is ruinous to observation.

In acquiring a telescope, it is utterly useless to purchase one of the really cheap kind—the type with a very light and unsteady mounting. No good objective can be offered new at a very low price, and the defining power of such a lens is often so poor that no satisfaction is possible. Besides this the mounting *must* have a certain rigidity, or else when a breeze comes up or when the tube is touched ever so lightly, the tube will take on tremors which become magnified when we do observing, and nothing can be done until the image becomes quiet. With a very bad mounting the image almost never is quiet enough.

As to prices of new telescopes, obviously exact prices cannot conveniently be given, for they depend chiefly upon the make, also choice of accessories, and for foreign instruments, upon the rate of exchange. However, a good 3-inch American altazimuth telescope (refractor) costs in the neighborhood of $300, and an equatorial of this size, about $400. A 6-inch reflector professionally made, with circles and equatorial, costs about $350, while a home-made mirror telescope can be constructed for about one-third of this. However, a really excellent and well-tried second-hand instrument can be picked up at times for a reasonable sum.

What the prospective buyer of a telescope should do is to have an expert telescopist test out either the new or the second-hand objective (or the mirror) before completing the purchase. We have encountered new apochromatic objectives even from the best manufacturers, that proved to be defective (by accident, having suffered jar perhaps or maladjustment); similarly we have found objectives of exquisite qualities hidden in an obscure telescope tube and outfit. And one *cannot* properly test an objective by the use of a daylight object; it should be a single point of light, either a real star or an artificial one.

The simplest telescope mounting is the altazimuth type, the commonest kind found in small instruments. In the least desirable forms, it consists of nothing more than a universal joint that allows movement in any direction but seldom has the necessary rigidity. An improvement on this is the forked support for the tube, which has greater firmness and allows motion in either altitude or azimuth.

The greatest drawback of the altazimuth mounting lies in the fact that, as the earth rotates, the star moves out of the field of view, and the telescope must be moved in two directions or their resultant to follow it. With the altazimuth mount, this following of a star cannot be done easily by hand or mechanically by clockwork or motor, and consequently observatories and many private astronomers have their instruments set on an equatorial mounting.

The equatorial is unquestionably the best type, and the only kind feasible for serious observing and for astro-photography. These are more costly to buy or to have constructed, but many amateurs have made their own with crude materials and found them entirely practicable.

The equatorial mounting consists of a polar axis and a declination axis. The polar axis is adjusted so that it is parallel to the earth's axis and points exactly toward the celestial pole. Its inclination to the horizontal, of course, is precisely equal to the latitude of the station. In the finished instruments of the observatory, and of professional manufacture, the polar axis has attached to it a graduated circle known as the *hour circle*, on which are marked hours and fractions thereof. The declination axis, at right angles to the polar axis, carries the *declination circle*, graduated in degrees, and also a counterweight that balances the weight of the telescope.

The telescope tube itself is attached to one end of the declination axis, while the polar axis rests firmly (in a manner that permits rotation) on the tripod or pier which supports the entire instrument, as the accompanying diagram shows.

The advantages of the equatorial mounting are great. For one thing, when an object is in the field of view, it can be kept there by only one movement of the telescope—in hour-angle. The declination axis is not touched, and the telescope is only rotated in hour-angle, in a direction opposite to that of the earth's rotation. It can be done by hand, or by means of a driving mechanism that will do it automatically and allow greater freedom for the observer.

With this method photographs of long duration can be made, for the counter-motion about the polar axis offsets

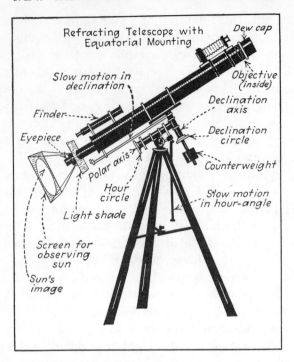

Refracting Telescope with
Equatorial Mounting

Dew cap

Slow motion in
declination

Objective
(inside)

Finder

Declination
axis

Eyepiece

Declination
circle

Polar axis

Counterweight

Hour
circle

Slow motion
in hour-angle

Light shade

Screen for
observing
sun

Sun's
image

the rotation of the earth and keeps the object centered in
the telescope field. Additional guiding, though, is needed
for good photographs, and this is a manual process requiring
considerable practice. *Photographs cannot be made with the
altazimuth mount,* for the star images take on a "skewed"
appearance.

The other principal advantage of an equatorial is that an
invisible object can be easily located simply by setting the
circles to the hour-angle and declination of the object. For
this we need three things: the sidereal time at the moment,
the right ascension, and the declination. Sidereal time is
read from a clock, but to set the clock it is necessary to
make computations (see Appendix IV). The right ascension
and the declination of the object are known. In the case of
stars they are taken from the nautical almanacs (if fairly

bright stars) or from star atlases; or if faint stars, from star catalogs. Nebulae and star clusters have their places recorded in atlases, also catalogs like Dreyer's *New General Catalogue*. Faint planets and the asteroids have their coördinates in nautical almanacs and special publications; while ephemeral objects like comets are found in various astronomical magazines and bulletins, like the *Harvard Announcement Cards*.

Having the sidereal time and right ascension, we use these to find the hour-angle, according to the formula

$$t - R.A. = h.a.$$

where t is the sidereal time, $R.A.$ the right ascension, and $h.a.$ the hour-angle. We set off the hour-angle on the hour-circle of the mounting and start the driving clock at once. This hour-angle measures the angle of view away from the meridian. Next, the declination is set off on the declination circle of the mounting.

When the telescope is adjusted to the hour-angle and declination the object will be near the middle of the field of view. Here is where the finder helps, in showing on a small scale the configuration of stars involved. In the main telescope tube, it is usually best to use first a low-power ocular to pick up the image. In the case of an asteroid, faint satellite, etc., with image of stellar appearance, it may be necessary to make a plotting on a star chart, in order to distinguish the image from a star. Once an object is in the middle of the field of view, as long as the driving clock is running, the object will stay there, as the telescope is now following the stars in their diurnal motion. If the mounting has no driving clock, the telescope must be guided by hand.

The objective (or mirror) is by far the most valuable part of the telescope, being the most expensive and needing the most protection. The main feature is the aperture, or diameter. The larger the aperture, the more light is gathered, and the fainter the object that can be viewed. The word "power" is a loose term and is specifically used to refer to magnification, not to light-gathering power. Magnifying power of a given objective varies with the ocular (eyepiece) used, and is found by dividing the focal length of the objective by the focal length of the eyepiece. If we have a $4\frac{1}{4}$-inch (110-mm) refractor and are using an ocular of 18-mm focus, we find the magnification thus. The focal length is stated by the maker, or we find it roughly by experiment by removing the eyepiece and throwing the image of an extremely distant object onto a screen at the eye end, and measuring the distance from the optical center of the lens to the screen. We use the focus of the objective in millimeters (1 inch = 25.4 mm). Suppose our $4\frac{1}{4}$-inch refractor has a focus of 1650 mm: the ocular mentioned would give a magnification of $\frac{1650}{18}$, or 91.6 or 92 times. (This would be one of the best powers to use on such an instrument.)

The greatest magnification obtainable with a given instrument depends upon quality of objective, quality of eyepiece, mounting, state of atmosphere. The combination of the nature of the celestial object and the state of the atmosphere determines the proper power at the moment.

It is a mistake common to most beginners to use high magnification in an effort to distinguish detail. On the contrary, the lowest power that gives the necessary enlargement is to be preferred. According to the state of the atmosphere at the time and the quality of objective or mirror, we can magnify only to a certain point, beyond which the image is not clear or is too hard to keep in the field on account perhaps of tremors due to wind. Even under the best conditions we do not always want highest magnification, as, for example, in viewing a large region on the moon or in examining sun-spots, or again in looking at double stars like Albireo or Mizar. Thus, with a given state of air and quality of lens or mirror, each object itself has in general its own power needed.

Experienced observers are found to use, for most work, a magnification of about 30 to 40 for each inch of aperture. Yet occasionally they use as high as 100 to the inch under ideal conditions and for special work, like very close double stars; and a good lens will stand this power when the atmosphere will allow it. There are cases, like sweeping for comets, when a power of only about 5 to the inch is used, in order to get the widest field of view possible.

There is some color in the objects and phenomena of the heavens, notably in planets, some stars, and eclipses. When this is an important matter to us, we should use either a highly corrected objective in our refractor, or else use a reflector. An objective should be as free as possible from chromatic aberration, which causes colors to form around a brilliant object. The three-lens "apochromat" lens is superior to all others as a telescope objective. And of course for all colored objects the reflecting telescope cannot be beaten. In making color estimates, it is not safe to judge colors within about 15° of the horizon, for absorption and irregular refraction cause images to exhibit spurious colors.

Irrespective of magnification, the aperture itself of a lens or mirror has certain features we should remember. These are light-gathering power and resolving power. One of the more abstruse optical qualities that concerns the telescope-user is this matter of *resolving power*. Of two telescopes having the same magnifying power at the moment—if they have different apertures of objective or mirror, they will have different abilities to resolve double stars, or to see lunar detail, etc.; one of them may "split" Gamma Andromedae, for instance—show it as two stars— and the other may not. So we say that resolving power is the limit of the ability of an optical system to record fine detail in the object viewed. For any given diameter there is a definite limit to resolving power, set by optical principles, and suffice it to say that this limit depends upon the diameter of the lens or the mirror; the larger the diameter, the greater the resolving power. The following formula may be taken as an average guide:

$$p = \frac{5''.0}{a}$$

where p is the resolving power and a the aperture in inches. Thus a 12-inch mirror will show as two separate stars, a double star whose components are separated by about 0''.4 or more, under good conditions.

There is some variation from the above value on account of the difference in the components of a double star. The value refers to double stars with components of about equal brightness and about sixth magnitude. When the components are fainter or the brightness more unequal, it takes a larger aperture to resolve them than otherwise. The limit we give is exceeded by some telescopes and observers. The full resolving power of any instrument is only attained under perfect atmospheric conditions. Resolving power explains why a more perfect view of the moon or Jupiter is given with large apertures, when the magnification is kept the same.

The faintest star visible in a telescope depends upon several factors. The chief ones are diameter of instrument, clarity of atmosphere, and observer. If we suppose the atmosphere to be of the clearest and the observer's eye of the keenest, we have left the instrument. With any given aperture there is a limit for the faintest possible magnitude of star that can be seen.

From our Appendix VI we find that a twelfth-magnitude star is the faintest one visible in a 4-inch glass. But this means ideal conditions, and we must use high enough magnification in order to bring this about. The larger the telescope the fainter the star, so that aperture is the most important means of getting faint objects. But we must keep in mind that any particular magnitude is brighter or dimmer by $2\frac{1}{2}$ times than a star one magnitude away.

Oculars are a small but important part of the telescope optical equipment. The most important consideration is to choose a good manufacture. Strangely enough, expensive telescopes are sometimes fitted with poor eyepieces that result in low observing efficiency.

Oculars are compound magnifiers, and their function is to magnify the primary image formed by the objective or mirror of the telescope. Their size is marked in focal length. There are several types and the three most useful are the *Huygenian*, the *Kellner*, and the *orthoscopic*. The Huygenian is the simplest and cheapest. There are two plano-convex lenses with their convex sides away from the eye, and the image formed by the objective falls between the lenses. The eye lens is the lens next to the eye, and the field lens is the one toward the objective.

Looking into an eyepiece we find before us a circular field of view. A diameter of this circle subtends an angle always constant with any particular ocular, whether used on the telescope or held in the hand; this angle is the *apparent field of view*. The makers generally state the apparent field for a certain type of eyepiece. The best Huygenian oculars have an apparent field of view of 50°.

The two principal advantages of a Huygens ocular are the cheapness and large apparent field. They are commonly used where low magnification is needed, on account of the poorer optical corrections, and where a wide angle is an advantage.

For telescopes over 3 inches in aperture it is well to have a *finder* attached to the telescope tube. It is a miniature low-power instrument, with which to locate objects before examination with the regular lens. In case there be no finder, an object is first located most easily by use of the lowest power on hand, so that as many of the stars of the region as possible can be included in the field of view. This applies especially to picking up an asteroid whose path has been plotted; in observing a comet whose tail requires a wide field; and for star clusters, many of which extend beyond the field of view except under low power and wide field. The Huygens ocular is the best for such purposes.

Another kind of field of view is the actual angle in the sky that is taken in by a telescope. This *actual field of view* on the sky varies with the magnification: the more we magnify, the smaller the actual field becomes. The actual field is constant with any individual ocular as used with a certain telescope. It depends upon the apparent field of the ocular and the magnification. To get the actual field, divide the apparent field by the magnification.

Suppose we use a $4\frac{1}{4}$-inch refractor of 1650-mm focus. It is well to own one Huygenian of the best manufacture, so that with the above instrument we shall select one of 60-mm focus. We assume the maker gives the apparent field as 50°, or we could determine it by experiment. To get the magnification used with it, we apply the formula F/f as follows: $\frac{1650}{60} = 27\frac{1}{2}$; thus on this instrument, a large 60-mm eyepiece has a power of $27\frac{1}{2}$ diameters. To find the actual field covered on the sky we have $50 \div 27.5 = 1°.8$, so that this eyepiece on our glass will always include 1°.8 of the heavens, which is a comparatively large field and is not often exceeded in telescopes. Finders, however, commonly include larger angles, like binoculars, which are therefore better when a field of 2°.5 or more is needed.

The Kellner ocular (a modification of the Ramsden type) has a single field lens of plano-convex glass with plane side toward the objective, and an eye lens of smaller diameter, made of two cemented lenses. The ocular has better corrections than the Huygens type, but the field of view is smaller, usually 40°. The "field stop," or diaphragm, is in front of the field lens, where the image from the objective comes to a focus. It is well to own a good Kellner for medium magnification. Its corrections and the clarity of the glass give immense satisfaction to the user.

The very finest type of ocular is the orthoscopic. The or-

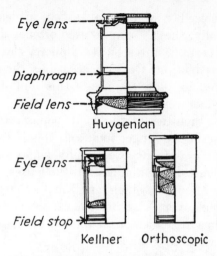

Eye lens

Diaphragm

Field lens

Huygenian

Eye lens

Field stop

Kellner   Orthoscopic

TELESCOPE EYEPIECES

Diagrams of three of the best types of astronomical oculars, the chief parts of each being labeled. Of these, the Huygenian is the simplest and least expensive, and is best adapted to wide angle of view. The 4-lens orthoscopic is the best type made, as it has superior corrections.

thoscopic is a quadruple system; the field lens is a three-lens component, color-corrected, consisting of two outer biconvex (positive) crown lenses and, cemented between them, a biconcave lens of heavy flint glass. And then there is the eye lens, a single plano-convex lens with the plane side next the eye and only a small air space between this lens and the field lens, so that they are nearly in contact.

The optical qualities of the orthoscopic are such as to make it a superb lens. The apparent field of view is 40°. In general, it has the best definition, flatness of field, color correction, and absence from internal reflection ("ghost") and distortion of any ocular. On account of the superior corrections, it is the best eyepiece for high magnification. Nor is there any disadvantage in using it for low magnification —except when a wider field of view is necessary.

Orthoscopics are made in focal lengths from 3^{mm} to 50^{mm}. The 3^{mm} and the 5^{mm} give such high magnification that they can seldom be used to advantage—except in clearest atmosphere. Naturally, the 5^{mm} can be used oftener than the 3^{mm}. However, in certain states of atmosphere, the 3^{mm} can be used with satisfaction. On rare occasions the air is sufficiently tranquil to allow the use of this short-focus ocular even on a $2\frac{7}{8}$-inch refractor.

The optical qualities of the small oculars appear to be equal to those in the longer foci; and this is especially remarkable in view of the exceedingly small size of these complicated lenses. The diameter of the lenses in the 3-mm ocular is only $2^{mm}.5$ or $\frac{3}{32}$ inch, and the diameter of the field stop is not much over 1^{mm}. Until one uses a good orthoscopic eyepiece, he has little idea of the quality of image which the best oculars are able to give.

Let us suppose we wish to equip with eyepieces a 110-mm ($4\frac{1}{4}$-inch) telescope. The focus of the objective is 1650^{mm}. The following would constitute an ideal equipment for such a telescope.

Focus mm	Type of ocular	Magnification
60	Huygenian	27.5
40	Kellner	41
25	Orthoscopic	66
18	Orthoscopic	92
12.5	Orthoscopic	132
9	Orthoscopic	183
7	Orthoscopic	236
5	Orthoscopic	330
3	Orthoscopic	550

The above selection of foci and types are very carefully chosen and are based on extensive experience. Not everyone will desire to have all of the above eyepieces. The magnifications listed apply only to the focal length above. The set of oculars, however, is suited to almost any telescope, of shorter or longer focus. Reflectors generally will not be able to use the longer foci. If the list has to be cut to five oculars, eliminate the two longest and the two shortest. In this case, the 25^{mm} should be a Huygenian, and the 18^{mm} a Kellner. When the telescope is provided with a good finder having a wide field, the long-focus oculars giving lower power are not needed so much as otherwise. It is also possible to be limited at first to two oculars, in which case procure a 25-mm Huygens and a 12.5-mm orthoscopic.

In the case of large telescopes in observatories, in order to obtain low magnification, more oculars on the long-focus end (at the top of the list) are necessary. A long-focus ocular, such as a 60-mm Kellner, used on a medium-sized observatory telescope, say of 16 inches aperture, affords views of the heavens that are absolutely entrancing.

Objectives and eyepieces will last indefinitely if handled with care. Naturally, they are not to be jarred or scratched, and, in order to keep away dust and scratches, no optical surfaces should be left exposed when not in use. The objective cap is always to be kept on while the lens is not in use, and oculars likewise should be covered when not on the telescope and kept either in individual boxes or all of them kept in an ocular box.

A zenith prism is almost an essential piece of equipment for observing objects nearly overhead. It affords greater comfort by directing the image at right angles to the telescope, so that the observer does not look straight through the tube and assume an awkward position for zenith objects. But while the image seen in an astronomical refractor with ordinary eyepiece is turned upside down, it suffers a worse fate when observed with a zenith prism. It is then reversed in such a way that certain objects, say the moon, cannot be compared easily with the charts, and the observer cannot turn the moon chart in any position to coincide with the telescopic view without looking through the back of the paper. When looking straight through a refractor, he simply turns the chart upside down—if indeed it may not already be published so, with north at the bottom, etc. Yet reversals do not matter for some objects, like star clusters.

A *dew-cap* is an extension of the telescope tube beyond the objective. It is not to be confused with the objective cap, which fits snugly over the lens. Some makers provide dew-caps, but most of them do not. The caps are of advantage in two ways. They actually tend to keep the dew from forming on an objective—which is apt to happen under certain conditions of the night air. When dew forms on a lens, the definition of the image is at once ruined, and the moisture must be carefully wiped off with a soft, clean cloth. Another use of the dew-cap is to block off extraneous light that might be entering the objective. The precaution is needed more in the city for bright lights than for dew; in the country it is needed more for dew than for lights.

A dew-cap may be made with cardboard fixed around the end of the telescope tube at the objective end. It should not project far enough to cut off any of the field of view, and this possibility can be ascertained by looking through the telescope from the eye end, with ocular removed. Dew-caps should not be so long as to become visible when looking thus; about 1 foot is right for a 5-inch refractor of 75 inches focus. Inside surfaces of dew-caps are always painted a dull black to absorb stray light.

When using a flashlight to look at the atlas or notes at the telescope, cover it with a red cloth or a few thicknesses of red tissue paper, so that the glare does not affect the dark-adapted eye. After the eye is completely dark-adapted, use only the barest minimum of light in looking at the atlas; otherwise it will again take considerable time to become accustomed to the darkness.

In cleaning lenses, always use the softest tissue or well-worn clean handkerchief and rub gently. Sometimes you will need to moisten the rag with clean water or pure alcohol to clean the lens, but the latter must be wiped dry.

The phenomenon of "averted vision" is useful to apply

in the telescope while observing excessively faint objects like nebulae, comet tails, or anything at the limits of vision. To use averted vision, we direct the eye deliberately a little away from the object under examination; now a strange thing takes place: it is noticed that distinctly more detail against the sky is seen, and often an otherwise hopeless situation can thus be saved. The region of most distinct vision in the human eye lies in the "fovea centralis" (an area in the retina behind the pupil) but the fovea does not lie in the axis of the eye, which is the line-of-sight directed toward the object.

There is a modified form of inverted vision which is of advantage at times. Suppose we have in the telescope field the section of a comet's tail, which is so faint as to be at the limit of vision, and we wish to trace the visible length to note its extent. If while looking at the comet we move the telescope field somewhat, rather fast, causing the image to go from side to side, the faintest possible parts of the tail will stand out against the darker sky, thus becoming visible where they may not have been otherwise. Often one can apply this procedure to faint stars and planets.

Directions in a telescopic field are at first perplexing, and they become more complicated when accessories like the zenith prism are used, and are notoriously so with reflecting telescopes. Subpolar areas of the sky likewise give confusing directions until they are studied. An ordinary astronomical telescope inverts the naked-eye view, turning everything upside down and reversing right for left. It takes additional lenses (or prisms) to form an erected field as in a spy-glass or prism-binoculars, but no erected field is needed in astronomy, so that these additional partial absorbers of light are purposely omitted.

Suppose we are northern observers looking out at the heavens toward the south. If we look straight into an astronomical (inverting) telescope, we find our north direction of the starry field actually at the bottom of the field of view of the instrument, and south at the top. East is at the right and west at the left side, so that the real naked-eye directions are all reversed. If we now institute a zenith prism and look down into it (at right angles to the telescope tube), we find north at the top of the field of view and south at the bottom, but east and west are as before—for we have mirrored the original inverted image—and east in the field is still at the right side, while west in the field is still at the left side, so the directions are somewhat mixed up.

But these conditions are relatively simple and easily understood, while observing near the meridian, that is, facing due south. The complication enters when the telescope is moved off the meridian: now our directions rotate, so that, for example, if we look toward the west point of the horizon, the west-east line in the field of view points directly at the west point and becomes more vertical—indeed would be exactly so if we were at the equator. Complications of direction in a reflecting telescope can be straightened out by viewing the moon and comparing the image with known directions as indicated on a chart of the moon.

Do not expect any of the stars to show discs, no matter how large the telescope or how great the magnification: they are too far away. In fact, it would be well if we could present our readers with the exact idea of how much can be seen in a telescope. It has been faithfully stated that one who has never looked through a telescope has no adequate idea of the wonders of the heavens. This statement is true, yet it is also true that the reader who studies the various specimens of fine celestial photography made with our largest instruments is apt to think he can have the same views in almost any telescope. Consequently he is doomed to a big disappointment; because the usual spectacular photograph has been made with exposure of many hours and so shows detail not even visible to the eye in a large telescope.

Besides this, and the smaller size of the telescope used, the observer is confronted with another condition more or less disconcerting. At the surface of the earth we are living in an ocean of atmosphere which compared to a tranquil, homogeneous fluid, is in a state of greater or lesser turbidity with difference of density and refraction, so that images of distant objects are subject to disturbances; hence the twinkling of stars. Such effects vary from night to night—even from hour to hour—and they are worse with large apertures than with small. The effect, when bad, is known as "boiling" of the air; it is an incessant rippling with all kinds of modification. So the telescope enthusiast should not expect to see the canals of Mars or the delicate spiral structure of certain nebulae on looking into even a large glass. Similarly the lunar mountain-ringed plains under high magnification are seldom as quiet as in their pictures, although outside of these disturbances of image they look more realistic than their pictures. The phenomenon of boiling is connected with temperature changes and convection currents of the air; the effect is greatest down near the horizon.

For good "seeing" conditions we want a tranquil atmosphere, with minimum irregularities. Keep the telescope line-of-sight out of the way of chimneys and other sources of heat. There seems to be no particular season when best seeing is attained, but it depends upon local atmospheric conditions. In the cold of winter-time it is often true that we have many clear skies; then the stars twinkle most and because of the clarity of atmosphere, we can see the faintest stars. But this is not the time for the finest "seeing" as we need a quieter atmosphere, and curiously enough a little mist, smoke, or haze is well known to give steadier images, particularly useful for planet observations.

If too much haze exists, then too many of the fainter stars are blotted out from lack of transparency. Thus, in metropolitan areas, even in a cloudless sky there is notoriously bad "seeing" and fifth- and sixth-magnitude stars which should be visible to the unaided eye seldom are seen at all. For example, we have never yet seen *perfectly* normal

skies from New York City, as we can from many places a
few miles away, with the Milky Way a clear band against
a black sky; although occasionally there are fairly good
nights even in New York, and we have really seen sixth-
magnitude stars here at those exceptional times. Visibility
of magnitude 6 with the unaided eye is usually taken as one
of the tests of a normal sky and a good vision. Sometimes
stars down to magnitude 8 or slightly fainter can be seen
in particularly good locations, like Arizona, Peru, or South
Africa, by eyes that are super-normal, but these conditions
are exceptional.

One method of overcoming some of the worst of bad seeing conditions is to reduce the aperture of the objective or
mirror, by means of a cardboard ring. By making the aperture relatively less compared to the air waves, such a ring
often improves the seeing at the moment. Obviously, one
can tell only by experiment what reduction will enhance
the seeing most, but the method is practicable.

It is to be stressed that bad seeing conditions cannot be
improved by high magnification; indeed, all other things
being equal, use the lowest power that will give the desired
effect.

An exceedingly valuable and detailed book on telescopes
and instruments is J. B. Sidgwick's *Amateur Astronomer's
Handbook*. A companion volume by this author, *Observational Astronomy for Amateurs*, is likewise very superior for
observing celestial objects. These 1955 books are obtainable
from the Hayden Planetarium, New York. They are fairly
advanced and quite comprehensive, and they have extensive bibliographies.

21

Astronomy for the Traveler

No matter where one travels on the earth, there are familiar guide-posts in the sky. As one travels east and west, there is little change overhead except in time. This is described in the chapter on time. As one goes north and south, many changes occur overhead. Sun and stars climb the sky and new ones come into view, or the sun and moon appear lower in the sky as new stars climb into view. These changes are described in the chapter on southern skies. From the position of the stars it is possible to tell your geographic position, and this is described in the chapter on navigation. But there are still other ways in which a traveler can better enjoy his travels by knowing something about the appearance of the sky and the history of astronomy.

In the South Seas, the Polynesian sailor is well worth watching. He navigates the trackless ocean without sextant or radio. He watches birds and cloud formations, but he is largely dependent on the sun and stars. Some of their remarkable feats of sailing are very hard to understand unless you realize that the Polynesians make excellent use of their navigation stars.

In the arctic north, most people are more conscious of the changing altitude of the sun than people of the middle latitudes. To people of Iceland and northern Norway, Sweden and Lapland, Alaska and Siberia the sun's position gives warning of the approach of the long winter night when, for months, only moon and stars and an occasional bright aurora will light the sky. During the night the endlessly circling stars reel off the hours but give scant hint of when the sun will rise again. With the rising sun come the long arctic days when the few hardy crops grow continuously in almost constant sunshine.

The visitor to Spitzbergen and the polar ice or one who crosses Asia on the Trans-Siberian railway has an excellent opportunity to see fine displays of the northern lights. He would doubtless see better displays if he could plan his trip during a period of maximum sun-spots—but his chances are good even at minimum sun-spot occurrence.

The mountain climber or the person crossing the ocean has the best chance to see the zodiacal light—that faint cone of light sometimes visible in the west after sundown or in the east before sunrise. Any time when one has uninterrupted horizon and clear air is also the ideal time to try to see the gegenschein—that phenomenon usually supposed to be a faint reflection of the sun occasionally visible on the opposite side of the ecliptic, or sun's path.

For the traveler there are many things to see not in the sky. There are astronomical buildings, monuments, instruments, and historic sites. There are the works of prehistoric and primitive peoples, the ruins of ancient civilizations, and strange customs of remote people of our own time.

In England one can see the Stonehenge, where early people erected a great stone colonnade from which to watch the sun. Some 90 stones remain today arranged in a circle almost 100 feet across. Three stones, one laid across the top of the other two, make the doorway. The Stonehenge is thought to have been used to mark the time of equinoxes and solstices, for some of the stones are arranged so as to give an exact line-up for these observations. It was probably the scene of many colorful ceremonies. Many mounds, or barrows, as these Stone Age earthworks are called, are associated with Stonehenge. In fact, 160 of them lie within 3 miles of it.

In Mexico there are many astronomical sites. The great pyramid of the sun at Teotihuacán, not far from Mexico City, is especially interesting when you remember that there are 91 steps on each of four sides. When you count the top platform, you have 365—one for each day of the year. In the National Museum the ancient calendar stone recalls the unusual calendar the early people of this area used. On the stone are carved symbols of the 20 days of their short month and the symbols for the 18 regular months of these 20 days, plus a short month of just 5 days to make up the difference. In a remarkable system, which repeated every 52 years, it was possible to place any day of ten thousand or more. The early Mexicans, the Mayans, also had a moon calendar and one based on the phases of Venus. All three calendars are thought to have worked together in an almost unbelievable astronomical and mathematical system. There are records of eclipses on their stone monuments, too. When one sees the fine architecture and art of these people, it is easier to understand their early mastery of some phases of astronomy.

In southern Mexico, in the state of Oaxaca, there is an astronomical observatory at the ruined city of Monte Alban. Recently excavated by the Mexican government, the building has slits and openings for observations and many unusual features. Less elaborate ruins in other parts of the country also have certain features which suggest that they were used as observatories.

In Peru, the early Spanish conquerors discovered wonderful temples to the sun and moon. Prescott in his history describes the large gold and silver discs, representing the sun and moon, that were mounted on the inner walls of these two buildings. Of course, the gold and silver long ago disappeared, but it is a strange and wonderful experience to stand in the massive stone rooms and imagine them with their former rich fittings. And if one is lucky enough to make the arduous trip back into the mountains to the mountaintop city of Machu Pischu, he can see the further evidence of the astronomical interests of these sun worshipers. A huge stone sun-dial crowns the summit of this dramatic and mysterious sky-high ruined city.

In India there are numerous places of astronomical interest—perhaps the most striking is Jaipur. Here a giant sun-dial 100 feet long and almost as high still remains from ancient times. It is a massive and impressive sight. To erect it the labor of many people was required over a long period of time. It is visited today only by the rare traveler who knows of its existence—but there was a day more than one thousand years ago, surely, when observations from it were made frequently and people eagerly observed the shadow's slowly creeping edge.

In Egypt several thousand years ago the great pyramids were erected at Giza near Cairo. It is thought that there may be some astronomical significance in the central shaft down which the light of certain stars may fall at certain times of the year. Of course, to the Egyptians we owe the basic structure of our calendar, for they were the first to reckon the year by the sun's position rather than by the less regular periods measured by the moon.

In China, where eclipses were carefully observed several thousand years ago, there are a number of sites of astronomical importance. Perhaps the most impressive is the Imperial Observatory at Peiping, where there is a fine collection of early instruments. Among the most beautiful are the ancient astrolabes, exquisitely designed and made in bronze.

Historical and archeological sites like these are found in many countries with a rich tradition in early times. But there are many astronomical ideas and practices among modern people that reward the inquiring traveler. There

are unusual customs among the remote people of China and
South America and among the primitive tribes of Africa
and Australia. The American Indian, too, has an interesting
star lore. The accounts of anthropologists who study these
people usually yield unique ideas that have sprung from
their study of the sky or their effort to explain some
celestial phenomenon.

And in the remote outposts of the world are places where
happenings of astronomical importance have taken place.
In Arizona, Siberia, and Estonia are scars on the earth's
surface where meteorites have fallen. The huge crater in
Arizona, nearly a mile across and 500 feet deep, is well
worth a visit. When this fall occurred is not known, but the
fall in Siberia was only about forty years ago. There are
still people living who remember the blinding flash, the
thunderous sounds, and the tremendous vibrations of
the impact of the fall. Although few travelers have visited the
site, photographs have been taken of the area now marked
by numerous water-filled craters and countless fallen trees.
The crater in Estonia is older, and new brush and trees
have already partly disguised the ragged scar. The great
Hoba West, the largest meteorite known, is still in the
ground, near Grootfontein in South-West Africa. Partially
excavated, it is estimated to weigh some 60 tons or more.

Less exciting perhaps, but equally interesting to many
people are observatories where important discoveries have
been made and places where astronomers have gone to make
observations. In the Hudson Bay region important auroral
studies have been made, while eclipse expeditions have
gone to the Andes, South Sea Islands, Brazil, and many
other places.

Capetown, at the southern tip of Africa, is where John
Herschel went over a hundred years ago for his famous
studies of the southern skies. And in Capetown today is
the Royal Observatory of South Africa, founded during
the time of Herschel's studies. In Bloemfontein, South

Africa, there are two important observatories—the southern stations of Harvard College and of the University of Michigan. And at Johannesburg are the southern station of Yale University and the Observatory of the Union of South Africa, founded in 1903. The other stations are about twenty years old.

There are famous observatories with long and eventful histories all along the traveler's route. Not far from London, Greenwich Observatory is the center of time for all the world, for the world time zones begin here. They all refer to Greenwich as the zero, or prime, meridian. There is not a ship at sea or a plane in the air that does not owe its navigating to Greenwich.

The observatory in Paris is distinguished for Cassini's observations of Saturn and other planets, for Antoniadi's observations of Mars, and for the works of other astronomers of note. The Pulkowa Observatory in Russia is famous for the work of Struve, the first of several important astronomers of that name. When Pulkowa was founded, it was the most modern and best equipped observatory in the world.

While Herschel, the discoverer of the planet Uranus, made reflectors as large as 48 inches in diameter, the planet Neptune was found in the 9-inch refractor at the Royal Observatory in Berlin. The planet Pluto, however, was discovered photographically when plates made in the 13-inch camera telescope were examined with the Blink microscope at the Lowell Observatory in Flagstaff, Ariz Flagstaff is known also for Percival Lowell's studies of Mars, as is also the Royal Observatory in Milan, where Schiaparelli carried out his long program of observation of Mars.

The traveler who covers the globe will find many a station along his way where important astronomical programs are carried out. He may visit Sydney, Australia; Wellington, New Zealand; Lembang, Java; Kodaikanal, India; Bondzareak, Algiers; or Stockholm, Vienna, Marseille, Florence,

Versailles, Potsdam, and many other cities. In each he will find observatories making studies of double stars, or clusters, or nebulae, or the sun, or other astronomical phenomena. Astronomers circle the globe. Theirs is a truly universal interest, and they explore the depths of space in stations at the ends of the earth.

The United States is the country where astronomical observatories offer the greatest challenge to the traveler. Most of the world's largest telescopes and the most completely equipped and staffed observatories are now in the United States. California is the state most favored—it has the two largest telescopes. The 200-inch is at Palomar Mountain, the 100-inch and the 60-inch at Mount Wilson, Pasadena. The installation of the gigantic 200-inch telescope was delayed by the Second World War, but the actual operation of this scientific wonder has only recently gotten started. The 100-inch reflector near Pasadena remains one of the world's wonders, and the 60-inch is still among the 10 largest mirrors. The 170-foot vertical solar telescope is also of great interest. And near San Francisco is Lick Observatory with the second largest refracting telescope.

The largest refractor is the 40-inch at Yerkes Observatory at Williams Bay, Wis. It is just one of many instruments at the University of Chicago observatory. The other large reflectors are at Ann Arbor, Mich.; Mount Locke, Tex.; Toronto, Ont., and Victoria, B.C.; Delaware, Ohio; and Oak Ridge, Mass. Reflectors below 60 inches are found at Córdoba, Argentina; Berlin-Babelsburg, Germany; and Melbourne, Australia, as well as at the U. S. Naval Observatory in Washington, D.C., Flagstaff, Ariz., and other places.

Everyone enjoys a visit to an observatory. When the observatory roof opens, like a large eye opening in the night, and then turns like an owl preparing for flight, it is an absorbing experience. When the huge telescope swings noiselessly into position, its several tons of weight moving like a fine watch, the traveler knows it has been well worth a side trip, or a bus ride, or even a long journey. And when he peers into space and sees the landscape of the moon, or the rings of Saturn, or the countless suns in some huge cluster, the traveler is impressed at the same time by the ingenuity of man and his insignificance in the vast and wonderful scale of things.

And so the traveler may find that time, place, and sky conditions make it possible to observe phenomena rarely seen, or he may find along his way some of these places made more interesting when he knows their astronomical history.

Appendix I

The Greek Alphabet

Letter	Name	Letter	Name	Letter	Name
A, α	Alpha	I, ι	Iota	P, ρ	Rho
B, β	Beta	K, κ	Kappa	Σ, σ	Sigma
Γ, γ	Gamma	Λ, λ	Lambda	T, τ	Tau
Δ, δ	Delta	M, μ	Mu	Υ, υ	Upsilon
E, ϵ	Epsilon	N, ν	Nu	Φ, ϕ	Phi
Z, ζ	Zeta	Ξ, ξ	Xi	X, χ	Chi
H, η	Eta	O, o	Omicron	Ψ, ψ	Psi
Θ, θ	Theta	Π, π	Pi	Ω, ω	Omega

Appendix II
The Plotting of Planet Paths

MERCURY and Venus and the other planets in the sun's retinue are always fascinating material for observation, but to study them one must know where they are. Since they change position constantly, the observer must have a map or he must subscribe to one of the periodicals containing regular positions of the planets. But such charts as mentioned can be prepared only for a limited time in advance, and the periodicals may not always be available.

The alternative, then, is for the amateur to construct such maps for himself. Four items are needed: a hard pencil, a good ruler (preferably one measuring millimeters and half-millimeters—like the Keuffel and Esser ruler No. 1460 P), an atlas of the sky—whatever kind is available—and the *American Ephemeris and Nautical Almanac* (published each year by the Naval Observatory, Washington, D. C.) which contains daily planet and sun positions.

Objects are located in the sky by means of two coördinates which correspond respectively to geographic longitude and latitude—their right ascension (distance on the celestial equator from the vernal equinox measured eastward to the star's hour-circle, in hours) and their declination (distance north or south of the celestial equator, in degrees).

The ephemeris gives these positions for the planets, but with far greater accuracy than necessary for the present work; as a result it is advisable to "round out" the numbers given. For example, Mercury's position for January 1, 1952, is given as: right ascension, $17^h6^m56^s.93$; and declination, $-20°21'27''.1$. After the numbers have been simplified, this right ascension becomes 17^h7^m, and the declination, $-20°21'$. But this is for 0^h universal time and would be used for 7 p.m., E.S.T. of December 31, 1949. When the R.A. or Dec. is over 30 seconds, add another minute.

With the position so stated, it is easy to indicate the point on the atlas, and the same procedure should be followed for other positions of the planet at intervals of 5 days for Mercury, 10 or 15 days for Venus, and a month or more for the outer planets. With these points determined, a smooth curve drawn through them shows the planet's apparent path among the stars for a given period. One factor remains to be considered, that of visibility. In drawing your own maps, you will wish to indicate when the planet can be seen. The best criterion for visibility is to determine whether the planet is within about 15° of the sun. If it is outside this purely arbitrary limit, it may be presumed visible. One way to ascertain this is to plot the sun on the same chart.

Neptune, asteroids, and comets below fifth magnitude must be plotted on an atlas with stars to the eighth magnitude and fainter. Only a few atlases are suitable for this; an especially good one for the purpose is the *Stern-Atlas*—a set of charts by Beyer-Graff (Hamburg, 3d ed.) which may be ordered from Stechert-Hafner, Inc., 31 East 10th St., New York 3, N. Y.

All atlases are constructed with stated fixed coördinates for a certain year. But because of precession, the stellar reference points are constantly shifting. This precessional allowance must be accurately computed for telescopic objects (below sixth magnitude). The amount of precessional variation for different regions of the sky appears directly on some charts or in tables accompanying them. According to this, make allowance for the precession and change the given values for the planet position to a new set that fits the chart. (For precession by formula, see end of this appendix.) When this is done you may proceed to plot as with the brighter planets.

Charts of Neptune and the other planets are published

yearly in the *Observer's Handbook of the Royal Astronomical Society of Canada* (252 College Street, Toronto, Ontario). Planet charts appear in the *Handbook of the British Astronomical Association*. *Sky and Telescope*, published by the Sky Publishing Corp., Cambridge 38, Mass., has planet material and various kinds of astronomical articles by professional and other astronomers; write for a free trial issue.

An example of computation work for precession allowance follows. Column 1 gives the date of the original ephemeris position. Column 2 gives the corresponding right ascension of the planet. The next step is to compute precession for this position and change it to fit the Beyer-Graff charts, which are made for an equinox of 1855. A table of computed values of what the precession allowance should be was computed by the author and used for the example, but is similar to and more exact than that offered in Stuker's *Stern-Atlas* or the Beyer-Graff *Stern-Atlas*. In the table, column 3 gives the yearly precession in R.A. thus computed, and column 4 shows the allowance for (1938 − 1855) or 83 years. Subtracting column 4 from 2 we have column 5, the correct right ascension for 1855, which is the R.A. the body would have if the equinox were still in the same position as in 1855. The remaining columns give the data for declination. The final positions as derived are plotted onto the 1855-equinox star atlas, and the planet should be found on the apparent path drawn on this chart.

The most difficult part of the computing is to take proper care of the minus signs in the case of south (minus) declination, and also to watch for the proper sign of declination allowance, for sometimes it is minus and sometimes plus. We subtract column 4 from column 2, because we are going backward in time from 1938 to 1855. Similarly, column 8 is subtracted algebraically from column 6, thus: $-11°12'.2$ $-(-15'.2) = -11°12'.2 + 15'.2$ or $-10°57'.0$. If, with the 1938 data, we wished to reduce the positions to, say, the equinox of 2021, we should add algebraically instead of subtracting: $-11°12'.2 + (-15'.2) = -11°27'.4$.

EXAMPLE OF PRECESSION ALLOWANCE FOR VESTA, 1938

1	2	3	4	5	6	7	8	9
0^h	R.A., 1938	1^y	83^y	R.A., 1855	Dec., 1938	1^y	83^y	Dec., 1855
	h m s	s	m s	h m s	° ′	″	′	° ′
Jun. 3	15 46 47	3.28	+4 32	15 42 15	−11 12.2	−11.0	−15.2	−10 57.0
11	15 39 59	3.29	+4 33	15 35 26	−11 29.5	−11.5	−15.9	−11 13.6
19	15 34 40	3.30	+4 34	15 30 6	−11 55.3	−11.8	−16.3	−11 39.0
27	15 31 13	3.31	+4 35	15 26 38	−12 29.0	−12.1	−16.7	−12 12.3
Jul. 5	15 29 50	3.33	+4 36	15 25 14	−13 9.9	−12.2	−16.8	−12 53.1

Manifestly, the greatest obstacle to the whole method is to find star charts available with stars fainter than sixth magnitude. There are almost none in existence. For comets and the brightest asteroids, plotting can be done on atlases like Schurig's or Norton's, when the object is not fainter than about 7. In the case of fainter objects, they could still be plotted but would likely be indistinguishable on the sky from neighboring stars of the same magnitude, that do not show on the Schurig or Norton. When this method must be resorted to, one can still rely upon movement of the comet or asteroid from night to night to identify it, whereas, with proper charts, one can perform the identification definitely on the first night of observation. In general, we might say that most comets worth seeing can be plotted on such an atlas as Norton or Schurig. Neptune's position when once located on one of these charts can be followed for the entire season.

Precessional change may be calculated by formula. The annual rate of change in R. A. $= m + n \sin \alpha \tan \delta$; and in declination, $n \cos \alpha$; where $\alpha =$ R. A., $\delta =$ dec., $m = 3^s.07234 + 0^s.0000186(t - 1900)$, and $n = 20''.0468 - 0''.000085(t - 1900)$; in which t is the year in question, as 1938 in example above.

Appendix III

Minor Planets "Nearest" to the Earth

The following data on the five asteroids at present known to approach nearest to us indicate unusual orbital features. The data on Hermes are the most uncertain, because of paucity of observation at the time of appearance.

Planet	Discoverer and year	Minimum distance from earth, miles	Revolution period, years	Estimated diameter, miles	Stellar magnitude M	Semi-major axis, astronomical units	Eccentricity	Inclination of orbit to ecliptic °
433 Eros............	Charlois and Witt, 1898	13,900,000	1.76	20	10	1.458	0.223	10.8
1221 Amor...........	Delporte, 1932	10,400,000	2.67	1½	18	1.923	0.437	11.9
Apollo (1932 HA).....	Reinmuth, 1932	2,500,000	1.81	1	17	1.486	0.566	6.4
Adonis (1936 CA).....	Delporte, 1936	1,200,000	2.76	¾	19	1.969	0.779	1.5
Hermes (1937 UB).....	Reinmuth, 1937	475,000	2.	¾	18	1.29	0.5	5.

Appendix IV
Sidereal Time

SIDEREAL time is used principally in the astronomical observatory or by the individual observer. Certain observations can be recorded by this time, and one of its uses is in connection with the transit of stars. Another main function of sidereal time is in setting the telescope, for which purpose the sidereal time is simply read from a sidereal clock or watch.

Sidereal time is *nearly* but not exactly star time; it is *vernal-equinox time*, and is a measure of the earth's rotation with respect to the equinox rather than to the sun. A sidereal day being shorter than a mean solar day by $3^m56^s.555$ sidereal time or $3^m55^s.909$ mean solar time, the sidereal timepiece is rated to gain that much in a mean solar day over an ordinary mean-solar timepiece.

A typical sidereal watch or clock has 24 hours on the dial and is rated to sidereal time. But, in the absence of such an instrument, an ordinary clock or watch can be used by having it made to run fast by the above amount daily. This can be achieved and the clock set most conveniently by the following means. We choose a certain hour of the day when the radio time signals can be received on the short-wave set. Then we compute the sidereal time for that moment for each day, for a number of days. By choosing such an hour we can check our mean-time clock and so know the correct time, both standard time and local civil time. Knowing therefore what the sidereal time should be at a certain moment each day, we read our sidereal clock and note the error (or the correction). By keeping record of the correction, we can rate the timepiece accurately. Once the method is learned, the process is very simple. For instance, the writer, in checking his sidereal watch every day, takes out one quantity from the nautical almanac, adds a constant quantity (see below), and then knows what the true sidereal time should be when the electric clock comes to $0^h0^m0^s$.

Suppose we have computed the true sidereal time for 0^h E.S.T. for several days by the aid of the nautical almanac; then we know what the sidereal time should be, and we can get the error of the clock. A table should be drawn up by which the performance of the clock over a period of time is shown. The following is an example, the almanac values being given for universal time.

Date	Sidereal time at 0^h U.T. from almanac	Reading of sidereal clock at 0^h U.T.	Correction to clock reading	Rate of clock
1940 Feb. 1	h m s 8 40 15.0	h m s 8 40 8.5	s +6.5	s
				0.0
2	8 44 11.5	8 44 5.0	+6.5	
				−0.5
3	8 48 8.0	8 48 2.0	+6.0	
				−1.0
4	8 52 5.0	8 52 0.0	+5.0	
				−1.5
5	8 56 1.0	8 55 57.5	+3.5	

The above table indicates well the performance of the clock for a four-day interval. (The time is here given in even half-seconds but expressed decimally.) On February 1, at 0^h mean time, the sidereal clock is read, as per column 3, which on comparison with column 2 yields the information that the clock is $6^s.5$ slow. Therefore the *error* of the clock is $-6^s.5$. We do not, however, need any column for the error, but rather we change the sign of the latter quantity and call it the *correction*. The *correction* in scientific work is a quantity that must be added algebraically to an observed quantity (here the reading, column 3) to give the true quantity. In astronomy it matters little how large the actual correction is, for it is easy enough to add the amount to the observed reading; the chief point is to do the reading accurately.

By studying column 4 as a whole, we can determine still more. Upon subtracting each quantity from the one following, we obtain the *rate* of the clock. Thus, between February 4 at 0^h, and February 5 at 0^h, we have $+3.5 - (+5.0)$ $= -1.5$, meaning that the clock *gained* $1^s.5$ during this day. In the quantities denoting correction and the rate, a plus sign indicates *slow* and a minus sign *fast*. Looking at column 5, we observe that between February 1 and 2 the clock kept perfect time (to the half-second); but between February 2 and 3 it gained $\frac{1}{2}$ second per day, and each day thereafter it gained $\frac{1}{2}$ second per day more than the day before, or it was accelerating by $\frac{1}{2}^s$ per day. The most important feature concerning the accuracy of a clock is to have the *rate uniform*, whether the rate is the same each day or accelerating or decelerating. The more uniform the clock, the better the performance. The best pendulum clocks in the world (like the Synchronome Free Pendulum) gain or lose but a very few thousandths of a second a day, but these are of exceptional accuracy.

Of course in order to check the sidereal clock we must know how to calculate the sidereal time by the use of a nautical almanac, for a given place and time. (Short explanations are given in the almanacs, but they are not very detailed.) As an example, assume that you are at Columbus, Ohio, at longitude 83°W. and that you have a short-wave radio. If you tune in on station NSS at 10:55 to 11:00 p.m., E.S.T., on 4390 or 9425 kilocycles, you get [1948] the best time signals for this moment of mean time, thus correcting your mean-time clock. At 10 p.m., read the sidereal clock to obtain its correction, knowing what the sidereal time should be. For 0^h E.S.T., tune in at 9425 kilocycles. Obtain from the U. S. Naval Observatory the current list of radio stations over which the time signals are sent; they may vary from the above from year to year. Signals are received at practically every hour of the day.

Your assumed longitude of 83° is equal to 5^h32^m of time, inasmuch as $15° = 1^h$. Now the problem is to find the sidereal time for 10 p.m. E.S.T. on September 21, 1940, or $22^h0^m0^s$, or $21^h28^m0^s$ in terms of your local civil time, for the time signals tell you when that will be. Looking at page 12, *American Ephemeris and Nautical Almanac* for 1940, we find the sidereal time of 0^h universal time for September 21 to be $23^h58^m52^s.208$. But at that moment it is not yet 0^h civil time at your meridian, and, by the time it is 0^h, the sidereal clock will have gained on the mean time. For this amount, add correction from Table III (American Ephemeris), $54^s.539$. The sum of these two quantities equals the sidereal time for 0^h of your local meridian. In other words, your sidereal clock gains $54^s.539$ in the interval between the turning of the earth from 0° to 83° of longitude.

However, we need now the sidereal time for a later period, 21^h28^m, rather than 0^h, so add local civil time, 21^h28^m. But during this mean-time interval the sidereal clock gains $3^m31^s.586$ over the mean time, so add that quantity. The sum of all the quantities (deducting 24^h) is $21^h31^m18^s.333$, local sidereal time for 10 p.m., E.S.T., or 9:28 p.m., Columbus local mean time. We tabulate the above to find sidereal time for 10 p.m., E.S.T., or $22^h0^m0^s$ "zone time". First, subtracting 32^m for difference between local meridian and standard meridian, we get $21^h28^m0^s$ for local civil time.

	h	m	s
Sidereal time of 0^h universal time, Sept. 21, from American Ephemeris.........................	23	58	52.208
Reduction for longitude (5^h32^m), table III, American Ephemeris, mean solar into sidereal............			54.539
Local civil time................................	21	28	0.000
Reduction for local civil time, table III...........		3	31.586
Local sidereal time for 10 p.m., E.S.T............	21	31	18.333

If we add the last 3 of the 4 tabulated quantities we obtain $21^h32^m26^s.125$, which is a *constant correction*, to be added to the sidereal time of 0^h U.T. for any day desired, to get the local sidereal time of that particular longitude and that particular time (10 p.m.), hence simplifying the calculations each day to only one addition.

It is important to note that every year or so the schedule of time signals is changed; hence the proper procedure is to obtain the current issue of *The Naval Observatory Time Signals*, from the Nautical Almanac Office, U. S. Naval Observatory, Washington, D.C. This consists of several sheets of very useful information. Signals from NSS (Annapolis) are controlled directly by the Naval Observatory.

One should also send for the schedule of time signals from the National Bureau of Standards, Washington, D.C. These signals (from WWV, near Washington) are an exceedingly valuable feature and are somewhat different from the above. Signals [1948] are broadcast on 2.5, 5, 10, 15, and other megacycles, some being sent out continuously, night and day. Signals from WWV are based on Naval Observatory time-determinations.

Appendix V

Dark-room Procedure

WE MENTION a few points in connection with King's chapter "Development and Handling of Plates" in *Manual of Celestial Photography*. In some places we take issue with him. Rodinal is a developer highly recommended by King. This is not necessarily the best developer. From extensive experience we find that pyro is still the best developer in general photography; especially would we recommend it for lunar photography or other extended areas such as comets, but not necessarily always for star work. Best gradations and shadow detail are attained with pyro. Otherwise metol-hydroquinone and ortol cannot be beaten. Some of the modern fine-grain formulas are excellent. The finest grain we have attained has been with the developer paraphenylene-diamene, an agent somewhat difficult to work. It should be used only where ample exposure can be given.

Another point is that in stellar work we develop for contrast, but not in photos of the moon, for by doing so with the latter we ruin the gradation of tone. As to the hypo solution, the best one is not a plain hypo bath. The English acid fixing-bath formula with the potassium metabisulfite proves to be a superlative bath for everything (including papers), except extreme hot-weather negative-developing work or where one has difficulty with the hardening of the emulsion. A suitable formula is:

	English	Metric
Hypo	4 to 6 oz.	200 to 300 grams
Potassium metabisulfite	½	25
Water to	20	1000 cc.

Dissolve first the hypo, and, when this is dissolved, the hypo bath being cool, add the metabisulfite. The advantage over the hypo-alum bath commonly used in America is the clearness of the solution together with ease of mixing it. If the temperature in the dark room is very high, the usual hypo-alum bath recommended by plate-makers may be used.

The scientific method of plate development is the thermo-time ("time-and-temperature") system. A deep green safelight is the best to use in the dark room and can be used for all negatives. We never use the inefficient and outmoded red light. When we find by experiment that a certain developer gives the proper contrast in x minutes at a certain temperature with our standard formula, we thereafter develop for x minutes in that developer at that temperature, not looking at the plate during development, but rocking the tray or moving the developing hanger during the process and watching the clock instead. Indeed no adequate inspection can be given a fast panchromatic plate, and no better method is known than this standardized system. The tray or tank should be covered or left in absolute darkness.

Panchromatic emulsions are not difficult to work, particularly when the technique is standardized. It is to be stressed that these plates or cut-films are the best for nearly every purpose; in fact the red-blind type is naturally defective and should have only limited use. The Ilford, Eastman, and other companies manufacture various grades of special plates suited to astro-photography, and there are some remarkable emulsions. When plates are used, it is of advantage, and in many cases quite essential, as in pictures of the moon, to use backed or double-coated plates rather than single-coated ones. Another bit of advice not usually known is that *unexposed plates preserve their keeping qualities much better when stored in the electric refrigerator.*

Appendix VI
Table of Faintest Magnitude and Resolving Power

IN COLUMN 3 are the theoretical limits of faintest magnitude discernible with a given aperture of telescope lens or mirror. The values are based upon the formula

$$m = 9 + 5 \log A$$

where m is the magnitude and A the aperture in inches. The results are "ideal", and apply to excellent seeing conditions, normal vision, and normal aperture-ratio of telescope.

In column 4 is the theoretical resolving power for various apertures. For example, an 80-mm objective can resolve a double star whose components are at least $1''.5$ apart. The values are based upon the formula

$$r.p. = \frac{5''.0}{A}$$

1	2	3	4
Aperture, mm.	Aperture, in.	Faintest magnitude	Resolving power, seconds of arc
		m	''
50	2	10.5	2.5
60	$2\frac{3}{8}$	10.9	2.1
80	$3\frac{1}{8}$	11.5	1.5
110	$4\frac{1}{4}$	12.1	1.1
130	$5\frac{1}{8}$	12.5	0.97
150	6	12.9	0.83
200	$7\frac{7}{8}$	13.5	0.63
250	10	14.0	0.50
300	12	14.4	0.42
380	15	14.9	0.33

where *r.p.* is the resolving power, and *A* the aperture in inches. This applies to pairs of about equal brightness and sixth magnitude. (When the pairs are unequal and the mean magnitudes fainter, the numerator must be considerably increased.) Under exceptional conditions, slightly closer stars than the above may be resolved; whereas, under poor conditions, the given limits may not be attained.

Appendix VII
The Constellations

Constellation	Meaning
Andromeda	Andromeda
Antlia	air-pump
Apus	bird of paradise
Aquarius	water carrier
Aquila	eagle
Ara	altar
Aries	ram
Auriga	charioteer
Boötes	herdsman
Caelum	chisel
Camelopardalis	giraffe
Cancer	crab
Canes Venatici	hunting dogs
Canis Major	larger dog
Canis Minor	smaller dog
Capricornus	sea-goat
Carina	keel
Cassiopeia	Cassiopeia
Centaurus	centaur
Cepheus	Cepheus
Cetus	whale
Chamaeleon	chameleon
Circinus	compasses
Columba	dove
Coma Berenices	Berenice's hair
Corona Australis	southern crown
Corona Borealis	northern crown
Corvus	crow
Crater	cup
Crux	cross
Cygnus	swan
Delphinus	dolphin
Dorado	swordfish
Draco	dragon
Equuleus	little horse
Eridanus	river Eridanus
Fornax	furnace
Gemini	twins
Grus	crane
Hercules	Hercules
Horologium	clock
Hydra	water-monster
Hydrus	water-snake
Indus	Indian
Lacerta	lizard
Leo	lion
Leo Minor	smaller lion
Lepus	hare
Libra	scales
Lupus	wolf
Lynx	lynx
Lyra	harp
Mensa	table mountain
Microscopium	microscope
Monoceros	unicorn
Musca	fly
Norma	square
Octans	octant
Ophiuchus	serpent-bearer
Orion	hunter
Pavo	peacock
Pegasus	Pegasus
Perseus	Perseus
Phoenix	phoenix
Pictor	easel
Pisces	fishes
Piscis Austrinus	southern fish
Puppis	stern
Pyxis	compass
Reticulum	net
Sagitta	arrow
Sagittarius	archer
Scorpius	scorpion
Sculptor	sculptor
Scutum	shield
Serpens Caput	serpent—head
Serpens Cauda	serpent—tail
Sextans	sextant
Taurus	bull
Telescopium	telescope
Triangulum	triangle
Triangulum Australe	southern triangle
Tucana	toucan
Ursa Major	larger bear
Ursa Minor	smaller bear
Vela	sails
Virgo	virgin
Volans	flying fish
Vulpecula	little fox

Appendix VIII

Planetary Data

	Mean distance from sun		Sidereal period	Synodic period‡	Eccentricity of orbit	Inclination to ecliptic	Diameter	Period of rotation on axis	Inclination of equator to orbit plane	Surface gravity (earth = 1)	Oblateness	Stellar magnitude (maximum)	Albedo	Mean velocity in orbit	Known moons
	Millions of miles	Astronomical units		days		° '	miles		°					miles/sec.	
Sun......	......	......	......	......	......	......	865,380	25d.38	7.?	28.0	0	−26.7	......	......	......
Moon......	......	......	(27d.322)‖	29.53	0.055	5 9‡	2,159.9	27d.322	6½	0.16	0	−12.6	0.07	0.63	......
Mercury...	36.0	0.387	87d.969	115.88	0.2056	7 0	3,008.5	88d	<7 ?	0.26	0	−1.2	0.07	30§	0
Venus.....	67.2	0.723	224d.701	583.92	0.0068	3 24	7,575.4	*	?	0.90	0	−4.4	0.59	22	0
Earth.....	93.0	1.000	365d.256	......	0.0167	0 0	7,926.7†	23h56m	23¼	1.00	1/297	......	0.45	18½	1
Mars......	141.5	1.524	1y.881	779.94	0.0934	1 51	4,215.6	24h37m	24	0.38	1/192	−2.8	0.15	15	2
Jupiter....	483.5	5.203	11y.862	398.88	0.0484	1 18	88,698†	9h50m	3	2.40	1/15	−2.5	0.5	8	12
Saturn.....	886.1	9.539	29y.458	378.09	0.0557	2 29	75,060†	10h14m	26⅔	0.95	1/(9.5)	−0.4	0.6	6	9
Uranus.....	1783	19.182	84y.013	369.66	0.0472	0 46	30,878	10h.8§	98	0.96	1/14	+5.7	0.6	4	5
Neptune....	2793	30.058	164y.793	367.49	0.0086	1 46	27,700	15h.8§	29	1.00	1/50	+8	0.7	3	2
Pluto......	3675	39.518	248y.430	366.73	0.2486	17 9	3,600	?	?	?	?	+15	?	3	0

* The rotation of Venus is still uncertain but is probably a few weeks or months.
† The equatorial diameters are tabulated. The polar diameter of the earth is 7900.0 miles, of Jupiter 82,789 miles, and of Saturn 67,170 miles.
‡ Approximately.
§ Mean.
‖ Period of revolution around the earth.

[327]

Appendix IX

Messier Objects

MESSIER's catalog of star clusters and nebulae contains a number of the best objects for observation. The original list was published in 1784 in the *Connaissance des temps*. We give below the entire list, together with the corresponding NGC. numbers. Our list, however, is modernized, with positions for the equinox of 1950 and the constellations according to the standard official boundaries. In column 5 we give the kind of object as revealed in the large telescopes; in a few cases these differ from the older descriptions in Dreyer's *New General Catalogue*.

The *galactic clusters* are the open star clusters. For the spiral nebulae we use the term *spiral galaxies*. We give first for convenience a classification of star clusters and nebulae, with well-known typical examples. Many of the Messier clusters and nebulae occur in the Selected List at the end of Chap. 14.

Star clusters
{
galactic (or open): M 44; M 45
globular: M 3; M 13
}

Nebulae
{
galactic {
diffuse: M 8; M 20; M 42
planetary: M 27; M 57; M 97
}
extra-galactic (external galaxies)
{
regular galaxies {
elliptical (spheroidal): M 32; M 60; M 87
spiral {
normal: M 31; M 51; M 81
barred: NGC 5850; NGC 7479
}
}
irregular galaxies: M 82; NGC 2070; NGC 6822; Magellanic Clouds
}
}

Messier	NGC	Position, 1950 R.A.	Position, 1950 Dec.	Constellation	Type of object	Special name
		h m	° ′			
1	1952	5 31.5	+21 59	Taurus	Galactic nebula*	Crab Nebula
2	7089	21 30.9	− 1 3	Aquarius	Globular cluster	
3	5272	13 39.9	+28 38	Canes Venatici	Globular cluster	
4	6121	16 21.6	−26 24	Scorpius	Globular cluster	
5	5904	15 16.0	+ 2 16	Serpens Caput	Globular cluster	
6	6405	17 36.8	−32 11	Scorpius	Galactic cluster	
7	6475	17 50.7	−34 48	Scorpius	Galactic cluster	
8	6523	18 0.6	−24 23	Sagittarius	Diffuse nebula	Lagoon Nebula
9	6333	17 16.3	−18 28	Ophiuchus	Globular cluster	
10	6254	16 54.5	− 4 2	Ophiuchus	Globular cluster	
11	6705	18 48.4	− 6 20	Scutum	Galactic cluster	
12	6218	16 44.6	− 1 52	Ophiuchus	Globular cluster	
13	6205	16 39.9	+36 33	Hercules	Globular cluster	Hercules Cluster
14	6402	17 35.0	− 3 13	Ophiuchus	Globular cluster	
15	7078	21 27.6	+11 57	Pegasus	Globular cluster	
16	6611	18 16.0	−13 48	Serpens Cauda	Galactic cluster	
17	6618	18 17.9	−16 12	Sagittarius	Diffuse nebula	Omega, or Horseshoe,
18	6613	18 17.0	−17 9	Sagittarius	Galactic cluster	[Nebula
19	6273	16 59.5	−26 12	Ophiuchus	Globular cluster	
20	6514	17 59.3	−23 2	Sagittarius	Diffuse nebula	Trifid Nebula
21	6531	18 1.7	−22 30	Sagittarius	Galactic cluster	
22	6656	18 33.3	−23 57	Sagittarius	Globular cluster	
23	6494	17 54.0	−19 1	Sagittarius	Galactic cluster	
24	6603	18 15.5	−18 27	Sagittarius	Galactic cluster	
25	4725†	18 28.7	−19 17	Sagittarius	Galactic cluster	
26	6694	18 42.5	− 9 26	Scutum	Galactic cluster	
27	6853	19 57.5	+22 35	Vulpecula	Planetary nebula	Dumbbell Nebula
28	6626	18 21.5	−24 54	Sagittarius	Globular cluster	
29	6913	20 22.2	+38 21	Cygnus	Galactic cluster	
30	7099	21 37.5	−23 25	Capricornus	Globular cluster	

* M 1 has been classified as a planetary nebula. But in form it is more like a diffuse type—and apparently an expanding nebula, as if from the former site of the great explosion of a nova.

† In this case, 4725 refers to the *Second Index Catalogue*, published in 1908 as the second supplement to Dreyer's NGC. The nebula is known as IC 4725. The (first) *Index Catalogue* was published in 1895.

‡ M 102 has been identified as "perhaps" NGC 5866 by Bailey of Harvard. But in 1947 researches by Dr. Helen S. Hogg revealed the fact that a letter by Pierre Méchain (written in 1783 and recently discovered) announced that M 102 was an error and was the same nebula as M 101. [*Jour. Roy. Ast. Soc. of Canada*, Sept.–Oct., 1947, p. 269.]

§ According to Dr. Hogg, Méchain discovered many of the objects in Messier's list, and in his letter, mentioned above, he lists additional nebulae, of which Dr. Hogg finds these four ought to be put with the original list with the numbers given here.

Messier	NGC	Position, 1950		Constellation	Type of object	Special name
		R.A.	Dec.			
		h m	° ′			
31	224	0 40.0	+41 0	Andromeda	Spiral galaxy	Great Nebula in An-
32	221	0 39.9	+40 35	Andromeda	Elliptical galaxy	[dromeda
33	598	1 31.0	+30 24	Triangulum	Spiral galaxy	
34	1039	2 38.8	+42 34	Perseus	Galactic cluster	
35	2168	6 5.7	+24 21	Gemini	Galactic cluster	
36	1960	5 32.9	+34 7	Auriga	Galactic cluster	
37	2099	5 49.0	+32 33	Auriga	Galactic cluster	
38	1912	5 25.3	+35 48	Auriga	Galactic cluster	
39	7092	21 30.4	+48 13	Cygnus	Galactic cluster	
40	....	12 19.8	+58 23	Ursa Major	[Likely 2 stars]	
41	2287	6 44.9	−20 41	Canis Major	Galactic cluster	
42	1976	5 32.8	− 5 25	Orion	Diffuse nebula	Great Nebula in Orion
43	1982	5 33.0	− 5 18	Orion	Diffuse nebula	
44	2632	8 37.2	+20 10	Cancer	Galactic cluster	Praesepe (Beehive)
45	....	3 44.5	+23 57	Taurus	Galactic cluster	Pleiades [Cluster
46	2437	7 39.5	−14 42	Puppis	Galactic cluster	
47	2478	7 52.4	−15 17	Puppis	Galactic cluster	
48	....	8 11.5	− 1 48	Hydra	Galactic cluster	
49	4472	12 27.3	+ 8 16	Virgo	Elliptical galaxy	
50	2323	7 0.5	− 8 16	Monoceros	Galactic cluster	
51	5194	13 27.8	+47 27	Canes Venatici	Spiral galaxy	Whirlpool Nebula
52	7654	23 22.0	+61 19	Cassiopeia	Galactic cluster	
53	5024	13 10.5	+18 26	Coma Berenices	Globular cluster	
54	6715	18 51.9	−30 32	Sagittarius	Globular cluster	
55	6809	19 36.9	−31 4	Sagittarius	Globular cluster	
56	6779	19 14.6	+30 5	Lyra	Globular cluster	
57	6720	18 51.7	+32 58	Lyra	Planetary nebula	Ring Nebula in Lyra
58	4579	12 35.1	+12 5	Virgo '	Spiral galaxy	
59	4621	12 39.5	+11 55	Virgo	Elliptical galaxy	
60	4649	12 41.2	+11 50	Virgo	Elliptical galaxy	
61	4303	12 19.4	+ 4 45	Virgo	Spiral galaxy	
62	6266	16 58.0	−30 2	Ophiuchus	Globular cluster	
63	5055	13 13.6	+42 18	Canes Venatici	Spiral galaxy	
64	4826	12 54.3	+21 57	Coma Berenices	Spiral galaxy	
65	3623	11 16.3	+13 22	Leo	Spiral galaxy	
66	3627	11 17.6	+13 16	Leo	Spiral galaxy	
67	2682	8 48.5	+12 0	Cancer	Galactic cluster	
68	4590	12 36.8	−26 28	Hydra	Globular cluster	
69	6637	18 28.1	−32 23	Sagittarius	Globular cluster	
70	6681	18 39.9	−32 21	Sagittarius	Globular cluster	

Messier	NGC	Position, 1950		Constellation	Type of object	Special name
		R.A.	Dec.			
		h m	° ′			
71	6838	19 51.5	+18 39	Sagitta	Globular cluster	
72	6981	20 50.7	−12 44	Aquarius	Globular cluster	
73	6994	20 56.2	−12 50	Aquarius	Galactic cluster	
74	628	1 34.0	+15 32	Pisces	Spiral galaxy	
75	6864	20 3.1	−22 4	Sagittarius	Globular cluster	
76	650	1 39.1	+51 19	Perseus	Planetary nebula	
77	1068	2 40.1	− 0 13	Cetus	Spiral galaxy	
78	2068	5 44.2	+ 0 2	Orion	Diffuse nebula	
79	1904	5 22.1	−24 34	Lepus	Globular cluster	
80	6093	16 14.1	−22 51	Scorpius	Globular cluster	
81	3031	9 51.5	+69 18	Ursa Major	Spiral galaxy	Great Spiral, Ursa Major
82	3034	9 51.9	+69 56	Ursa Major	Irregular galaxy	
83	5236	13 34.2	−29 37	Hydra	Spiral galaxy	
84	4374	12 22.6	+13 10	Virgo	Elliptical galaxy	
85	4382	12 22.9	+18 28	Coma Berenices	Spiral galaxy	
86	4406	12 23.7	+13 13	Virgo	Elliptical galaxy	
87	4486	12 28.3	+12 40	Virgo	Elliptical galaxy	
88	4501	12 29.5	+14 42	Coma Berenices	Spiral galaxy	
89	4552	12 33.1	+12 50	Virgo	Elliptical galaxy	
90	4569	12 34.3	+13 26	Virgo	Spiral galaxy	
91	....	12 40.6	+13 33	Coma Berenices	[Probably a comet]	
92	6341	17 15.6	+43 11	Hercules	Globular cluster	
93	2447	7 42.4	−23 45	Puppis	Galactic cluster	
94	4736	12 48.6	+41 24	Canes Venatici	Spiral galaxy	
95	3351	10 41.3	+11 58	Leo	Spiral galaxy	
96	3368	10 44.1	+12 5	Leo	Spiral galaxy	
97	3587	11 11.9	+55 18	Ursa Major	Planetary nebula	Owl Nebula
98	4192	12 11.2	+15 11	Coma Berenices	Spiral galaxy	
99	4254	12 16.3	+14 42	Coma Berenices	Spiral galaxy	
100	4321	12 20.4	+16 6	Coma Berenices	Spiral galaxy	
101	5457	14 1.4	+54 35	Ursa Major	Spiral galaxy	
102‡	5866‡	15 5.1	+55 57	Draco	Spiral galaxy	
103	581	1 29.9	+60 26	Cassiopeia	Galactic cluster	
104§	4594	12 37.4	−11 20	Virgo	Spiral galaxy	
105§	3379	10 45.2	+12 51	Leo	Spiral galaxy	
106§	4258	12 16.6	+47 35	Canes Venatici	Spiral galaxy	
107§	6171	16 29.7	−12 57	Ophiuchus	Globular cluster	

For footnotes, see page 329.

Appendix X

The Brightest Stars

THE subjoined list of brightest stars in the sky is arranged in order of magnitude, beginning with the brightest. The measure of brilliance is by *magnitude;* and, in column 3, "Mag." represents the apparent visual magnitude.

The positions of the stars are for the standard equinox of 1950; while none of the "fixed stars" is really fixed, their motions in space as perceived by us are so slow that the tabular positions are quite correct for a considerable number of years around 1950.

Column 4 gives the spectral type, for reference, and the color of the star as seen by the eye. These color-designations are by no means guaranteed but probably on the whole are essentially correct. In a majority of cases they are based on the corresponding spectral type; yet the color does not always rigidly follow the type. Besides, the matter of color is notoriously uncertain for another reason, namely, that various observers are apt to record colors differently.

In column 5, the distance of the star from us is computed from the parallax, from the formula

$$d = \frac{3.258}{p},$$

where d is the distance in light-years and p is the parallax in seconds of arc. The distances are in fairly round numbers and should not be considered extremely accurate, because parallaxes, which are excessively small angles, are difficult to measure. Moreover, it is often necessary to use the mean of the trigonometric and the spectroscopic parallaxes, and there may be a large discrepancy between them. Our basic data are computed from authoritative parallax determinations.

The radial velocity in column 6 indicates motion of a star in the line of sight. It is the speed of approach to the center of the solar system or recession from it. A plus sign signifies an increasing distance or recession, while a minus sign signifies a decreasing distance or approach. As it is usually given in kilometers per second, we have recorded it so. (1 km. = 0.62137 mile.)

Column 7 indicates very closely the date when the star transits the observer's meridian at 9 p.m., local civil time.

Star		Position, 1950 R.A.	Dec.	Mag.	Spectrum and color		Distance	Rad. vel.	Meridian 9 p.m.
		h m	° ′				light-years	km/sec	
α Canis Majoris	Sirius	6 42.9	−16 39	−1.58	A0	bluish	8	− 7.5	Feb. 16
α Carinae	Canopus	6 22.8	−52 40	−0.86	F0	yellow-white	650	+20.5	Feb. 11
α Centauri		14 36.2	−60 38	+0.06	G0, K5	yellow, orange	4	−22.2	June 16
α Lyrae	Vega	18 35.2	+38 44	0.14	A0	bluish-white	23	−13.8	Aug. 15
α Aurigae	Capella	5 13.0	+45 57	0.21	G0	yellow	42	+30.2	Jan. 24
α Boötis	Arcturus	14 13.4	+19 27	0.24	K0	orange-yellow	32	− 5.1	June 10
β Orionis	Rigel	5 12.1	− 8 15	0.34	B8	bluish-white	545	+23.6	Jan. 24
α Canis Minoris	Procyon	7 36.7	+ 5 21	0.48	F5	yellow-white	10	− 3.0	Mar. 2
α Eridani	Achernar	1 35.9	−57 29	0.60	B5	bluish	70	+19	Nov. 30
β Centauri		14 0.3	−60 8	0.86	B1	bluish	130	−12	June 7
α Aquilae	Altair	19 48.3	+ 8 44	0.89	A5	yellow-white	18	−26.1	Sept. 3
α Orionis	Betelgeuse	5 52.5	+ 7 24	0.92	M0	reddish	300	+21.0	Feb. 3
α Tauri	Aldebaran	4 33.0	+16 25	1.06	K5	orange	54	+54.1	Jan. 14
α Virginis	Spica	13 22.6	−10 54	1.21	B2	bluish	190	+ 1.6	May 28
β Geminorum	Pollux	7 42.3	+28 9	1.21	K0	yellow	31	+ 3.3	Mar. 3
α Scorpii	Antares	16 26.3	−26 19	1.22	M0	reddish	170	− 3.2	July 14
α Piscis Austrini	Fomalhaut	22 54.9	−29 53	1.29	A3	white	27	+ 6.5	Oct. 20
α Cygni	Deneb	20 39.7	+45 6	1.33	A2	white	465	+6 to −9	Sept. 16
α Leonis	Regulus	10 5.7	+12 13	1.34	B8	bluish-white	70	+ 2.6	Apr. 9
β Crucis		12 44.8	−59 25	1.50	B1	bluish	465	+20.0	May 18
η Carini		10 43.1	−59 25	1.0 to 7.4	Peculiar		...	−25.0	Apr. 17
α¹ Crucis		12 23.8	−62 49	1.58	B1	bluish	150	−12.2	May 13
α Geminorum	Castor	7 31.4	+32 0	1.58	A0	greenish-white	44	+60	Feb. 28
γ Crucis		12 28.4	−56 50	1.61	M3	red	...	+21.3	May 15
ε Canis Majoris		6 56.7	−28 54	1.63	B1	bluish	325	+27.4	Feb. 19
ε Ursae Majoris		12 51.8	+56 14	+1.68	A0	white	50	−11.9	May 20

γ Orionis	Bellatrix	5 22.4 + 6 18	+1.70	B2	bluish	215	+18.0	Jan. 27
λ Scorpii		17 30.2 −37 4	1.71	B2	bluish	205	var.	July 30
ε Carini		8 21.5 −59 21	1.74	K0, B	orange	325	+11.5	Mar. 13
o Ceti	Mira	2 16.8 − 3 12	1.7 to 9.5	M5	red	250	+57.8	Dec. 11
ε Orionis		5 33.7 − 1 14	1.75	B0	bluish	405	+25.8	Jan. 29
β Tauri		5 23.1 +28 34	1.78	B8	bluish-white	115	+ 8.0	Jan. 27
β Carinae		9 12.7 −69 31	1.80	A0	white	⋯	− 5	Mar. 26
α Trianguli Australis		16 43.4 −68 56	1.88	K2	orange	130	− 3.7	July 18
α Persei		3 20.7 +49 41	1.90	F5	yellow-white	190	− 2.4	Dec. 27
η Ursae Majoris		13 45.6 +49 34	1.91	B3	bluish	220	−10.9	June 3
γ Geminorum		6 34.8 +16 27	1.93	A0	white	65	−11.3	Feb. 14
ε Sagittarii		18 20.9 −34 25	1.95	A0	white	165	−10.8	Aug. 12
α Ursae Majoris		11 0.7 +62 1	1.95	K0	orange	90	− 8.6	Apr. 22
δ Canis Majoris		7 6.4 −26 19	1.98	F8	yellowish	410	+34.3	Feb. 22
β Canis Majoris		6 20.5 −17 56	1.99	B1	bluish	235	+34.4	Feb. 10
δ Velorum		8 43.3 −54 31	2.01	A0	white	85	+ 2.2	Mar. 19
θ Scorpii		17 33.7 −42 58	2.04	F0	yellow-white	135	+ 1.4	July 31
ζ Orionis		5 38.2 − 1 58	2.05	B0	bluish-white	300	+18.8	Jan. 31
β Aurigae		5 55.9 +44 57	2.07	A0	white	65	−18.1	Feb. 4
α² Crucis		12 23.8 −62 49	2.09	B1	bluish	150	+ 0.3	May 13
α Pavonis		20 21.7 −56 54	2.12	B3	bluish	235	+ 1.8	Sept. 12
α Ursae Minoris	Polaris	1 48.8 +89 2	2.12	F8	yellowish	1085	−17.4	Dec. 4
α Ophiuchi		17 32.6 +12 36	2.14	A5	white	54	+15	July 31
σ Sagittarii		18 52.2 −26 22	2.14	B3	bluish	160	−10.7	Aug. 20
α Andromedae		0 5.8 +28 49	2.15	A0	white	95	−13.0	Nov. 8
ζ Ursae Majoris	Mizar	13 21.9 +55 11	2.16	A2	green-white	80	− 9.9	May 28
α Hydrae		9 25.1 − 8 26	2.16	K2	orange	190	− 4.4	Mar. 29
α Gruis		22 5.1 −47 12	2.16	B5	bluish	90	+11.8	Oct. 1
κ Orionis		5 45.4 − 9 41	2.20	B0	bluish	545	+20.1	Feb. 1
λ Velorum		9 6.2 −43 14	+2.22	K5	orange	215	+18.4	Mar. 25

Star		Position, 1950 R.A.	Dec.	Mag.	Spectrum and color		Distance light-years	Rad. vel. km/sec	Meridian 9 p.m.
		h m	° '						
γ² Velorum		8 8.0	−47 11	+2.22	Oa	bluish	...	+35	Mar. 10
β Persei	Algol	3 4.9	+40 46	2.3 to 3.5	B8	bluish-white	100	+ 5.7	Dec. 23
β Leonis	Denebola	11 46.5	+14 51	2.23	A2	white	40	− 2.3	May 4
α Arietis		2 4.3	+23 14	2.23	K2	orange	70	−14.3	Dec. 8
β Ceti		0 41.1	−18 16	2.24	K0	orange	60	+13.1	Nov. 17
β Gruis		22 39.7	−47 9	2.24	M3	orange	325	+ 1.6	Oct. 17
β Ursae Minoris		14 50.8	+74 22	2.24	K5	orange	110	+16.9	June 20
γ Cassiopeiae		0 53.7	+60 27	2.25	B0	bluish	95	− 6.8	Nov. 20
ι Carinae		9 15.8	−59 4	2.25	F0	yellowish-white	...	+13.3	Mar. 27
θ Centauri		14 3.7	−36 7	2.26	K0	orange	55	+ 1.3	June 8
ζ Puppis		8 1.8	−39 52	2.27	Od	bluish	815	−24	Mar. 8
γ Andromedae		2 0.8	+42 5	2.28	K0	orange	165	−11.7	Dec. 7
α Coronae Borealis	Gemma	15 32.6	+26 53	2.31	A0	white	60	+ 1.7	June 30
γ Cygni		20 20.4	+40 6	2.32	F8	yellowish	405	− 7.6	Sept. 12
ε Scorpii		16 46.9	−34 12	2.36	K0	orange	85	− 2.5	July 19
β Andromedae	Mirach	1 6.9	+35 21	2.37	Ma	red	80	+ 0.1	Nov. 23
γ Centauri		12 38.7	−48 41	2.38	A0	white	130	− 7.5	May 17
γ Draconis		17 55.4	+51 30	2.42	K5	orange	125	−27.8	Aug. 6
β Cassiopeiae		0 6.5	+58 53	2.42	F5	yellow-white	40	+11.4	Nov. 8
η Canis Majoris		7 22.1	−29 12	2.43	B5	bluish	270	+40.4	Feb. 26
β Ursae Majoris		10 58.8	+56 39	2.44	A0	white	75	−12.1	Apr. 22
α Phoenicis		0 23.8	−42 35	2.44	K0	orange	80	+74.6	Nov. 12
α Cassiopeine		0 37.6	+59 16	2.47	K0	orange	190	− 3.8	Nov. 16
δ Orionis		5 29.4	− 0 20	2.48	B0	bluish-white	465	+19.9	Jan. 28
κ Scorpii		17 39.0	−39 0	2.51	B2	bluish	360	−10	Aug. 1
ε Pegasi		21 41.7	+ 9 39	2.54	K0	orange	170	+ 5.2	Oct. 2
γ Ursae Majoris		11 51.2	+53 58	2.54	A0	white	100	−11.1	May 5
γ¹ Leonis	Algieba	10 17.2	+20 6	+2.61	K0	orange	135	−36.8	Apr. 11

Appendix XI

Eclipses

THE subjoined table includes lunar and solar eclipse data of interest to the observer; it lists

1. Total eclipses of the sun from 1948 to the year 2000. Column 2 indicates the approximate track of the total phase, over the earth's surface. Partial phases occur over a wide area on either side of this path of totality.

2. Annular eclipses occurring from 1957 to 1990.

3. Total eclipses of the moon occurring from 1957 to 1984. The approximate time (in Eastern standard time) is given, as well as the computed duration of totality. In column 4 is the general region on the earth from which the eclipse is visible.

The next total solar eclipse over New York City occurs on 2024 April 8. The next annular eclipse of the sun over New York City occurs on 2111 August 4.

Our data are derived and computed from the basic work, *Canon der Finsternisse*, by Oppolzer.

1. TOTAL SOLAR ECLIPSES, 1948 to 2000 A.D.

Date	Path of Total Phase
1948, May 9.....	Indian Ocean, southeastern Asia, across the Pacific Ocean
1948, Nov. 1.....	Central Africa, south Indian Ocean to the Pacific west of New Zealand
1950, Sept. 12....	North polar regions, northeastern Siberia, into mid-north Pacific Ocean
1952, Feb. 25....	Across north Africa and Arabia, into central Asia
1954, June 30....	Central United States, northeastern Canada, Greenland, southern Scandinavia, across Russia into India
1955, June 20....	Indian Ocean, south India, across southeastern Asia, to north Pacific Ocean
1956, June 8.....	South Pacific Ocean
1958, Oct. 12....	South Pacific Ocean, ending in southern South America
1959, Oct. 2.....	Eastern New England, across the north Atlantic and north Africa to the north Indian Ocean
1961, Feb. 15....	Bay of Biscay, across France, northern Italy, southeastern Europe, northwestern and northern Asia, to the Arctic
1962, Feb. 5.....	Borneo, New Guinea, central and northern Pacific Ocean
1963, July 20....	Japan, Bering Sea, Alaska, northern Canada, mid-north Atlantic Ocean
1965, May 30....	South Pacific: New Zealand—Marquesas Islands—Peru
1966, May 20....	Atlantic Ocean, NW Africa, Mediterranean Sea, across Asia
1966, Nov. 12....	Pacific, west of Galápagos Islands, across southern South America, across the south Atlantic to the Indian Ocean
1967, Nov. 2.....	Antarctic Ocean, Antarctica
1968, Sept. 22....	Arctic Ocean, northern Russia, to central Asia
1970, Mar. 7.....	Central Pacific Ocean, Mexico, Florida, to mid-north Atlantic Ocean
1972, July 10....	Northeastern Asia, Alaska, northern Canada, to mid-Atlantic Ocean
1973, June 30....	Northern South America, Atlantic Ocean, across northern Africa to mid-Indian Ocean
1974, June 20....	Southern Indian Ocean and Antarctic Ocean, south of Australia
1976, Oct. 23....	East Africa, across the Indian Ocean and Australia to a point near New Zealand
1977, Oct. 12....	Mid-north Pacific Ocean, southeastward, extending into northern South America
1979, Feb. 26....	North Pacific Ocean, northwest tip of United States, across Canada, Hudson Bay, into central Greenland
1980, Feb. 16....	Atlantic Ocean, across central Africa, Indian Ocean, India, southern China
1981, July 31....	Southeastern Europe, across Siberia, to mid-north Pacific Ocean

1983, June 11.... South Indian Ocean, across the East Indies, to western Pacific Ocean

1984, May 30.... Pacific Ocean, across Mexico, southern United States, across the Atlantic to northern Africa

1984, Nov. 22.... East Indies, across the south Pacific Ocean to a point off the coast of Chile

1985, Nov. 12.... Antarctic Ocean

1986, Oct. 3..... [A short eclipse.] In the Atlantic just off the southeast coast of Greenland

1987, Mar. 29.... Patagonia, across the south Atlantic Ocean, across Africa

1988, Mar. 18.... Eastern Indian Ocean, across Sumatra, the Malay Peninsula, into the north Pacific, across the Philippine Islands to a point south of Alaska

1990, July 22.... Finland, the Arctic Ocean, northeastern Asia, across the north Pacific

1991, July 11.... Mid-Pacific Ocean, across Mexico, central America, northern South America, into Brazil

1992, June 30.... Southeastern South America, across mid-south Atlantic to the Indian Antarctic Ocean

1994, Nov. 3..... Pacific Ocean south of the Galápagos Islands across South America and the south Atlantic Ocean to the western Indian Ocean

1995, Oct. 24.... Southwestern Asia, across northern India, the Malay Peninsula, into mid-Pacific Ocean

1997, Mar. 9..... Central Asia, across NE Asia, into the Arctic Ocean

1998, Feb. 26.... Mid-Pacific Ocean, across the northern tip of South America, across the Atlantic Ocean to the Canary Islands

1999, Aug. 11.... Atlantic Ocean south of Nova Scotia, across the north Atlantic, across central Europe, southern Asia, and northern India

2000 .... [No total solar eclipse]

2. ANNULAR ECLIPSES, 1957 to 1990 A.D.

Date	Path of Annular Phase

1957, Apr. 29.... [A short eclipse.] Beginning in northern Russia; mostly in the Arctic Ocean

1958, Apr. 19.... North Indian Ocean, across southeastern Asia into mid-north Pacific Ocean

1959, Apr. 8..... South Indian Ocean, across Australia, into west Pacific Ocean

1961, Aug. 11.... South Atlantic Ocean, Antarctic Ocean, Antarctica

1962, July 31.... Northern South America, across Atlantic Ocean, the Sahara and east Africa, to Madagascar

1963, Jan. 25..... South Pacific west of Chile, across southern South America, into the Antarctic Ocean and to Indian Ocean east of Madagascar

1965, Nov. 23.... Northwestern India to coast near Calcutta, across Malay peninsula, Borneo, and New Guinea, into mid-north Pacific

1969, Mar. 18.... Across the Indian Ocean and the East Indies islands
1969, Sept. 11.... Northern and eastern Pacific Ocean into Brazil
1970, Aug. 31.... The East Indies and into the south Pacific Ocean
1972, Jan. 16..... Marie Byrd Land and eastern Antarctica
1973, Jan. 4...... South Pacific, South America, into the south Atlantic
1973, Dec. 24.... Across northern South America, Atlantic Ocean, ending in North Africa
1976, Apr. 29.... Atlantic, North Africa, Mediterranean Sea, south-central Asia
1977, Apr. 18.... South Atlantic, across South Africa to the Indian Ocean
1979, Aug. 22.... Across Amundsen Sea into west Antarctica
1980, Aug. 10.... Mid-Pacific Ocean into Brazil
1981, Feb. 4..... Pacific Ocean, from south of Australia to near South American coast
1983, Dec. 4..... North Atlantic Ocean, across central Africa
1987, Sept. 22.... Central Asia to mid-Pacific Ocean
1988, Sept. 11.... West Indian Ocean to south Pacific south of New Zealand
1990, Jan. 26..... South Indian Ocean and south Atlantic Ocean

3. TOTAL LUNAR ECLIPSES, 1957 to 1984

Date	Time	Dur.	Region of visibility
	h m	h m	
1957, May 13..	17 32	1 20	Africa, Europe, partly North and South America
1957, Nov. 7...	9 28	0 32	Asia, Australia, western and mid-Pacific Ocean
1960, Mar. 13..	3 30	1 36	North and South America
1960, Sept. 5...	6 23	1 30	Mid-Pacific, part of North America
1961, Aug. 25..	22 8	0 14	North and South America, western Africa, Europe
1963, Dec. 30..	6 7	1 24	Mid-Pacific, and partly in North America
1964, June 24..	20 7	1 38	Africa, Europe, South America, eastern North America
1964, Dec. 18..	21 35	1 4	South America, most of North America, western Africa, Europe
1967, Apr. 24..	7 7	1 22	Pacific Ocean and Australia
1967, Oct. 18..	5 16	0 56	Pacific Ocean, western North America
1968, Apr. 12..	23 49	0 56	Most of United States, Mexico, South America
1968, Oct. 6...	6 41	1 2	Pacific Ocean and Australia
1971, Feb. 10..	2 42	1 18	S. Canada, United States, part of South America
1971, Aug. 6...	14 44	1 42	Part of Africa, India, west Indian Ocean
1972, Jan. 30..	5 53	0 42	Pacific Ocean, western North America
1974, Nov. 29..	10 16	1 16	Eastern Asia and Australia
1975, May 25..	0 46	1 30	Southern United States, Mexico, South America
1975, Nov. 18..	17 24	0 46	Europe and Africa
1978, Mar. 24..	11 25	1 30	Southern Asia, and Australia
1978, Sept. 16.	14 3	1 22	Most of Africa, southern Asia
1979, Sept. 6...	5 54	0 52	Pacific Ocean, eastern Australia
1982, Jan. 9...	14 56	1 24	Part of Africa, eastern Europe, southern Asia
1982, July 6...	2 30	1 42	South Pacific Ocean, Mexico, western South America
1982, Dec. 30..	6 26	1 6	Central Pacific Ocean
1983..........	.. ..	. ..	[No total lunars in 1983–1984]

Glossary

The list of definitions included here is not intended to be a complete roster of astronomical terms, instruments, and phenomena, but a ready reference list of words with which the reader may come into frequent contact. For reference to more detailed descriptions or words not contained here, consult the Index.

aberration in lenses and mirrors. The failure of light rays to meet at the places where they are expected by simple theory. In *chromatic aberration* the images formed by the differently colored components of light are not brought to the same focus in one plane and are of unequal sizes. In *spherical aberration*, the marginal rays (even in monochromatic light) are brought to a focus nearer the lens or mirror than the central rays. There are also various other types of optical aberration, such as astigmatism, coma, etc.

aberration of light. The apparent displacement of an object in the sky caused by the effect of the earth's motion on the direction in which light seems to reach us. The effect is very small because of the tremendous velocity of light as compared to the speed of the earth.

albedo. The ratio of the amount of light reflected by the entire lighted side of an opaque body to the amount of light falling on the body. When the moon's albedo is given as 0.07, it means that $\frac{7}{100}$ of the light falling on it is reflected.

altitude. The angular distance of a given object above the horizon, measured along the object's vertical circle from the horizon toward the zenith.

aphelion. The point in the earth's orbit farthest from the sun.

apogee. The point in the moon's orbit farthest from the earth.

apparent solar time. The time kept by the actual or apparent sun, or the hour-angle of the apparent sun. It is not uniform throughout the year, but is sometimes ahead of, and sometimes behind, the mean solar time.

astronomical unit. The average or mean distance of the earth from the sun, the value now used being 93,003,000 statute miles.

azimuth. The angular distance on the horizon, from the south point to the point at which the object's vertical circle intersects the horizon, measured westward around the circle from 0° to 360°. Note, however, that in navigation, it is the distance on the horizon between the north point and the foot of the vertical circle, measured eastward around the circle through 360°.

binary. A system of two stars under a gravitational bond and revolving around their common center of gravity.

bolide. A bright meteor (fire-ball), especially one that explodes near the end of its path in the atmosphere.

celestial globe. A globe somewhat similar to a terrestrial globe but representing the constellations on the background of sky, together with the principal circles of the celestial sphere. A celestial globe must necessarily represent the stars reversed or as if seen from outside the heavenly vault.

celestial latitude. The distance of an object from the ecliptic in degrees, minutes, and seconds as measured along a great circle that passes through the ecliptic poles and the object, and therefore at right angles to the ecliptic. If the object is toward the north ecliptic pole, it is marked +; if toward the south, −.

celestial longitude. The distance along the ecliptic in degrees, minutes, and seconds from the vernal equinox to the point of intersection with the ecliptic, of a great circle passing through the object to be measured and the ecliptic poles. It is measured from the equinox in the direction of the sun's apparent motion, from 0° to 360°.

celestial poles. The two intersections of the earth's axis prolonged, with the celestial sphere.

celestial sphere. An imaginary sphere of very large (infinite) radius which surrounds the observer, who is supposed to be at its center. For many astronomical purposes, celestial objects are considered as if they were all located on the surface of this sphere.

colure, equinoctial. The great circle passing through the celestial poles and the equinoxes. The *solstitial colure*, similarly, passes through the poles and the summer and winter solstices.

conjunction. The situation or aspect whereby two objects in the sky have the same right ascension *or* the same longitude, it being understood which one is meant. In the case of Mercury or Venus, *inferior conjunction* occurs when the planet is between us and the sun; *superior conjunction* occurs when the planet is on the other side of the sun from us.

coördinate, celestial. One of two or more values which specify the position of a point on the celestial sphere—such as altitude, declination, hour-angle, etc.

declination. The distance of an object north or south of the celestial equator, measured in degrees, minutes, and seconds. If north, it is indicated by the sign +; if south, by −.

diurnal circle. The circular path of a celestial object in its apparent daily (diurnal) motion across the sky. Diurnal circles are all parallel to the celestial equator and to each other.

eccentricity. The degree of flattening of an ellipse, or its departure from a circle. Its value is obtained by dividing the distance between the center of the ellipse and one focus by half the length of the longest axis.

eclipse. The darkening of a heavenly body by another. In a solar eclipse, the sun's light is cut off because of the interposition of the moon between us and the sun. In a lunar eclipse, darkening occurs as the moon enters the earth's shadow in space. The term *eclipse* is to be distinguished from occultation.

ecliptic. The great circle made by the intersection of the plane of the earth's orbit on the celestial sphere. A less proper definition: the apparent path of the sun around the sky during the year.

elongation, greatest (applied to an inferior planet). The greatest distance from the sun, on either the east or west side, which the planet seems to reach between any two consecutive conjunctions with the sun.

ephemeris. A table of computed positions of a celestial object for certain given dates.

equation of time. The difference in minutes at the moment between the apparent solar time and the mean solar time. It is used in two senses: the *equation of time, mean minus apparent*, is the correction to be added algebraically to apparent solar time, to give mean time. When it is marked +, the real sun is *slow* over the mean sun; when marked −, the real sun is *fast* over the mean sun. The *equation of time, apparent minus mean*, is the correction to be added algebraically to mean time, to give apparent time. When marked +, the real sun is *fast* over the mean sun; when marked −, the sun is *slow* over the mean sun.

equator, celestial. The great circle of the celestial sphere half-way between the celestial poles, and 90° from each. It is the projection of the plane of the terrestrial equator onto the celestial sphere.

equinox. One of the points of intersection of the ecliptic and the celestial equator. The *vernal equinox* is the point of 0° longitude and 0° latitude, where the sun crosses the equator about March 21; and the *autumnal equinox* is the point of 180° longitude, where the sun crosses the equator about September 22. The word equinox also refers to the *time* of the sun being at the equinox point.

evening star. One of the naked-eye planets (not a star) so described when it sets after the sun. More exactly, in the case of an inferior planet (Mercury or Venus), it is evening star between the times of superior and inferior conjunction with the sun. If a superior planet (Mars, Jupiter, or Saturn), it is evening star between opposition and conjunction with the sun.

galaxy. A vast system of stars in space, such as our Milky Way, which is often called "the Galaxy" and contains a few billions of stars.

great circle. A circle on a sphere where the plane of the circle passes through the center of the sphere. The ecliptic, celestial equator, horizon, and meridian (together with the anti-meridian) are great circles of the celestial sphere.

horizon. A great circle on the celestial sphere, half-way between the zenith and the nadir, and 90° from either. This is the astronomical or true horizon, the visible horizon being the boundary between the sky and the visible landscape.

hour-angle. The angle formed at the celestial pole between the celestial meridian and the hour-circle of a given object in the sky, measured westward from the meridian. Also measured as distance in arc along the celestial equator, from the meridian to the intersection of the object's hour-circle. Usually given in hours, minutes, and seconds, but may be written in arc, where $1^h = 15°$ of arc.

hour-circle. A great circle passing through both celestial poles and a given object in the sky. Every star or other object in the heavens has its own hour-circle, which appears to move with it in its diurnal motion. The term *hour circle* applies also to the circle attached to the polar axis of a telescope. It is graduated in hours and minutes and indicates the point in hour-angle at which the telescope is set.

international date-line. A fixed, imaginary line in the Pacific Ocean, west of which the new day begins. It coincides throughout a large part of its extent with the 180th meridian.

interpolation. The mathematical process of finding intermediate values in a given series of values.

ionosphere. The zone of maximum ionization of the earth's atmosphere, also known as the Kennelly-Heaviside layer. It is far above the stratosphere and the ozone level, and is at about 50 to 80 miles above the surface of the earth.

libration. An oscillation by which a satellite or planet, which otherwise would always turn precisely the same face to its primary, shows at times some of the usually hidden side. The moon and Mercury exhibit the phenomenon.

light-year (a unit of distance, not of time). The distance that light travels in one year. At a speed of 186,270 miles per second, the value is 5.880×10^{12} (= 5,880,000,000,000) miles.

magnitude, stellar. The apparent brightness of a star. Magnitude does not refer to the apparent angular diameter or to the actual size of the star.

meridian, celestial. The half of the great circle passing through the observer's zenith and the celestial poles that is above the horizon. It is the projection on the celestial sphere of the plane of the observer's terrestrial meridian. The *anti-meridian* is the invisible half of the same great circle which passes through the observer's nadir and the celestial poles.

morning star. One of the naked-eye planets (not a star) so described when it rises before the sun. More exactly, in the case of an inferior planet, it is morning star between the times of inferior and superior conjunction with the sun. If a superior planet, it is morning star between conjunction and opposition with the sun.

nadir. The point on the celestial sphere to which a plumb-line extended through the earth points. It is opposite the zenith and 180° from it.

node. The point of intersection of two great circles—commonly used to refer to the intersections (with the ecliptic) of a great circle determined by the plane of an object's orbit.

oblateness. The flattening of a spheroid, such as the earth. The value is determined by dividing the difference between the equatorial and polar diameters by the equatorial diameter.

obliquity of the ecliptic. The angle of inclination between the celestial equator and the ecliptic. It is equal to about 23°27′.

occultation. The hiding of one object in the sky by another, especially when the moon passes in front of a star or a planet (but the term does not apply to an eclipse of the sun although this *is* an occultation). The term also applies to the case of a satellite passing behind a planet, and this is to be distinguished from an eclipse, for in an eclipse the object is plunged into the *shadow* of the primary.

opposition. The situation or aspect in which an object is distant 180° from another, usually the sun. (This difference may be either in longitude or right ascension, one or the other being specifically meant.) The sun, the earth, and the object, therefore, are in a straight line, with the earth between.

parallax. The angle between the direction of two bodies, as seen from two different points of view.

perigee. The point in the moon's orbit nearest to the earth.

perihelion. The point in the earth's orbit nearest the sun.

period, sidereal. The time taken for one revolution of a body in space around another, with respect to the stars. The *synodic period* is the interval between two successive times when the two revolving bodies have the same heliocentric longitude; for example, the time interval between two inferior conjunctions of Mercury with the sun, or between two successive full moons.

perturbation. Deviation of an object from an orbit that has been computed without taking into account all the factors involved in determining the object's motion.

position angle. The angle expressing the direction of one object from another (called the "principal" one of the two) on the celestial sphere.

It is the angle formed at the principal object between a line drawn from it due north, and a line drawn from it to the second object. It is always measured from the line drawn northward around to the line connecting the two objects in an easterly, etc., direction and may range from 0° to 360°.

precession of the equinoxes. The very slow westward motion of the equinox points among the constellations.

prime vertical. The great circle on the celestial sphere passing through the east and west cardinal points and the zenith; or the vertical circle at right angles to the meridian.

proper motion. The angular rate of change in a star's position on the celestial sphere. It is the measure of a star's drift in space in a direction perpendicular to the line-of-sight from the earth. The real drift in space is more or less at an angle to the line-of-sight, the two components of this drift being the proper motion and the *radial velocity* or motion toward or from the earth.

refraction. In general, a bending of light rays out of their otherwise straight path. *Atmospheric refraction* is the effect of the terrestrial atmosphere, by which light rays are bent toward the earth's surface, so that a star seems to be displaced toward the observer's zenith.

retrograde motion. The "backward" or westward apparent movement of a planet on the celestial sphere, with respect to the stars. Retrograde motion takes place during a comparatively short time in each synodic period of a planet.

revolution. The motion by which a body moves around another body, as the earth going around the sun.

right ascension. The distance of an object east of that half of the equinoctial colure which passes from pole to pole through the vernal equinox. It is measured along the star's parallel of declination, always eastward completely around the circle. Commonly expressed in hours, minutes, and seconds, it may also be written as degrees, minutes, and seconds ($1^h = 15°$).

rotation. The motion of a body by which it turns on its axis.

sidereal time. The hour-angle of the vernal equinox. Sidereal time is measured by the earth's rotation with respect to the stars (nearly), not the sun. The zero hour is the moment when the vernal equinox is on the observer's meridian. Sidereal time is counted up to 24^h, and one day (24^h) of sidereal time is $3^m55^s.909$ (of mean solar time) shorter than a mean solar day.

solstice. One of the two places where the sun assumes its greatest declination, these points being half-way between the equinoxes. The *summer solstice* is the point on the ecliptic (at longitude 90°) where the sun is at its maximum northern declination ($+ 23\frac{1}{2}°$); the *winter solstice* is the point on the ecliptic (at longitude 270°) where the sun is at its maximum southern declination ($-23\frac{1}{2}°$). The word solstice is also applied to the *time* when the sun is at a solstice point.

spectral lines. Lines crossing the spectrum of a luminous body and indicating its physical and chemical characteristics.

spectrum. An arrangement of radiant energy in a series according to wave-length, as when a beam of light passes through a prism and is split up into colors. When white light is thus analyzed, the spectral colors are those of the rainbow—red, orange, yellow, green, blue, indigo, and violet.

terminator. The sunrise or sunset line on the moon.

time, mean solar. The hour-angle of the "mean sun" $+12^h$. Mean solar time is kept by a uniform clock so designed that its time coincides yearly with the solar time when the sun crosses the vernal equinox. It has the same number of days, hours, etc., in a year as the apparent time. A mean solar day is therefore of uniform duration; its length is the average of all the apparent solar days in the year; and is $3^m 56^s.555$ (of sidereal time) longer than a sidereal day. Mean solar time is the time kept by the ordinary clocks used in civil life; and such clocks are set to the mean time of the standard-time meridian of the zone in which they are stationed. When this is done, it is known as *standard time*, and this time is alike over a particular zone arbitrarily fixed, and within which all clocks running on standard time are set to the same hour, minute, and second. *Civil time* is mean solar time; when mean solar time marks the time of an observer's local meridian, it is called *local civil time* (sometimes ambiguously called "local time"), as contrasted with standard time. *Universal time* is the technical designation of Greenwich civil time, or local mean time (civil time) of 0° longitude running through Greenwich, England. It is abbreviated UT.

transit. The passing of a heavenly body over or in front of another, or across a line or circle, as the transit of an inferior planet across the sun's disc, the transit of a Jovian satellite over Jupiter's disc, or the transit of a star across the meridian.

twilight. An atmospheric phenomenon caused by reflection of sunlight from the upper layers of the atmosphere. *Evening twilight* takes place after the setting sun, and *morning twilight* or *dawn*, before sunrise. Evening twilight is technically defined as the period of time between sunset and the time when the sun's center is 18° below the horizon; and morning twilight begins with the sun 18° below the horizon. The above terms refer to *astronomical twilight*. *Civil twilight* is defined as ending (or beginning, as the case may be) when the sun is 6° below the horizon.

vertical circle. An arc of a great circle, extending from the zenith through any given object on the celestial sphere to the horizon and at right angles to the latter.

zenith. The point directly above the observer, to which a plumb-line extended upward, points. (This is the astronomical, not the geocentric zenith.)

Index

★ NOTES ★

★ NOTES ★

★ NOTES ★

★ NOTES ★

★ NOTES ★

★ NOTES ★

★ NOTES ★